Social Interaction and Patient Care

SOCIAL INTERACTION
AND
PATIENT CARE

Edited by:

JAMES K. SKIPPER, JR., Ph.D.

*Research Associate, Department of Sociology and
Child Study Center, Yale University*

ROBERT C. LEONARD, Ph.D.

*Associate Professor of Sociology, University of
Arizona; formerly Assistant Professor of Research
in Nursing and Sociology, Yale University*

Introduction by:

HANS O. MAUKSCH, Ph.D.

*Dean, College of Liberal Arts,
Illinois Institute of Technology*

Foreword by:

HELEN NAHM, Ph.D.

*Dean, School of Nursing,
University of California,
San Francisco Medical Center*

J. B. LIPPINCOTT COMPANY
Philadelphia · Montreal

FOR JOAN AND JEAN

Contributors

Margaret Aasterud, R.N., M.S.
University of Nevada

Barbara J. Anderson, R.N., M.S.N.
Yale University

Barbara Baumann, A.M.
Hunter College

Anna T. Baziak, R.N., M.S.N.
Yale University

Norman H. Berkowitz, Ph.D.
Boston University

Brian Bird, M.D.
Western Reserve University

Paul H. Brauer, M.D.
Mt. Sinai Hospital, New York

Esther Lucile Brown, Ph.D.
Private Consultation

Josephine M. Callahan, M.Ed.,
M.P.H.
*National Institute of Neurological
Diseases and Blindness,
National Institutes of Health,
Bethesda, Md.*

Ronald G. Corwin, Ph.D.
Ohio State University

Rose Laub Coser, Ph.D.
Harvard Medical School

Robert Knox Dentan, B.A.
Ohio State University

Joan S. Dodge, Ph.D.
University of Illinois

Rhetaugh Graves Dumas, R.N.,
M.S.N.
Yale University

Ruth Elder, R.N., M.S.N.
Yale University

Dorothy E. Gregg, R.N., M.A.
Western Reserve University

Donald P. Jewell, M.A.
*American River Jr. College,
Sacramento, Calif.*

Miriam M. Johnson, Ph.D.
University of Oregon

Malcolm W. Klein, Ph.D.
University of Southern California

Richard F. Larson, Ph.D.
Oklahoma State University

Henry D. Lederer, M.D.
Medical College of Virginia

Robert C. Leonard, Ph.D.
*University of Arizona
and Yale University*

Mary F. Malone, R.N., M.S.
Boston University

Harry W. Martin, Ph.D.
University of North Carolina

Hans O. Mauksch, Ph.D.
Illinois Institute of Technology

Robert K. Merton, Ph.D.
Columbia University

Mary E. Meyers, R.N., M.S.
University of California at Los Angeles

Peter Kong-Ming New, Ph.D.
University of Pittsburgh

Gladys Nite, R.N., M.A.
University of Washington

Humphry Osmond, M.D.
New Jersey State Bureau of Research in Neurology and Psychiatry

Benjamin D. Paul, Ph.D.
Stanford University

Julina P. Rhymes, R.N., M.S.N.
Yale University

William A. Rushing, Ph.D.
Washington State University

Julian Samora, Ph.D.
University of Notre Dame

Lyle Saunders, M.A.
Ford Foundation, New York

Bernard E. Segal, Ph.D.
Dartmouth Medical School

James K. Skipper, Jr., Ph.D.
Yale University

Robert Sommer, Ph.D.
University of California at Davis

Daisy L. Tagliacozzo, Ph.D.
Illinois Institute of Technology

André M. Tao-Kim-Hai
Kailua, Oahu, Hawaii

Mary Ann Bochnak Tarasuk, R.N., M.S.N.
University of Minnesota

Phyllis A. Tryon, R.N., M.S.N.
Yale University

Robert N. Wilson, Ph.D.
University of North Carolina

Preface

That health has important social and psychological aspects as well as physical is no longer often debated. Since the end of World War II, the study of social and psychological factors in health and disease has been spiraling. Reports of empirical social research concerning various diseases, patients, physicians and nurses, hospitals and health programs, etc., are now sprinkled throughout the major journals in sociology, psychology, psychiatry, medicine and nursing. The newly-founded *Journal of Health and Human Behavior* is devoted entirely to the interrelationship between health and human behavior. Recently, several "handbooks" and "reading" texts have been published. Those volumes make excellent source books of the important research which has been done. However, they either attempt to cover the entire health field, or they focus specifically on some aspect of illness, medical practice or the cure process. The care process, as distinct from cure, has been relatively neglected. The present volume was written in an attempt to remedy that situation.

Social Interaction and Patient Care brings together with editorial commentary papers which focus on social and psychological aspects of patient care, in contrast to illness and cure. Throughout this book, the role of the nurse, the key functionary in the care process, is the focus of attention. However, this is not a book about nurses, but rather about nursing, that is *the process of patient care*.

This volume has the advantage of including many authors. There are selections written by physicians, nurses, psychologists, psychiatrists, anthropologists, sociologists and former patients. The articles range from the careful rational analysis of the scientist to intense emotional experiences of former hospital patients. Some are based on clinical experience and observations, others are the products of empirical studies which provide the reader with a great deal of quantified data. A wide variety of research designs, methods and techniques are represented. There are case studies, rigorous clinical experiments, and others with a survey research design as their base. Several of the research reports used interviews and questionnaires to collect data, while others relied on observational techniques both structured and unstructured.

Regardless of how else one may want to classify the selections in this volume they all have at least this in common; they deal with some phase of the communication process in the hospital setting as it is related to patient care. It is our belief that in a service or helping profession such as patient care, the key phases of professional practice are basically a communication process. Therefore, the process of communication is the key concept which threads together the five sections of this book. It is the hope of the editors that this book will live up to its primary reason for being: to furnish practitioners and students with a rational approach to the social context of their professional acts, in order that they may exploit their potential to its fullest despite the conflicting demands of bureaucracy, technical function, and the inescapable humanity of their patients and fellow workers.

JAMES K. SKIPPER, JR.
ROBERT C. LEONARD

New Haven, Connecticut
August, 1964

Introduction

Hans O. Mauksch

This volume should be a welcome addition to the increasing number of books of readings which bring together various viewpoints on the relationships of the social sciences to the health professions. It should be of special interest to nurse educators and students since it is specifically planned to emphasize the nursing point of view. The most modest claim of this volume lies in the fact that it makes available to institutions with sometimes limited library resources, a carefully compiled list of selections that should provide stimulation and enrichment to the nursing curriculum.

In a more important way, this book also represents an opportunity to examine a range of topics in which social scientists have made contributions to nursing education, or in which members of the nursing profession have examined those principles of nursing practice derived from the social sciences.

The student who enters a school of nursing does not expect to find much emphasis on the social sciences in her curriculum. Like the physician and the lawyer, she does not see the interpersonal aspects of her occupation in terms of a scientific endeavor. On the contrary, the nursing student visualizes nursing as an expression of a natural mothering instinct. The scientific aspect of nursing she sees in the biological and medical sciences. She does not anticipate that taking care of a sick person involves different, more complex and more consciously analyzed interpersonal skills than those employed in the relationship between mother and child. Too often, the student is not prepared to cope with these complexities, despite her motivation to learn proper techniques. Inadequacy in interpersonal clinical competence accounts for much frustration in the practice of nursing.

Let us turn now to an examination of the environment in which the nurse practices. We take it for granted that the young girl, the young adult, can enter the hospital and take care of patients. We simply assume that with a little bit of good will and cheer, she will be able to cope with the reality that confronts her on the patient-care unit. What are some of the things that the nursing student will have to face within a relatively short period of time? She is a young person who, probably for the first time in her life, sees adults in a condition of dependence and weakness. This adolescent who is at the developmental stage between dependence on parents

xi

and the struggle for independence from the home is groping for a new station in life. At this point, she must face the adult patient who, clad in an undignified hospital gown, is full of anxiety about his or her own fate, and handicapped with physical limitations. The patient reaches for support to this young person who is not prepared emotionally or intellectually to respond effectively. In all of the studies, in all of the interviews that have been collected, this phase, rather than some more dramatic aspect of nursing, appears to be the chief trauma—the main learning challenge—of the young student nurse.

Some other factors seem more obvious in a society in which it is normal for human beings to seek escape from crises, from death and dirt. Although we find young people who have deliberately chosen to seek such situations, there is a vast difference between conscious choice and the reality of the first experience. Death especially, because of its tragedy and because of the implied failure of the healing profession, comes as a severe shock to the young student.

Acquiring security in handling an ill patient, when just touching him may cause him anguish, must be learned. Coping with physical exposure and rendering care of the most intimate nature demands a real amount of understanding of one's own feelings and an understanding of those of the patient. Only when such understanding has been acquired can one act securely and successfully. Quite aside from the point of modesty, the human body is traditionally inviolable; through our psychological development and through our biological nature, it seems to us to be sacrosanct. The assumption can be made that it is probably harder for the surgeon to initiate the first incision than any of the subsequent steps of surgery that must be taken. The first experiences in the necessary manipulation of this body are difficult for the nursing student. All these realities involve the management of the nurse's own feelings as well as those of the patient. This conscious control requires knowledge and skills which rest on psychological and sociological theory; the commonsense application of the natural mothering instinct is not sufficient by itself.

Another application of social science in nursing practice emerges from an examination of the role of the nurse in the hospital. Most of her activities here involve on the one hand interpretation, observation and interaction with the patient; and on the other hand, coordination, mediation and administration of a complex working force that meets at the patient's bedside. From the physician's point of view, as study after study reveals, the nurse and her qualities appear quite different than from the administrator's view. Both these professions differ, in turn, from the picture that nurses and the nursing profession paint of themselves. The hospital combines two lines of authority: that of administration and patient care vested in administration and nursing; and the authority of patient care, the therapeutic processes, personified and promulgated by the physician. The nurse stands at the juncture of these two lines. She has to be prepared to translate an individual directive into an organized body of daily routines and activities; the emergencies of patients into the routine of her work day; the hospital policies into the ongoing activities of the patient-care unit; and the individual orders of the physician into a pattern of nursing care.

In the light of all this, the nurse has to become aware of many things. She has to see the patient as a person in a social role. His present role, that of patient, is one to which no consent is given. There is some degree of consent in every social role in the repertory of our culture but that of the patient is a role to which one may be committed without consent and without participation. Patients often exhibit an apparent desire to surrender rights, self-determination, and ego identification. The nurse must understand the mechanisms of human beings, their reaction to stress, their potential ability to rehabilitate their own egos in the face of illness, and their physical inadequacy and emotional tension.

The nurse must understand not only the patient in his capacity as such, but also those aspects of his behavior which he brings with him to the hospital and which affect not only his attitude toward his illness and the hospital, but the progress of his cure and rehabilitation itself. In addition to this, the nurse must also develop the ability to communicate with patients of both sexes, of all ages and personality types, and with widely varying socioeconomic and cultural backgrounds. The impact of family structure and family relations on disease and stress is a field which is becoming increasingly emphasized in medical care. The patient's social and ethnic background is an influencing factor on his disease and thus on his hospitalization and becomes an important clue to the kind of care that the nurse needs to offer.

The nurse is the one functionary of the hospital who is at the patient-care unit continuously. All others, including the physician, come and go. The nurse is the coordinator, the mediator and the observer for all the patient services. To participate in all of these events, she must understand herself, her own involvement, her own attitude toward disease, toward people and toward the work situation. The nurse must understand the principles of organization and administration because, in reality, whether she likes it or not, she has become *de facto* administrator in the complexity of patient care.

In the light of these comments, this volume makes a significant contribution to nursing education and nursing practice. It shows that client, practitioner and the professional process can become the focus of analysis for research in nursing. This book demonstrates the contributions of the social sciences in the use of research for professional education, exploration and experimentation. The selections assembled here show a range not only of focus, but also of method and of presentation. This variety of expression should give the nursing student a sense of the diversity and wealth with which professional communication can proceed. It is hoped, therefore, that this volume will not only contribute as a resource of knowledge made available to the members of the profession and their students, but also as an index of communication and as an appropriate expression of the dialogue of a profession.

Foreword

HELEN NAHM

Understanding the social and psychological aspects of the nurse's role, the importance of communication, the patient's view of his situation, the structural and cultural context of patient care, and the role and status relationships among doctors, nurses and patients is an undertaking of so great a magnitude that it almost defies hope of achievement. To a considerable extent the goals are elusive; for, with each new discovery, in any of the above areas, new areas for study and research are opened up. Nevertheless, the modern professional nurse must have a broad overview of these complex relationships if she is to achieve her maximum potential.

Traditionally, the importance of character and personality has been emphasized strongly in health and medical fields. In nursing, concern for the welfare of others has been considered of paramount importance, and each nurse has been expected to exhibit qualities of kindness and consideration toward others. However, in years past it was taken for granted that certain basic qualities were either present or not present in an individual. If present, it was a relatively easy matter for the school to inculcate proper ways of thinking and behaving. If not present, educators felt no compunction against advising the individual to leave the field. Though the importance of the learning environment was recognized, the freedom of the individual to develop in his own unique way was seriously hampered.

In comparatively recent times educators began to realize that such qualities could be cultivated in the student by means of new disciplines quite distinct from, but complementary to, her technical education. When the 1937 Curriculum Guide for Schools of Nursing was published, the importance of social sciences was stressed, particularly psychology and sociology. Nurses who were eager to improve their service and education programs began to include such courses in the curriculum. However, the early courses were didactic. Courses in psychology, for example, tended to include long lists of ways in which a nurse should behave to assure desired responses in patients and others. Rarely was recognition given to the importance of the total environment in which individuals were expected to function, to the interactions among various groups of personnel concerned with patient care, or to the relationships between environmental situations and responses of individuals and groups to those situations. Nevertheless, new knowledge was becoming available. During World War II and the postwar years, society was being faced with increasingly complex problems of patient care and continuing shortages of personnel to care for the sick.

The first of the social scientists to be consulted for assistance in ever-increasing numbers were the psychologists, particularly those involved in educational and personnel psychology. The importance of better methods of selecting students, staff nurses and other personnel was emphasized, as well as better methods of evaluating performance. Attention was directed to generally accepted theories of learning and the implications of these theories for curriculum planning and evaluation. Emphasis began to be placed on individual differences and the need for counseling programs to assist each individual toward his own maximum development. These and other changes had a direct impact on the welfare of students and employees in the field of patient care as well as on the patients for whom they were responsible.

Since the end of World War II the sciences of sociology, social psychology and cultural anthropology have gained increasing recognition as fields that have much to offer to nursing as well as to other of the health professions. The impact of these sciences on patient care has been both direct and indirect. The direct effect has come from recognition that interactions among varying groups of nurses, patients, physicians and other health workers are determined largely not only by personality characteristics of each individual involved but also by his social and cultural background. Furthermore, the importance of the settings in which interactions take place has come to be recognized as a factor of paramount importance.

The indirect effect of social and behavioral sciences on nursing has come through the effect that these sciences have had on psychiatry. Historically, there have always been some who have been concerned about the plight of psychiatric patients. However, it was not until the 1930's that nurses in any large number in the United States began to concern themselves about the needs of these patients. It is only during the past 15 years that the importance of psychiatric nursing as an essential component of the education of all nurses has come to be generally accepted. Such acceptance has been due not only to advances in the field of psychiatry itself but also to the impact that the social and behavioral sciences have had on psychiatric treatment and care. As the emphasis has shifted to prevention and early treatment of psychiatric disorders, new roles for nurses are being created, and the need for broader preparation for these roles is being emphasized. Interestingly, educators are becoming increasingly aware of the importance of teaching basic psychiatric principles and techniques before the student's field experience in this area, realizing their utility in the care of general hospital patients.

The papers selected for this book give a comprehensive picture of the impact that social and behavioral sciences have had on patient care and on roles of nurses in such care. They indicate that it is through the care aspects that nurses can perfect their art and can demonstrate the unique relationships that exist between prevention of and recovery from illness and the skills through which one human being expresses concern for another. But the skills of the future must be grounded in science and the scientific method of approach to problems. The papers in this volume illustrate how the findings of social and behavioral sciences may be used to transform patient care from the performance of routine tasks to a highly creative art of tremendous importance to the welfare of mankind.

Acknowledgments

This book is a joint outcome of two sociologists' separate but related encounters with the nursing profession and the problems of patient care in large urban general hospitals. To our colleagues and students at Presbyterian-St. Luke's Hospital, Chicago, and those at the Child Study Center, School of Medicine, and School of Nursing, Yale University, we must acknowledge a great indebtedness for willing induction of novices to the mysteries of the hospital culture, for tolerance and courtesy beyond reasonable expectations, and active administrative and financial support for research. In addition to those who directly contributed to this book as authors, special mention is due: Milton J. E. Senn, M.D., Florence S. Wald, R.N., Virginia A. Henderson, R.N., August B. Hollingshead, Ph.D., and Powhatan J. Wooldridge, Ph.D. For tolerant forbearance of our excitement over hospital esoterica: our sociological colleagues in Linsly Hall, and especially the members of the F.E.P.C. For stimulation in developing our conception of the patient care process: the students of Sociology 65a. For sustained interest, support, encouragement, and patience beyond the call of duty: David T. Miller, Editor, of the J. B. Lippincott Company.

Essential secretarial assistance on this manuscript was provided by Lorna Bonfield, Patricia McNeil, Germaine Boucher and Betty Flagg.

Contents

Section 1

Social and Psychological Aspects of the Nurse's Role

Introduction 3

MEETING PATIENTS' PSYCHOSOCIAL NEEDS IN THE GENERAL
HOSPITAL 6
Esther Lucile Brown

THE IMPORTANCE OF THE EXPRESSIVE FUNCTION IN
PREOPERATIVE PREPARATION 16
Rhetaugh Graves Dumas,
Barbara J. Anderson and
Robert C. Leonard

A SOCIOLOGICAL ANALYSIS OF THE NURSE ROLE 29
Miriam M. Johnson and
Harry W. Martin

THE ROLE OF THE HOSPITAL NURSE: IS IT INSTRUMENTAL OR
EXPRESSIVE? 40
James K. Skipper, Jr.

Section 2

The Importance of Communication

Introduction 51

COMMUNICATION AND THE HOSPITALIZED PATIENT 61
James K. Skipper, Jr.

EXPLANATION TO THE PATIENT 82
Margaret Aasterud

NURSES' SENSE OF ADEQUACY AND ATTITUDES TOWARD KEEPING
PATIENTS INFORMED 87
Joan S. Dodge

THE EFFECT OF TYPES OF COMMUNICATION ON PATIENTS'
REACTIONS TO STRESS 92
Mary E. Meyers

xxi

TALKING WITH PATIENTS 101
Brian Bird

WHAT IS THE PATIENT SAYING? 102
Ruth G. Elder

AN EXPERIMENTAL TEST OF THE IMPORTANCE OF COMMUNICATION
SKILLS FOR EFFECTIVE NURSING 110
Mary B. Tarasuk, Julina P. Rhymes and
Robert C. Leonard

GIVING THE PATIENT AN ACTIVE ROLE 120
Phyllis A. Tryon and
Robert C. Leonard

REASSURANCE 127
Dorothy Gregg

Section 3

The Patient's View of His Situation

Introduction 139

ORIENTALS ARE STOIC 143
André M. Tao-Kim-Hai

HOW THE SICK VIEW THEIR WORLD 155
Henry D. Lederer

"SHOULD THE PATIENT BE TOLD THE TRUTH?" 167
Paul H. Brauer

A WAY OF DYING 179
Anonymous

A CASE OF A "PSYCHOTIC" NAVAHO INDIAN MALE . . . 184
Donald P. Jewell

ANTHROPOLOGICAL PERSPECTIVES ON MEDICINE AND PUBLIC
HEALTH 195
Benjamin D. Paul

DIVERSITIES IN CONCEPTIONS OF HEALTH AND PHYSICAL FITNESS . 206
Barbara Baumann

THE NURSE FROM THE PATIENT'S POINT OF VIEW 219
Daisy L. Tagliacozzo

Section 4

The Structural and Cultural Context of Patient Care

Introduction 229

THE SOCIAL STRUCTURE OF A GENERAL HOSPITAL 233
Robert N. Wilson

IT DEFIES ALL LOGIC—BUT A HOSPITAL DOES FUNCTION . . . 245
Hans O. Mauksch

THE NURSE: COORDINATOR OF PATIENT CARE 251
Hans O. Mauksch

TOO MANY NURSES MAY BE WORSE THAN TOO FEW 266
Peter Kong-Ming New,
Gladys Nite and
Josephine Callahan

THE LANGUAGE OF THE HOSPITAL AND ITS EFFECTS ON THE PATIENT 272
Anna Teresa Baziak and
Robert Knox Dentan

MEDICAL VOCABULARY KNOWLEDGE AMONG HOSPITAL PATIENTS . 278
Julian Samora,
Lyle Saunders and
Richard F. Larson

SOME SOCIAL FUNCTIONS OF LAUGHTER 292
Rose Laub Coser

THE SCHIZOPHRENIC NO-SOCIETY 306
Robert Sommer and
Humphry Osmond

Section 5

Doctor, Nurse and Patient: Role and Status Relationships

Introduction 325

BECOMING A NURSE: A SELECTIVE VIEW 327
Hans O. Mauksch

THE PROFESSIONAL EMPLOYEE: A STUDY OF CONFLICT IN NURSING
ROLES 341
Ronald G. Corwin

INTERPERSONAL CONFLICT IN THE OUTPATIENT DEPARTMENT . . 356
Mary Malone,
Norman H. Berkowitz and
Malcolm W. Klein

SOCIAL INFLUENCE AND THE SOCIAL-PSYCHOLOGICAL FUNCTION OF
DEFERENCE: A STUDY OF PSYCHIATRIC NURSING 366
William A. Rushing

STATUS-ORIENTATIONS IN NURSING 377
Robert K. Merton

NURSE AND PATIENTS: TIME, PLACE, AND DISTANCE . . . 384
Bernard E. Segal

Index 395

Section 1

Social and Psychological Aspects of the Nurse's Role

INTRODUCTION

🖎 The nurse's traditional patient care role includes motivating the patient to care for himself, and cooperating with those aiding him toward a cure. Motivation is psychological, and it is through social interaction with the patient that the nurse can affect the patient's motivation. Therefore, the social sciences are basic to nursing as it traditionally has been conceived. In recent years increasing emphasis has been given to the use of the social sciences in nursing. The basic nursing student is expected not only to learn physical and biologic sciences but also to have at the very least a nodding acquaintance with some concepts and principles of the social sciences. Such concepts as "total patient care," "the patient as a person," "relating to the patient expressively" and "the role of the professional nurse" are so much in vogue today that one may hardly glance through a nursing publication without running across them several times. For many nurses and nursing educators this trend has raised questions. Some no doubt feel that the point of overemphasis on social science has been reached, perhaps even to the detriment of patient care. This feeling may arise because for many the relevance of social science to nursing has never been stated clearly. The basic purpose of this section is to make clear those assumptions about patient care that make the social sciences basic to professional nursing practice.

The first thing to understand is the relevance of the social sciences to the basic purpose of the health professions: cure of the sick person. To begin with, in order to utilize the increasing improvements in technology, medical practice has moved in the past half century from the home to specialized institutions such as the hospital. The hospital has become a workshop where doctors can use jointly the more expensive and complicated tools of their trade. In the hospital the job of taking *care* of the patient is joined with the business of achieving his *cure*. Care and cure are intimately related functions. This relationship is recognized implicitly when a physician decides to place a patient in the hospital in order to guarantee "proper care," as well as to carry out diagnostic and therapeutic procedures designed to cure the patient's condition. But it has become increasingly obvious that improvements and refinements in care function do not match the medical advances that have taken place. As everyone admits, patients are people. Yet in practice this fact often is ignored and the patient becomes "depersonalized."[1] This depersonalization has been recognized and identified as a trend that must be reversed if "proper care" is to be given. In our first selection for this section, Esther Lucile Brown says:

> As psychological factors become increasingly recognized as determinants of therapeutic progress, the need becomes clearer for hospitals, physicians, and nurses to consider the psychosocial and cultural needs of patients, to treat the whole person and not merely a disease entity.

Dr. Brown points out here that patient care has an important impact on cure. The experiment reported by Dumas, Anderson, and Leonard in our second selection illustrates this point. Proper care for the patient may speed up the cure and help to prevent complications.

Simply communicating the fact that "somebody cares" may help to promote cure by encouraging the sick person himself to care about getting well. In our third selection, by Johnson and Martin, this motivation of the patient to carry on in the difficult task of getting well is taken to be a particular instance of the "expressive function" that must be performed in order to keep any social system going. Cure of the patient is a specific instance of an "instrumental" task which, as we have pointed out, is the primary purpose of the doctor-patient-nurse social system. If we grant that performance of both instrumental and expressive functions is necessary for achieving the goal of the system— in this case cure of the ill person—the question still remains of who shall perform these functions.

In our third selection, Johnson and Martin go on to point out several reasons why the expressive function might be most congruent with the nurse's role. Dumas *et al.* point out that performance of this function for surgical patients is a matter of debate, but that the nurse can do it. In the paper by Skipper, conflicting opinions regarding what role the nurse actually takes is confronted by evidence. He shows that from the nurse's point of view the expressive function is just as important as the instrumental for the nurse role. To the extent that the opinions of the nurses surveyed in that study are shared by the nursing profession in general, the social sciences are especially basic to the nursing profession.

In addition to the importance of the nurse's traditional patient care role, which includes motivating the patient to care for himself, there are several other reasons why the social sciences are of value to nurses. These reasons will become more evident from a reading of the entire book. Here it may be sufficient simply to point out that nurses are people and they work in a social organization. Hence, as with any other profession, the nurse can make use of the social sciences in understanding the world of her work as well as the entire world in which she lives. It is worth pointing out specifically that for the helping professions, professional practice is a social process. One convenient way to conceive of the nursing process is in four steps: (1) identifying the existence of a patient need, (2) deciding how best to meet that need, (3) carrying out the action that is decided on, and (4) validating that, in fact, the action taken did meet the patient's need.[2] Professional process is a special case of social interaction between two persons; social interaction is to a large extent a communicative process. In the next section, on "the importance of communication," this point is elaborated and discussed in detail.

FOOTNOTES

1. It should be understood that when the social scientist points to a situation such as this "depersonalization" of the patient and its consequences, this in no way should be taken as a criticism of those engaged in patient care. Scientific description and explanation of a situation is one thing. Evaluation of it is quite separate. If depersonalization or its consequences for the patient are judged to be undesirable, then further research into its causes is called for, rather than simple exhortations to the practitioner to cease and desist. After all, those engaged in patient care are also people who must have *their* needs provided. As is discussed in the following contributions, there are perfectly understandable reasons why meaningful communication between patient and staff is difficult for the helping person as well as for the patient.

2. Orlando, Ida J., *The Dynamic Nurse-Patient Relationship*, G. P. Putnam's Sons, 1961. Wiedenbach, Ernestine, "The Helping Art of Nursing," *American Journal of Nursing*, Vol. 63, No. 11, November 1963, pp. 54-57.

Meeting Patients' Psychosocial Needs in the General Hospital

ESTHER LUCILE BROWN

Patients who enter hospitals are frequently, if not generally, people in trouble. There is "something wrong" with them that requires diagnosis, treatment, or both. That very fact, even though they may not be in pain, is often sufficient to arouse anxiety about their imminent hospital experience, what the diagnostic tests will show, and whether they will be really cured, left with physical disabilities, or faced with the likelihood of too early a death.

In addition, there are other kinds of troubles, which concern family, work, and financial matters, that patients take with them to the hospital. How will the family get along in the absence of the mother or the father; how will the bills be paid even though there be hospital insurance; will the breadwinner find his job waiting for him on his return, will he be able to do the kind of work he has always done, or will he be incapacitated? How long will it be before the mother and housewife is able to resume her indispensable role in the family? Sometimes there is the nagging question of whether the marital partner can be left foot-loose with safety for more than a day or two, or whether the children's affection will not be weaned away from the sick parent or grandparent.

These troubles differ, of course, according to the life circumstances and the basic personality structure of the particular individual. His socioeconomic background, education, and cultural attitudes and values are important determinants of how he will react to sickness and hospitalization. Many of his worries are neurotic in origin. A recent study, for example, suggested that no fewer than half of the eighty patients admitted to one

Reprinted with permission from the author and *The Annals of the American Academy of Political and Social Science*, Vol. 346, March 1963, pp. 117-125.

hospital with a diagnosis of appendicitis experienced neurotic anxiety. That some of the fears about minor surgery, financial difficulties, or the infidelity of a spouse may have little basis in reality does not make the discomfort less pronounced.

ADMISSION TO THE HOSPITAL

It is against this background of diversified troubles that the admission of patients to the hospital must be viewed. At the moment when most persons probably want individualized attention and sympathetic understanding, they are likely to find themselves confronted with a clerk who asks, in a matter-of-fact manner, for information that they may even resent as trespassing upon their private lives. Discussion of how the hospital bill is to be paid is often particularly disturbing not only to persons with limited economic resources but to those in favored circumstances who consider it a serious breach of etiquette to discuss money matters at so inappropriate a time.

Once the admission data have been obtained, the clerk calls an aide who, almost without comment, bustles the patient off, generally accompanied by an adult relative or friend, to an undesignated floor of the institution. In some hospitals, the patient is taken to his room in a wheel chair even though he arrived on two good feet. If he is not accustomed to hospital mores, this unexpected act is likely to raise the question in his mind of whether he is more sick than he realized. He discovers later in such hospitals that he is sent to X ray or elsewhere in a wheel chair or perhaps strapped on a stretcher, as if he were likely to lose consciousness. At discharge, he will again be wheeled to the outer door of the institution, where the hospital's legal responsibility for him ends.

Although impersonal admission procedures have come to characterize most large hospitals, many attempts have been made, often with temporary or limited success, to introduce some amelioration. Small hospitals are generally able to preserve more friendliness and informality. Unusual indeed, however, is the Community Hospital in Waterville, Maine, where the writer saw families received as guests by the nurse in charge of admissions or the nurse director of the hospital. Both women wore their white uniforms, hopefully as visible symbols of warmth, interest, and understanding. After a visit in a pleasant lounge designed to reassure the family, one of the two nurses escorted the family to the appropriate floor where she introduced them to the head nurse as if they were her personal friends. Opportunity was provided for them to examine the patient's room and the layout of the area and to learn something of how patient care was organized. If it seemed desirable, the suggestion was made that a member of the family might like to stay at least overnight and sleep on a folding cot readily at hand. When the patient left the hospital, a group of staff gathered at the door to wave a friendly good-by to him and his relatives.

The admission procedure is only the first of a long series of initiation rites into an institution that is differently organized and operated than any other with which the patient is familiar. In the usual hospital, the patient discovers that a bed has been assigned for his use, but, if he is the average patient, he will have no effective voice in deciding where the bed will be placed, how the room will be arranged or perhaps even ventilated, whether he can have quiet and privacy if he wishes, and who his roommates will be. Instead, a member of the nursing service will promptly suggest that he give her his money and any valuables to be locked in the safe. Unless he has the luxury of at least a semiprivate room, street clothes will also be taken away and carefully checked.

THE LOSS OF SELF-IDENTITY

Simultaneously, he is expected to check most of his individualized wants and desires and his long-standing habit of making decisions for himself and others. It is assumed that he will place himself implicitly in the hands of the medical and hospital staff and co-operate with them in what they are doing for his good. However, as the stripping process continues and its effect on him becomes cumulative, he often feels as if he were losing one layer after another of his self-identification. The patient is frequently not known as a college professor, an expert steel riveter, an exceptionally fine homemaker, or a champion fisherman; he is the occupant of the second bed in Room 34, or the patient with gallstones, a broken hip, "Ca," or "CVA." The individual has been reduced to the anonymity of a horizontal figure between white sheets. In his own estimation, he may be scarcely better off than the patient undergoing surgery of whom T. S. Eliot remarks in *The Cocktail Party*:

> All there is of you is your body
> And the "you" is withdrawn.

For some patients, this loss of self-identity is one of the most difficult aspects of hospitalization. The greater the degree to which a person has formerly been able to maintain himself as "the subject, the centre of reality," to quote Eliot again, the more he is likely to suffer from role deprivation and lack of recognition.

THE LOSS OF HOME

This loss of self-identity is closely related to and exacerbated by the alien physical environment in which the patient finds himself. Unless his life has been deviant from that of most other persons, he has spent much of it within the setting of a home, where both people and things have given him some sense of rootedness, where the *he* that he has become is in no small part the product of these associations. Whether he be conscious of it or not, his clothes and other possessions, his work and play, as well as his family and friends, form an enveloping and generally supporting environment.

Just when patients tend to be most in need of this environment, they are deprived of many of its significant symbols. They are deprived, perhaps, of items of food that have been their cultural heritage for generations, of their early-morning coffee and their regular meal hours; they are deprived of the particular furnishings, gadgets, or knickknacks that give them a peculiar sense of comfort; they discover that, in a society as compulsive about time as is the United States, the hospital has provided the rooms with neither clock nor calendar. Their possible craving for the companionship of a much loved dog or even bird will be unsatisfied, and—most unfortunate of all—they will have to forego seeing their children or grandchildren unless the youngsters are more than twelve or fourteen years of age. In spite of the progressive liberalization of visiting hours for adults, other members of their family may still visit them only at specified times and rarely are permitted to stay with them at night.

These deprivations would not be so burdensome if ample provision were made to keep the patient occupied and entertained to the extent that his condition permitted. Except for pediatric, psychiatric, and rehabilitation services, however, recreational facilities at best are often limited to books and magazines, radio or television, and perhaps, "canned" music. Rarely is there provision for meals to be served to ambulatory patients in small dining areas on the patient floors, for moving pictures to be shown, or for occupational therapists to engage at least a few bed patients in engrossing manual skills. Some hospitals do not even have cards, games, and drawing paper and crayons to distribute on adult medical and orthopedic floors where statistics show that a considerable proportion of patients are in residence for several weeks. Under such circumstances, is it remarkable that patients are bored, strained, querulous, and that time seems almost endless?

LACK OF INDIVIDUALIZED ATTENTION

Above all else perhaps, most patients hope that physicians and nurses will not only give them competent medical attention but will spend time with them, listen to their troubles, and comfort them. They often assume that they will be able to adjust reasonably well to the role deprivations, the unfamiliar routines, the sometimes alarming or painful treatments, and the lack of recreational facilities if only "their doctor" and "their nurse" explain things to them in language they can understand, give them a chance to talk about themselves, and show interest in them.

Unfortunately, in this era of rapid advances in the science and technology of medicine, this kind of service appears to be in increasingly short supply. This seems to be true even though much is heard about the necessity for "treating the entire person" and not simply the disease entity. If a patient is fortunate enough to have a private physician whom he already knows and who is his doctor in the hospital, the likelihood is good that he will receive some individualized attention. However, the frequent absence of the physician and the possibility in teaching hospitals that he will be accompanied by house staff, often deprive the patient of those few minutes with "his doctor" to which he looks forward from one day to the next. The average patient, moreover, does not have a private physician in attendance but must rely on members of the medical staff assigned him.

The nurses on the staff of the hospital are often heard to remark: "The nurse is with the patient twenty-four hours a day." In reality, this statement only means that the patient floors are under nursing supervision around the clock; it does not mean that each patient has "a nurse" unless he is ill enough to require private-duty nursing. During the three shifts of duty, several graduate nurses will give the prescribed medications and carry out the treatments and technical procedures that supposedly require more skill and judgment than practical nurses and aides possess. An even larger number of auxiliary nursing personnel will provide the routine care. With nursing so subdivided among many persons and so technically oriented, and with few graduate nurses trained as yet in the exacting task of encouraging patients to talk about their feelings and needs, it may be almost impossible for a particular patient to find a nurse to whom he can relate himself. Instead, he is likely to find himself bereft of the comfort of a mother figure that his illness may have caused him to want or need.

No fewer than twenty or thirty different staff persons may well go in and out of his room during the course of a day. Each has a small, sharply defined duty to perform such as drawing blood for laboratory tests, bringing the food trays, filling the thermos bottle with fresh water, mopping the floor. Duties may be as circumscribed as in instances where the man from the food service puts the tray on the patient's dresser but is not expected to roll up the bed and place the tray on the table over the bed. Many a meal has waited until cold, beyond the reach of a patient, because of an emergency that kept the appropriate nursing aide from checking the tray and moving it from dresser to table.

Some of the persons who go in and out of the rooms rarely speak to the patients, some appear unaware of their presence. The patient in turn knows few of these persons by name, and sometimes he does not even recognize the category of personnel to which they belong, so bewildering are the different uniforms. A few patients find welcome distraction in the frequent appearance of different members of the staff; often there is one person, perhaps the woman who mops the floor with whom spirited conversation is exchanged. More often patients complain to their visitors that the room is like a railroad station; the continuous coming and going is exhausting and annoying, and, instead of feeling less lonely, they feel psychologically deserted.

PATIENT-STAFF PERCEPTIONS

The foregoing pages described a few of the representative perceptions of patients about their hospital experiences as reported by them and their families, by staff, or by those social scientists who have recently begun to make studies of the hospital as a social institution. The growing body of evidence suggests more strain and stress within that institution than either it or the community it serves would like to admit. The picture presented here suffers from the distortion that occurs in most reports based on broad generalization without opportunity for extended qualifications. We think it safe to conclude, however, that, although some patients are well satisfied with and appreciative of the care they have received, many are not only dissatisfied but disturbed by the way in which patient care is organized and administered.

Although the hospital is also frequently disturbed by the quality of patient care provided, its staff have a set of perceptions, which are the product of their training and experience, that are sometimes very different from those of their patients. Often the divergencies are so great that it is difficult for doctors and nurses to understand why the sick person is critical, withdrawn, or depressed unless they can find the cause in the illness itself. It should be noted, however, that, when staff members become patients, their vision often undergoes rapid change. Some of the most illuminating comments the writer has heard have come from physicians and nurses who had vigorously disagreed with her statements about patient care until they themselves were ill.

SOCIALIZATION OF STAFF

Doctors and nurses undergo a long process of conditioning—or socialization, to use the terminology of behavioral scientists—to the hospital as a place for the practice of medical and nursing knowledge and skills. When they are first introduced to clinical training, they must have something of the sense of strangeness and apprehension that patients experience, but in time the hospital becomes so familiar an environment that they may not even recall how they felt initially. Occasionally, one hears members of the staff admit privately that *they* are afraid of some of the new machines and new forms of radical treatment, but they often fail to realize that large X-ray equipment and oxygen masks or tents that have long been familiar to them can create fear for patients, particularly those with limited education and life experience.

Staffs have seen hospitals undergo a radical transformation in physical appearance since World War II. The pleasant architecture, the often fashionable lobbies and visiting rooms, the cheerful colors in patients' rooms— these are changes that have relieved the hospital of its formerly cold and sterile atmosphere. Great efforts have been made, moreover, to provide staff with functional work areas and with time- and energy-saving equipment. Is it any wonder that they take it for granted that patients will find the results impressive? What they may not note is that many of the most impressive changes have occurred in the greatly increased space and facilities for diagnostic tests and treatments, nursing stations, administrative offices, laboratories, classrooms, and an auditorium for educational and research purposes, and lounges and coffee shops for visitors.

Except for the elimination of large open wards and the creation of more cheerful rooms, the modification of the patient units has not been comparable. Only now is the concept of comprehensive patient care beginning to be reflected in greater variation in construction and furnishing of these units. And, as yet, this variation rests scarcely at all on any systematic examination of how the physical environment can be utilized to meet the psychological needs of patients. So little attention has been paid to this subject in the clinical training of physicians, nurses, and hospital administrators that it is surprising that departments of pediatrics, psychiatry, and rehabilitation have sometimes been able to initiate conspicuous changes. Such departments often make use of an abundance of things and activities symbolic of normal recreation and work and of life outside the hospital. It is in the adult medical and surgical departments, which serve a large proportion of all patients, that staff find the greatest difficulty in perceiving that their patients, too, may need symbols of home, health, and community living.

STAFF RELIANCE ON DIAGNOSIS

From careful observation of the behavior of diseases and of surgical intervention, it has been possible to assemble statistical data predicting probable outcome. Once a diagnosis has been established, therefore, doctors and nurses know, at least in a general way, what to expect. If the diagnosis indicates that the disease or accident is of relatively minor importance and recovery is almost certain, staff write off the need for any apprehension on their part. This perception may be greatly at variance, however, with that of the patient who often does not know what his prognosis is and, hence, relies upon how he feels and on his frequently incorrect assumptions. Many a person has suffered unnecessary anxiety because staff failed to tell him that his chances for a successful recovery were good. Later, if staff discover that he is apprehensive, they may remark that they can not understand why Mr. B is "so worried when there is no reason for it."

The case of a woman who was to undergo surgery for a ruptured vertebral disc illustrates the degree to which long reliance upon scientific prediction may restrict the therapist's ability to foresee probable causes of patient anxiety. In this instance, the woman dreaded the acute pain that she assumed would result from the surgical wound. To her relief, she found that she had only slight discomfort from stiffness in the lower back. When she told the neurosurgeon, he showed surprise that she should have expected pain. At least half the patients on whom he performed this type of surgery, said he, did not have more than minor discomfort afterwards. Again he appeared surprised when the patient suggested that she would have been greatly reassured had he told her in advance that she had a fifty-fifty chance of escaping acute pain subsequent to the surgery.

THE PATIENT'S VIEWPOINT

Staff often take it for granted that patients think and feel much as they do about many matters. This is an error with unfortunate consequences. They forget that they are not only accustomed to the hospital and have the knowledge requisite for predicting the probable outcome of disease but also that they are well, fully occupied, often young, and generally interested in what they are doing. These factors are such important determinants of their attitudes and reactions that many experience difficulty in looking at situations from the point of view of patients and families whose orientation and experience are very different.

Staff personnel see themselves "running all day," as the nurses say, "to make the patients comfortable." So busy and often harried are they that they find themselves annoyed by the patient's many complaints about time dragging, the quality of the coffee, dinner at five o'clock, noise in the corridor, and so on. They are likely to dismiss these seemingly petty inconveniences with a curt, "Well, I guess Mrs. C can put up with things for a few days." Were they to listen to what patients are trying to tell them, they might conclude that the Mrs. C's are not so inflexible as it appears; what patients are perhaps doing, consciously or unconsciously, is using situations about which they feel free to complain as symbolic of deep-seated and significant protests.

Many psychiatrists, psychiatric nurses, and social workers are distressed by the failure of staff to see more clearly the patients' point of view, and they have succeeded in introducing some consideration of the psychological needs of patients into professional training. However, like so many efforts that are largely verbal, these discussions—unless accompanied by supervised practice in listening and interpretation—are likely not to have the emotional impact necessary to assure change in perceptions and attitudes. Perhaps, if medical and nursing students and prospective hospital administrators were given a ten-day experience as bed patients, they would be better able to recall later how patients feel; perhaps they could express more understanding and interest themselves in making changes wherever possible that might reduce patients' boredom, frustration, and worry.

LACK OF COMMUNICATION

One of the chief reasons why differences in perception go unrecognized and consequently produce misunderstanding both for patients and staff is the paucity of conversation, about other than strictly medical matters, between clinicians and patients, clinical nurses and patients, and between these doctors and nurses about the patients. Inasmuch as the medical history rarely gives staff a sufficiently inclusive picture of the patient's life background, one might assume that doctors and nurses would utilize every possible opportunity to get acquainted with their patients and to exchange information, clues, and suggestions with each other. In actuality, doctors and nurses appear too busy to carry on extended conversations with patients, and communication between the two professions is limited primarily to written doctors' orders and doctors' and nurses' progress notes about each patient.

Although lack of time is the reason usually given, many less obvious but perhaps more compelling reasons contribute to the inadequacy of communication. Some of them have already been discussed in the preceding articles, because they are basic causes of many of the problems that the hospital—or health agency—encounters. As seen in social-science perspective, they are the product of the organizational structure of the hospital, the attitudes inculcated by professional schools and associations, and certain insufficiently cultivated areas in the training of health personnel.*

Within the hierarchical organization of the hospital, communication moves primarily from top to bottom within each professional or service

---

* The writer has attempted to discuss these subjects in some detail in *Newer Dimensions of Patient Care: Improving Staff Motivation and Competence in the General Hospital* (New York: Russell Sage Foundation, 1962).

group; horizontal communication between the several health professions is sharply restricted. Every system of professional education attempts to develop knowledge and skills that are largely exclusive to it, and the professional associations promote the idea of "uniqueness." As a consequence, the professions are not greatly encouraged to share this heritage with patients or each other. Because of the long history of medicine as compared with that of the other health professions, physicians still view the newer groups primarily as their assistants. Thus, they see themselves in the role of giving orders and directing action. This attitude is reflected in their failure to initiate the exchange of more information with nurses about the welfare of their patients and in the seeming inability of nurses to insist upon needed discussions of patient care.

Most important, perhaps, among the causes of paucity of communication, is the fact that doctors and nurses are still trained almost exclusively to treat disease and to make patients physically comfortable. The concept of "total patient care" is extensively promoted, but it is only in the initial stage of becoming an operational concept. Behavioral scientists would probably question whether it can become more fully operational until communication between staff and patients is greatly increased. And such communication can scarcely be achieved until all doctors and nurses have had training similar to what psychiatrists, social workers, and clinical psychologists are now receiving in listening and talking to patients and to staff. To be able to use both verbal and nonverbal communication therapeutically is a skill of a high order. Without training in its use, staff will continue to find reasons for not permitting patients to talk about their troubles; the reason closest at hand is lack of time. Sometimes, however, physicians and nurses glimpse the probability that, had the patient been given the opportunity to pour out his feelings initially, or had they discussed with each other the planning and co-ordination of his care, time might ultimately have been saved and his recovery might have been more rapid.

The Importance of the Expressive Function in Preoperative Preparation

RHETAUGH GRAVES DUMAS · BARBARA J. ANDERSON · ROBERT C. LEONARD

THE THEORY

Psychological reactions of people to their illness and to their treatment have important consequences for their medical condition. Our theory also states that through social interaction with others these psychological reactions are changed for better or for worse. The specific hypothesis tested was that psychological preparation of surgical patients by a nurse would reduce the incidence of postoperative vomiting. The results support the hypothesis. Thus this experiment joins the growing body of evidence pointing to systematic inclusion of social and psychological variables in the patient care equation. By showing the impact of patient care on medical cure, it also presents a clear-cut illustration of the proposition that it is self-defeating to emphasize cure to the exclusion of care. Both the instrumental cure and the expressive care functions of the organization must be performed if its goals are to be achieved.

THE EXPRESSIVE ROLE: WHOSE IS IT?

Whether or not preoperative psychological preparation and support have positive effects is a scientific question, a matter of fact that can be tested by research. On the other hand, no research—social, scientific or otherwise—can determine who *should* provide such support, or whether it should be provided at all. These are questions of value, matters of policy decision that may be settled only by reference to many other facts and

This paper was prepared especially as an original contribution to this book. The research has been supported by several previous fellowships and grants, currently NIH Grant NU00060. Previous formulations have been reported in *Nursing Research* (Vol. 12, Winter 1963), *American Journal of Nursing* (Vol. 63, August 1963) and *Hospital Topics* (Vol. 42, 1964).

values. At the same time, professional opinions about the relative value of the expressive function and who should perform it are questions of fact, and are of interest to students of social organization. Although our study did not collect much data on these questions, a review of the literature on the subject is relevant here.

As Brian Bird points out, "The psychological care of patients is in many respects a 'no man's land' of surgery. Everyone has a claim on it, but no one really owns it."[1] He suggests that the main responsibility should be shared by the surgeon and the nurse. To the contrary, Janis lumps nurses with medical doctors as having training inappropriate to this task.[2] The implication is that the task calls for a psychiatrist. On the other hand, Bowers sees this as clearly the surgeon's job and advises against referral to a psychiatrist, even when the condition is psychogenic.[3]

Others question the adequacy of training, interest, or right of the nurse to provide this service for the patient. From their study of surgery, two psychologists conclude that the right social and psychological environment of the patient is essential for effective surgery; and they go on to say that student physicians, interns and even residents tend to be preoccupied with the purely physical aspects of the patient's problem. At the same time they note:

> . . . there is no consensus among these physicians concerning which aspects in the orientation of, and communication with, patients should be carried out by others (i.e. by nurses or social workers). [They add] . . . nor do many nurses believe that they should be given such responsibilities; rather, most incline to the traditional view that such matters either belong to the physician-patient relationship or that they require so heavy a drain on time and energy as to force them to minimum of attention.[4]

These conclusions are supported by a survey by Lentz and Michaels.[5] They found that nurses feel that the surgical patient does not need as much psychological support as the medical patient. Similarly, in a small interview study including eleven surgical nurses, DeLuca found that:

> . . . although nurses led surgeons and anaesthetists in consideration of psychic factors, none of them seemed to see her role in alleviation of this stress. In response to the open-ended questions they talked freely about stress and its causes. However, none of the nurses said anything about how she might help the patient with it. They all mentioned how nice it was that the anaesthetists saw all patients preoperatively and helped them with their problems.[6]

On the other hand, the nursing literature continues to show concern with the social-psychological aspects of patient care. Certainly, the providing of emotional support for the patient has been one of the traditional functions of the nurse. Tagliacozzo found that patients value the nurse who performs this function.[7] Johnson and Martin point out several reasons why this "expressive" function in the patient-doctor-nurse triad is particularly congenial to the nurse's role.[8] They suggest that it could be the unique function of the nurse as an independent professional. Harmer and Henderson explicitly include relief of the patient's preoperative anxiety as one of the consequences of good nursing.[9]

Of course, it may well be that every professional who interacts with the patient should take some responsibility for the expressive function as well as for his own particular instrumental tasks. But it seems important to point out that the nurse is often in the best position to note the patient's adverse psychological reactions to the hospital environment and take immediate corrective action. The responsibilities of the surgeon and the anesthesiologist leave relatively little time to spend with each patient preoperatively. Their deep involvement in highly specialized instrumental tasks may preclude also the development of the necessary interpersonal skills. On the other hand, nursing has contact with the patient 24 hours a day. If a patient is troubled or anxious, the nurse probably will be the first to notice it. In a sense, the nurse may become a liaison between the patient and whatever help he requires to alleviate his distress. The nurse may provide the help directly or may assist the patient to get it from someone else. This paper suggests some ways that the nurse might relieve much of the psychological stress which many patients may experience during the preoperative period.

But before deciding who should provide this function, whether or not to provide it at all must be determined. We shall see next that the dominant opinion and practice appears to view the patient's social environment as relatively unimportant. The instrumental functions of surgery designed to cure the patient take clear precedence over the expressive care functions. Probably for this reason a clear assignment of responsibility for attending to the patient's expressive needs is not to be found.

THE FOCUS OF PREOPERATIVE PREPARATION

A patient entering the operating room for a major surgical procedure very likely is embarking on one of the most significant and potentially threatening experiences in his life. His chances for an uneventful convalescence and full restoration of health are influenced greatly by the adequacy of his preoperative care. Ideally, this care begins the moment that his doctor elects surgery as the treatment of choice. The interaction of the physiological and psychological systems of man dictates that his preoperative care include effective measures to prepare him mentally as well as physically for the impending event. Those caring for the patient will have their most beneficial impact on his mental state if they work from the patient's own point of view.

The importance of the meaning of the hospital and surgical experience to the patient has been recognized explicitly by some authors, and implicitly by many others. Elman states that surgical patients often suffer from adverse emotional reactions that increase postoperative emesis and urinary retention, lower the threshold of postoperative pain and increase postoperative anorexia.[10] The most extreme "complication" is, of course, death. Felter *et al.* wrote:

> Many surgeons are most reluctant to operate on a patient who is convinced that he will not survive the ordeal. Indeed, it is believed that such a patient has very little chance of recovery from a major operation.[11]

Eckenhoff states that marked apprehension in a patient makes him a potential candidate for death in the operating room. This author cites four cases in which each patient died, apparently because of fear.[12] Bowers asserts:

> All things being equal, some patients will get a good result and others a mediocre result from the same operation. This indicates that the psychological preparation of the patient for operation is extremely important. All surgeons can quote instances where patients have been inordinately fearful to the point of predicting their death, actually succumbing with little pathological explanation.[13]

This effect is hypothesized also for many other less serious complications, including the one we chose to study: postoperative vomiting (emesis).

In spite of the recognition of the effects of the patient's definition of the situation, preoperative care still typically is guided only by the patient's medical condition and the technical requirements of the impending surgery. Preoperative care includes almost every aspect of preparation of "the body" for the surgical procedure. The serious implications of neglect of physical care are emphasized in most of the literature about care of the surgical patient. There is much research on surgical and anesthetic technics, preoperative medication and so forth, all directed to the prevention of postoperative complications. In contrast, preoperative care only incidentally includes concern with what the patient is thinking and feeling.

Thus in practice there is a tendency to assume knowledge of the patient's point of view. Hospital personnel tend to act on the implicit assumption that what is important, dangerous or discomforting to them has the same effect on the patient. This can result in well-meaning but ineffectual attempts at psychological preparation and supportive "reassurance."[14] For example, the surgeon often explains very carefully the basis of his decision to operate, the nature of the operation and some of the discomforts the patient is likely to experience. He may discuss certain procedures that are a part of the physical preparation. He tells the patient what time the operation is scheduled and offers other information about activities that the patient may expect on the day of surgery. Before he leaves he may give the patient a kind pat on the back and advise, "Now don't worry, everything will turn out just fine. We will take good care of you." The anesthesiologist may visit the patient the night before surgery. He discusses the choice and the type of anesthetic to be used and gives a simple explanation of the procedure. He too assures the patient that "everything will be all right." The nurse frequently takes the time to explain those procedures that she carries out as part of the routine physical preparation. In an attempt to reassure the patient, she might tell of other patients whom she has cared for who had the same surgery and who recovered quickly.

Although their intentions are the best, the surgeon, the anesthesiologist and the nurse in these examples are telling the patient about aspects of the surgery that are important to *themselves* in the performance of their own role. Since the scale of values is more or less shared by all of these specialists, they find little reason to doubt that it should be shared also by the patient.[15] In effect, what occurs is a sort of medical culture ethnocentrism in which the patient implicitly is given only a passive role to play. Yet a moment's reflection reveals that in fact the patient is the most important actor on the stage! What the patient needs is the motivation and the information necessary to carry out his own role. For this, can it be assumed that all patients need primarily to know the nature of the operation, the reasons behind the choice of anesthetic and the fact that other patients with similar conditions have fared well? Yet it is clear that this assumption has been made when the members of the surgical team approach all patients in the manner just described.

Unless their efforts are focused precisely on what the patient is experiencing, doctors and nurses will be offering nothing more than "pat reassurances" and platitudes, which will not accomplish the purpose intended —to prepare the patient for surgery. The following case illustrates this point.

> Mrs. X was admitted to the hospital two days before she was scheduled for surgery. She was obviously upset. Her face was flushed and perspiring. Her hands fingered the clasp of her handbag, alternately opening and closing it. Her surgeon spent a great deal of time with her, carefully explaining what was going to be

done and what results she might expect. She was having orthopedic surgery and would have her leg in a cast for quite a while,
and so he discussed her care after discharge. She had someone
at home to look after her and to take care of her family. She
assured the doctor that she anticipated no great convalescence
problems. The anesthesiologist also spent considerable time explaining what anesthetic was to be used and how it would be
given. The nurse tried very hard to relieve Mrs. X's distress. She
told the details of preoperative routines, the enema, the order for
"nothing by mouth," and so forth. She told Mrs. X what time she
would go to the operating room, explained the stay in the recovery
room, and advised her not to worry—she would be all right.

Mrs. X continued to be distressed to the time of her surgery.
Postoperatively she had frequent episodes of vomiting and suffered a great deal of pain. She remained quite uncomfortable for
days in spite of attempts to assure her that she was doing very
well. Her discharge had to be postponed twice because she had
an elevation in temperature the day before she was to go home.
When she was scheduled for discharge the third time, she dis-
solved into tears, explaining that she could not go home because
her husband had been unable to get money to pay the hospital
bill. She had paid a deposit on admission and was told then that
if her bill exceeded this amount, it would be due on the day of
discharge. This had worried her very much, because her husband
had depleted their savings to pay the deposit. He was "laid off"
from his regular job shortly after she was admitted to the hospital
and had been doing extra work and saving the money. She thought
that she would have to remain in the hospital until he had
obtained the money. Yet the longer she stayed, the greater her
bill! She had not mentioned this to her doctor or nurse because
she felt that it was her own personal problem, which really had
nothing to do with her illness. The major information that this
patient needed preoperatively was not related to the surgical
procedure, the mode of administration of anesthesia, or why she
would spend time in the recovery room. Her outstanding concern
was how her husband could raise enough money to pay the hospital bill when she was ready to go home. Finally an arrangement
for paying the bill relieved her worries, and she could be discharged. This might have been accomplished much earlier if those
trying to help her had directed their efforts to finding out what
was really important to the patient in that situation.

To meet the patient's psychological needs consistently, the nurse must
understand how each patient is experiencing his particular situation. She
must then be able to "use this information as a basis for highly personalized,
properly timed, and precisely focused, nursing actions."[16] In addition she
will need to evaluate the outcome of such actions in terms of their effects
on the welfare of the patient. There may not be a "recipe" that will assure

desirable outcomes for all patients. But certain "ingredients" are basic to effective nursing care. Their use is illustrated by the case of Mrs. Y:

Mrs. Y was admitted for a diagnostic dilatation and curettage. On the morning of her surgery the experimental nurse began by asking: "Mrs. Y, you look sad to me this morning. Are you?" The patient replied, "I'm all right." This response was very slow, and feeble, and the patient began fidgeting. The nurse pulled up a chair, sat by the patient's bed and put her hand on the patient's hand. She said, "What's the matter? Are you worried about your operation?" At this point, the patient began to talk a little more freely and to express her feelings.

Mrs. Y had come first into the gynecological clinic. There she was advised to come into the hospital that same *evening* for diagnostic surgery the following morning. She was told that she would be discharged the day after surgery. The doctor promised to contact her at home when he had received the results of the tests. He also told her that if further surgery were indicated, he would tell her when to come to the hospital again.

The nurse found out that the advice to come into the hospital on the same day that she was seen in the clinic meant to this patient that she had cancer. She had a longstanding fear of cancer because she had had several induced abortions during her younger years. She feared that these abortions would cause cancer. She believed that cancer would be "God's way of punishing her" for her sins.

Mrs. Y wondered about what the doctor was doing to her. She had read that cancer is treated best if it is "caught right away." Why was the doctor going to discharge her so soon? Why didn't he do the test while she was still on the operating table? Then, if she did have cancer, "he could remove it right away." The surgeon told the nurse that the patient had been advised to come into the hospital immediately because there happened to be a bed available. For administrative reasons, results of the tests would not be available for several days. The doctor felt that her case would not be an emergency even if further surgery were indicated. He knew that the patient worked and that she had a child at home. He felt that she would be anxious to get back to her job and child and was surprised to hear about her misunderstanding and strong reactions to this scheduling.

The nurse relayed the information to the patient, who indicated that she was relieved by saying: "I feel so much better. I haven't been able to talk to anyone about the things I told you in many years. I was so worried, just knew I had cancer, and I could just not imagine how my son would manage if I were to die now."

In this case the patient's confidence in the surgeon was restored, her fears of cancer and death were reduced, and she began to think again about the future after this operation. Perhaps most importantly, the patient came to feel that she was in a friendly atmosphere where she could get help whenever she needed it, no matter what it was. She had the feeling that the staff *cared* about what happened to her. This patient had a calm recovery from the surgery with no complaints of pain and no vomiting.

In her approach to Mrs. Y, the nurse initially explored with Mrs. Y her observations of her behavior to find out whether she was in distress. Secondly, she explored the nature of this distress to determine what was required to relieve it, rather than assuming the cause. Thirdly, the nurse initiated an appropriate course of action in order to meet these requirements. Finally, she validated with the patient whether this course of action relieved the distress.[17]

It is expected that patients nursed by this process (referred to hereafter as the *experimental nursing process*) will approach surgery with a minimum of distress. Consequently, these patients should have a lowered incidence of postoperative complications. To test this expectation, a series of experiments are being conducted.[18]

THE EXPERIMENTS

We report here the results of 4 separate experiments, involving a total of 83 gynecologic patients. The design was basically the same for each experiment, although refinements were made as the study progressed. Eligible patients were selected from the daily surgery schedule and alternately assigned to an experimental or a control group. The patients in the control group received the usual preoperative care. The other group received, in addition to the usual care, special support and preparation from the experimental nurse, who had graduate preparation in mental health and psychiatric nursing. The same experimental nurse conducted the first 3 experiments; another did the fourth. The experimental nurse saw her patients at least 1 hour before surgery. She was with them on the ward, went with them to the operating suite, and remained with them until they were taken into surgery. In the first 2 experiments, she was also in the recovery room to receive the experimental patients and care for them until they returned to the ward. The incidence of emesis in the recovery room was recorded for both the control and the experimental groups by the same nurse. She spent from 1 to 5 hours with each of her patients, the average being 2½. In the last 2 experiments, the experimental nurse did not care for her patients in the recovery room. Instead, an observer was hired to make a "blind" recording of postoperative emesis.

The steps in the investigation included a small pilot experiment, an epidemiologic survey of surgical records, an experience survey of doctors and nurses, and replications of the pilot experiment. Each experiment was a refinement over the previous one.

The Pilot Experiment. Eleven patients were assigned alternately to experimental and control conditions. Interactions between the investigator and the experimental patients were reconstructed from memory. The incidence of vomiting in the recovery room was observed and recorded by the investigator for all 11 patients. The ejection of any stomach content was considered a positive finding. Fifty per cent of the control patients vomited; none of the experimental patients did so (see Table 1). Although this difference was in the predicted direction, the probability that it was due to one of the randomized variables was rather high ($p \leq 13$). In other words, there were better than 13 chances in 100 that the experimental patients would have not vomited anyway, even if they had not received the experimental nursing. But these findings did definitely encourage further research, which proceeded as follows.

The Survey. This step was taken to explore ideas and experiences of nurses, anesthesiologists and surgeons concerning the incidence of postoperative vomiting.[19] This information was used in designing subsequent experiments. First, 8 surgeons, 11 nurses and 2 anesthesiologists in a 200 bed hospital were interviewed.[20] Nurses gave somewhat greater weight to psychic factors than did the doctors. Surgeons and anesthesiologists placed major emphasis on chemical and physiological factors as leading causes of postoperative vomiting. A similar survey was conducted in the setting where the experiments were done. Seven nurses, 3 anesthesiologists, and 2 surgeons were asked to rank 10 cards, each bearing a "cause" of postoperative vomiting. These respondents ranked "anesthetic agent" first as an important

TABLE 1. THE RELATIONSHIP BETWEEN NURSING APPROACH
AND POSTOPERATIVE VOMITING

NURSING APPROACH	EXPERIMENTS							
	I		II		III		IV	
	EXPERIMENTAL	CONTROL	EXPERIMENTAL	CONTROL	EXPERIMENTAL	CONTROL	EXPERIMENTAL	CONTROL
Vomiting	0	3 (50%)	3 (30%)	6 (60%)	1 (10%)	5 (50%)	5 (31%)	6 (38%)
No Vomiting	5 (100%)	3 (50%)	7 (70%)	4 (40%)	9 (90%)	5 (50%)	11 (69%)	10 (62%)
Total	5	6	10	10	10	10	16	16
Probabilities	.12 < P < .13*		.18 < P < .19*		.07 < P < .08*		NS	NS

All four experiments combined, sig at .05 level.
* Exact probabilities computed by the hypergeometric formula.

cause of postoperative vomiting. The interquartile range for "emotional state of patient" was from 2 to 8, which indicates low agreement. There was high agreement that "previous surgical experience" is the least significant among the causes of postoperative vomiting.

The general conclusion drawn from these surveys was that there are believed to be several causes of postoperative vomiting and that although psychic factors are included, they are not regarded as very important. This step in the study obtained *opinions* from people who are assumed to be in a position to know what the important factors might be. But clinical opinion is no substitute for facts.

The Epidemiologic Survey. Patients' charts were surveyed to get beyond opinion to more systematic evidence on the correlates of postoperative vomiting.[21] The recovery room nurses were asked to record the incidence of vomiting in an available space on each patient's chart. Information relevant to 13 variables was collected from 305 charts. This was coded onto key sort cards, which permitted sorting and cross tabulation. The highest vomiting rates were found among patients whose ages ranged from 26 to 56 years. The rates were also highest among general and gynecologic surgery. Women tended to vomit more frequently than men. Patients who had general anesthesia vomited more than those who had other types of anesthesia. These findings justified our choice of gynecologic patients having general anesthesia for the experiments. This restriction of the sample controlled sex and reduced the variability in type of anesthesia and type of surgery. Although this restriction limited the generality of the experiment, it increased its sensitivity. Patients who had nasogastric tubes were not included in the study.

Experiment II. This experiment included 20 patients. In an effort to obtain data on the preoperative emotional state of control patients, the research nurse interviewed nurses who were responsible for the care of these patients. To check the reliability of her evaluation of the preoperative emotional state, the investigator also interviewed all patients on the second or third postoperative day. Ninety per cent of the patients reported that they were distressed at some time; of these, 50 per cent had their distress relieved, and 50 per cent did not. Using the experimental nursing process, the investigator was able to relieve the distress of 70 per cent of the experimental patients. The distress of 20 per cent of the control patients was relieved by nurses who gave care to this group. Of the patients who either experienced no distress or whose distress was relieved, none vomited. This finding is just a correlation, but it suggests the rather interesting conclusion that contrary to prevailing opinion, psychic distress is a major cause of postoperative vomiting. In this experiment, 60 per cent of the control patients vomited, in contrast to only 30 per cent of the experimental patients.

This difference of 30 percentage points is large, and in the hypothesized direction. Because of the small sample the difference is statistically significant at only the .19 level. But combined with the results of the first experiment, the difference is significant at the .023 level (Table 1). Thus, the results of this second experiment increased our confidence that the difference being observed was not due to chance. A more important doubt remaining was the possibility of bias in the investigator's recording of the outcome of the experiments. The next replication was designed, therefore, to control for such bias.

Experiment III. This experiment was conducted in the same setting as the previous experiments and also included 20 patients. The investigator saw the experimental patients on the evening before as well as on the morning of surgery. Interactions between the investigator and her patients were tape recorded. The experimental treatment ended when the patients were put on the operating table. The investigator therefore had no contact with the study patients postoperatively. An observer was employed to record the incidence of vomiting in the recovery room. This observer had no way of knowing which patients were control or which were experimental. All postoperative interviews were conducted by a graduate student of nursing skilled in interviewing technics. She was not told which patients were experimental or control.[22]

The findings for this experiment were consistent with those of the previous experiments. Patients whose distress was not relieved preoperatively tended to vomit more than those whose distress was relieved. Ten per cent of the experimental patients vomited. Fifty per cent of the control patients vomited. The probability that this difference was due to the randomized variables, rather than the nursing treatment, is less than .08. The combined result for the 3 experiments, totaling 51 patients, is a 16 per cent vomiting rate in the experimental group and 54 per cent in the control group. This combined difference is statistically significant at the .01 level. Since the third experiment eliminated possibility of observer bias, it seems clear that the experimental nursing approach added to the patients' preoperative preparation was having the predicted effect of reducing postoperative vomiting. But what was producing the difference? Was it actually the particular nursing process that we have described, or was it some other unidentified element of the experimental nurse's approach? Could another nurse produce the same results if guided by the same approach? The fourth experiment was conducted in an attempt to answer this question.

Experiment IV. The fourth experiment was designed to be identical to the third except that the experimental treatment would be given by another nurse. This new experimental nurse held a master's degree from the same graduate program in mental health and psychiatric nursing, and had been taught the experimental nursing process by the same instructor, during the same period of time. Since the study was conducted on the same units of the same hospital, it was hoped that the conditions would remain the same as in previous studies for the "control" patients. But the results of the experiment give us reason to suspect that this hope was not realized. In the fourth experiment there was a slight difference between the 2 groups, and in the predicted direction (see Table 1). But the difference is so small as to be attributed easily to chance differences in the composition of the groups. One could conclude from this result that the 2 experimental nurses were not providing the same kind of preoperative expressive care, even though they were guided by the same theory. Analysis of tape recordings by the 2 experimental nurses does in fact show differences, but because the similarities seem greater than the differences, we suspect that there was some other unintended difference in the experiment IV that produced the divergent results. Evidence for this can be seen in the vomiting rates themselves. The fourth sample had the lowest control group vomiting rate of any of the experiments. Thus, it seems, the "control" conditions that had existed in the previous experiments were not repeated. At the same time, there remains the possibility that the elements which we have postulated here as the important ones in producing the differences in the first 3 experiments, also were actually present in the fourth experiment, where they did not come out with the same result because the effective element is in fact something we have not identified. The only way to answer this question is by further experimentation, which is now in progress.[23]

At the same time, it should be emphasized that these remaining questions in no way weaken our acceptance of the general socio-psychosomatic hypothesis which guided the study. There was considerably less postoperative vomiting among the experimental patients, and the only systematic difference in their treatment was that they were talked to by the experimental nurse before they had their operation. In other words, these results very strongly suggest that performance of the expressive function, whether by a nurse, someone else, or everyone else, contributes to the primary instrumental surgical function by decreasing the likelihood of undesirable postoperative complications. Some recently reported experiments with preoperative visits by anesthetists and surgeons using a different approach and in a different setting add further weight to this conclusion.[24]

FOOTNOTES

1. Bird, Brian, "Psychological Aspects of Preoperative and Postoperative Care," *American Journal of Nursing*, Vol. 55, June 1955, pp. 685-687.
2. Janis, I. L., *Psychological Stress; Psychoanalytic and Behavioral Studies of Surgical Patients*. New York, John Wiley and Sons, 1958, p. 374.

3. Bowers, Warner F., *Interpersonal Relationships in the Hospital*, Springfield, Illinois: Charles C. Thomas, 1960, pp. 52-53.
4. Brant, Charles S., and Kutner, Bernard, "Interpersonal Relationships and Comprehensive Surgical Care in a Municipal Teaching Hospital," (mimeographed).
5. Lentz, Edith M., and Michaels, R. G., "Comparisons Between Medical and Surgical Nurses," *Nursing Research*, Vol. 8, Fall 1959, pp. 192-197.
6. DeLuca, Virginia, Yale University School of Nursing, 1961. (Unpublished term paper.)
7. Tagliacozzo, Daisy L., "The Nurse from the Patient's Point of View," in this volume.
8. Johnson, Miriam, and Martin, Harry W. "A Sociological Analysis of the Nurse Role," *American Journal of Nursing*, Vol. 58, March 1958, pp. 373-377, and in this volume.
9. Harmer, Bertha, and Henderson, Virginia, *Textbook of the Principles and Practice of Nursing*. New York, Macmillan, 5th edition, 1960, p. 992.
10. Elman, Robert, *Surgical Care; A Practical Physiologic Guide*. New York, Appleton-Century-Crofts, 1951, p. 42.
11. Felter, R. K., *et al.*, *Surgical Nursing*. 6th edition, Philadelphia, F. A. Davis Co., 1952, p. 59.
12. Eckenhoff, J. E., "Some Preoperative Warnings of Potential Operating-room Deaths." *New England Journal of Medicine*, Vol. 255, December 6, 1956, pp. 1075-1079.
13. Bowers, Warner F., *op. cit.*, p. 30.
14. Gregg, Dorothy, "Reassurance," *American Journal of Nursing*, Vol. 55, February 1955, pp. 171-174.
15. Cf. Brown, Esther Lucile, "Meeting Patient's Psychosocial Needs in the General Hospital," *The Annals of the American Academy of Political and Social Science*, Vol. 346, March 1963, pp. 123-124, and in this volume.
16. Jourard, Sidney, "How Well Do You Know Your Patients?" *American Journal of Nursing*, Vol. 59, November 1959, pp. 1568-1571.
17. Orlando, Ida J., *The Dynamic Nurse-Patient Relationship; Function, Process and Principles*. New York, G. P. Putnam's Sons, 1961.
18. One current experiment is extending the preparation time back to the point at which the decision to operate is made. Others recently completed have concentrated on the nursing admission to the hospital. (See Roslyn R. Elms and Donna Diers, "The Patient Comes to the Hospital," and Patricia A. Moran, "Parents in Pediatrics," both in *Nursing Forum*, II, 1963.) Other reports should be forthcoming.
19. Selltiz, Claire, *et al.*, *Research Methods in Social Relations* (Revised), Henry Holt, 1960, pp. 55-59.
20. DeLuca, Virginia, *op. cit.*
21. Anderson, Barbara J., Yale University School of Nursing, 1961. (Unpublished term paper).
22. Ruggerio, Roslyn C., Yale University School of Nursing, 1962. (Unpublished term paper).
23. But the same general nursing approach as that used in the experiments reported in this paper appeared to reduce vomiting during labor. See Barbara L. Bender, "An experimental study of the relationship of nursing

care and the incidence of vomiting during labor," unpublished Master's Report, Yale School of Nursing (June 1963).
24. Egbert, Lawrence D., M.D., *et al.,* "Reduction of Postoperative Pain by Encouragement and Instruction of Patients," *New England Journal of Medicine,* Vol. 270, April 16, 1964, pp. 825-827.

A Sociological Analysis
of the Nurse Role

MIRIAM M. JOHNSON · HARRY W. MARTIN

The purpose of this paper will be to bring some aspects of sociological theory to bear on the problem of giving a precise though general statement of what the crucial functions of the nurse are. Much has been written about the functions of the nurse, but usually this takes the form of listing in very concrete terms what the nurse's activities include.[1, 2, 3] Sometimes attempts are made to generalize about the purpose of these activities, but this often leads into vague generalities, such as, "The purpose of the nurse is to meet the total needs of the patient." This paper does not purport to give *the* answer to this problem of the nurse's function, but it attempts to clarify the problem—"what the nurse is basically doing for the patient"—by presenting a frame of reference within which her activities may be analyzed.

The crux of this frame of reference involves not just viewing the nurse as an individual doing certain things in a certain way, but rather involves

Reprinted with permission from the *American Journal of Nursing,* Vol. 58, March 1958, pp. 373-377.

This paper was developed as a part of the investigation supported by a research grant from the National Institute of Mental Health, Public Health Services.

Although theoretical in nature, it is based upon data from four sources: (1) extended individual interviews with the faculty of a 4-year school of nursing, (2) group of interviews with the students of this school, (3) "patient care studies" on medical and surgical patients written by junior and senior nursing students, and (4) hospital and clinical observations.

Other data which lend empirical support to the analysis have been obtained during the course of several years of participation by one of the writers (HWM) in teaching medical students and in sociological research at the clinical level in a large southern medical teaching center.

thinking of the nurse as playing a role in the doctor-nurse-patient social system, and then asking what is the role's specific contribution to this social system.

INSTRUMENTAL AND EXPRESSIVE FUNCTIONS DEFINED

Any social system—that is, two or more people interacting with each other—regardless of its specific size or purpose, has certain functional problems which must be solved if the system is to maintain itself. First, the social system must make progress toward realizing the purpose of the group: it must move toward a goal. Second, the social system must maintain internal equilibrium: relationships between the social system members must be harmonious and integrated and each member must feel good both within himself and toward the other group members.

Thus we may think of any social system as having an external problem, that of moving toward the group goal, and an internal problem, that of maintaining integrated relationships among the members by managing the tensions in individuals in the group. We call actions which are directly related to moving the system toward its goal *instrumental*, and actions which are related to maintaining motivational equilibrium in the individuals composing the group *expressive*.[4]

By way of illustration, the reader may think of a committee meeting as a social system. Two things are going on. On the one hand, the members are attempting to come to a decision on a certain matter. The evidence is weighed and evaluated and some solution to the problem is reached. At the same time, other types of interactions are taking place. The members exchange pleasantries, they laugh, they overcome their ruffled feelings. These activities also have a function for the system, are tension releasing and integrative or expressive. Clearly in a committee meeting the greater number of activities are usually instrumental, but even here the members resort to some expressive action to release the pent-up tensions produced by their efforts to solve the problem.

It has been found, by using experimental groups, that a group which meets over an extended period of time to reach a solution to a problem presented by the experimenter will, in the course of member interaction, develop two different types of leaders.[5] One person becomes the instrumental specialist or task leader in the group. He is primarily concerned with working out a solution to the problem. His attention is directed away from the system and its internal relationships toward the objective problem of obtaining, evaluating, and utilizing information in the interest of solving the problem.

Another person assumes the role of expressive specialist or social-emotional expert. He is not primarily concerned with the objective problem but rather is consciously or unconsciously helping the group to keep the internal equilibrium of the system by managing the tensions which are set up in the group members by their efforts at problem solving. He is concerned with giving direct gratification to group members and creating harmony within the system. He is largely concerned with the attitude of group members toward him and toward each other rather than with the problem at hand. The instrumental specialist is usually considered by group members to be "the leader," while the expressive specialist is the "best liked."

THE DOCTOR-NURSE-PATIENT SOCIAL SYSTEM

Now, let us turn specifically to an analysis of the doctor-nurse-patient relationship viewed as a social system, but let us not get into the larger social system of the ward or floor with its more complex set of relationships. The instrumental problem in this system is clearly that of "getting the patient well," of utilizing the available knowledge to diagnose and treat the illness, and of securing the cooperation of system members (doctor, nurse, patient) in this effort. The expressive problem of the system is that of managing the tensions of the system members, that are, at least in part, generated by the activities necessary to restore the patient to health.

The patient, in this triad of doctor-nurse-patient, is in no position to assume leadership in the interaction. If he could "cure" himself he would not be in the hospital. Rather because he is ill he is thought of by society as a person who needs help, who is obligated to seek help, and who cooperates with those qualified to offer it. The patient then cannot be the leader of the interaction, but is a recipient of action on his behalf.

It is our contention, based on extensive interviews and observation in a large medical training center, that these instrumental and expressive system functions are not participated in equally by nurse and doctor, but that there is a clear division of labor in which the nurse assumes the role of expressive specialist and the doctor that of instrumental specialist.

Let us look at some of the activities of nurses and doctors and try to show how, in the last analysis, the nurse's function in the system is primarily expressive. Compared to the activities of the doctor, the nurse's activities are not directly related to the external problem of getting the patient well, but are designed—as it is sometimes put—"to establish a therapeutic environment." This may include a variety of specific behaviors from creating a comfortable, pleasant physical setting to the more directly nurturant activities of explaining, reassuring, understanding, supporting, and accepting the patient.

These acts are mainly meaningful as direct gratifications to the patient which serve to lower his tension level. It is important to recognize that many of the nurse's physical acts of care, although they may involve technical procedures, are primarily significant to the patient as reflections of her attitude toward him. By caring for the patient she shows that she cares about him. By making the patient comfortable, she comforts him. Thus both her physical acts and the attitudes they symbolize are direct gratifications to the patient which serve to maintain his motivational equilibrium.

The doctor's activities in examining, diagnosing, prescribing, and treating, on the other hand, are not directly gratifying to the patient. The patient understands that these activities are necessary as a means to his recovery but in themselves they are often felt by the patient to be embarrassing, painful, and anxiety-provoking. Indeed it is the doctor's instrumental activities which tend to produce the high levels of emotional tension in the patient which the nurse, by her explanations, reassurance, and comforting ministrations, can seek to reduce.

Because of the tension-reducing and hence directly rewarding aspect of her activities, the nurse receives from the patient an emotional response perhaps best described as "appreciation." The nurse tends to judge herself, and her colleagues judge her, in terms of whether the patient likes her and appreciates her. The doctor, in contrast, cannot expect to be "loved" by the patient in the way the nurse is. He has to judge his effectiveness, not in terms of the patient's attitude toward him, but in terms of whether the patient is in fact getting better. Thus, because the nurse plays an expressive role, she gets a reward of "appreciation" from the patient. The doctor gets rewarded less by the patient's attitude than by his own assessment of whether his technical treatment is in fact helping the patient.

Inasmuch as the doctor is primarily responsible for system goal attainment—i.e., getting the patient well—he must be the chief authority in the three-way relationship of doctor-nurse-patient. It is he who must define for the nurse and the patient what must be done in order to get the patient well. This technical-instrumental specialization of the doctor is the basis for the principle that only the doctor has the authority to prescribe medications. The nurse, in contrast, does not have the doctor's authority, but this does not mean that she is without power. She controls the patients, too, but not so much by giving orders as by subtle indirection. This indirect use of power fits with her expressive role. She cannot be the authority figure and at the same time the giver of direct gratifications.

The nurse's role in the three-way relationship is that of system integrator. She serves as a kind of intermediary between the doctor and the patient by interpreting the doctor and his activities to the patient. Thus while the doctor, as instrumental specialist, leads the system, the nurse, as expressive specialist, integrates it.

Now it is quite true that the nurse does perform technical functions, some of them quite complex. It is also true that the doctor performs expressive functions in that he too reassures the patient and shows that he understands. Our point is, however, that if one looks at all the things the doctor does in the doctor-nurse-patient social system the most obvious of them are found to be of an instrumental nature. At the same time, it is found that the nurse does far more for the patient which is of an expressive, immediately gratifying nature than the doctor does.

Functions	Doctor	Nurse
Instrumental	Primary	Secondary
Expressive	Secondary	Primary

In other words, instrumental functions are performed primarily by the doctor and secondarily by the nurse, and the expressive functions are primary for the nurse and secondary for the doctor.

This concept helps the reader to understand how so many radically different statements about nurses can exist. Nurses are aware that some people seem to think of them as "mere technicians" or, even worse, as a sort of "drudge" or "slave." On the other hand, nurses hear that they are wonderful people, "ministering angels." These two grossly contrasting pictures of the nurse exist in the public mind. Which statement best describes her seems to depend on which aspect of the nurse's activities attention is being focused upon. When the public thinks of the nurse as an instrumental specialist, she does not appear to be anything like as important as the doctor because, compared to the technical activities of the doctor, the nurse's technical activities are simply not that complex or crucial.

On the other hand, when the public thinks of the nurse as an expressive specialist because of her kindness, her willingness to listen and understand, her comforting care, she becomes a much more important figure, a "ministering angel." As expressive specialist she is doing something the doctor cannot do as well as she, and is making a unique and important contribution to the doctor-nurse-patient social system.

So far we have been talking about the importance of expressive functions in rather general terms. Let us turn now to a more detailed look at the situation of the ill and hospitalized patient, in order to show specifically what these expressive actions of the nurse are and why they are of such strategic importance in the therapeutic process.

THE THERAPEUTIC FUNCTION OF THE
NURSE'S EXPRESSIVE ROLE

The patient, by virtue of being sick, tends to be, to some extent, regressed. He is dependent, egocentric, subject to irrational fears, and in general his capacity for normal self-control is weakened.[6] When he is a patient in the hospital he is taken out of the whole meaningful complex of his ordinary life and isolated from his family and relatives. He is removed from the support his family could give him and placed in a highly impersonal, routine situation where much attention is given to technical instrumental activities. In the hospital the patient is subjected to probing examinations in semi-nude states, he is frequently exposed to technical descriptions of his condition which he does not understand, he may have to undergo painful treatments or operations, the outcome of which is uncertain.

Thus the patient, both by virtue of being ill and by virtue of being in the hospital, needs, more than does the normal adult, reassurance, support, acceptance, understanding, and meaningful explanations. Because of the patient's regressed state of mind and the threatening unfamiliarity of the hospital, if the purely instrumental aspects of restoring him to health are not balanced by tension-reducing expressive mechanism, a great strain is put on the patient's ability to "take it." Indeed, if his tension is built up to intolerable heights his illness may be intensified. The nurse, then, in playing an expressive role, serves the important function of maintaining the motivational equilibrium of the patient as he moves from illness to health.

How does the nurse do this specifically? We shall let the nurses answer this themselves. By quoting nurses on the subject of what they think their main contribution to the patient is, we can further clarify what we mean by expressive activities as they apply to the nurse role. These are some of the answers nursing instructors at a 4-year school of nursing gave to the question: "In your opinion, what is the most important contribution which the nurse makes to the patient?"

> I would say that of establishing a therapeutic environment. It includes a pleasant physical environment, an environment that is comfortable, pleasant, free from unnecessary noises.

> Her ability to understand, her ability to understand him as a person. It is important that we are able to have the patient know that we understand how he is feeling and that we react in a way which indicates our understanding.

> In my opinion, I think the most important contribution would be emotional support and understanding or acceptance of the patient.

> It's not just treating a person by order which includes medication, dressings and that sort of thing, but it's because you recognize their need for a sounding board, and you become that to them.

> I think her most important contribution is not always in what she says but lies in her ability to be there and to understand, to have courage to listen and not run away.

The patient is put in an environment where he doesn't know what is expected of him next and he needs to be made comfortable about confessing his ignorance to a person who will accept him even though he seems to be pretty dumb about what he is supposed to do.

Giving adequate explanations to the patient and breaking it down on his level, because many times the doctors are too busy and they don't stay with the patient.

It's what we can give the patient to help him to adjust.

If the nurse has prepared the patient to accept what is to come, then she has done a good job, perhaps a better job than giving him several injections of medications in preparation for his surgery.

What in essence do all these activities add up to? We are saying that the function of these behaviors is not so much to "cure" the patient as to maintain his motivational balance while he is undergoing the technical procedures necessary to get him well. We are not suggesting that the nurse's technical procedures are unimportant, but rather that their importance lies, not in their instrumental, but in their expressive significance. As we pointed out earlier, her physical acts of care are primarily important as expressions of her attitude toward the patient. By keeping the physical environment pleasant, by caring for the patient, she is expressing an attitude of "caring about" the patient which is so important to his emotional well being. If the nurse does treat the patient as a physical object rather than as a person whom she cares about, much of the therapeutic effect of her activities is lost.

It is our contention that these expressive functions cannot be carried out effectively by the doctor. Although it is important that he be aware of the importance of these expressive functions, it is hardly possible for him to directly implement them in his own role. In large, bureaucratically organized hospitals, which are becoming increasingly typical, the doctor sees the patient for only a few minutes at a time and the patient may have several doctors concerned with different aspects of his illness. The body of medical knowledge is growing at an accelerated rate and with it the technical considerations which the doctor must handle.[7]

Thus, the doctor, while he may certainly be aware of how his instrumental activities are affecting the patient and may attempt to cushion this effect by an attitude of understanding and reassurance, he is often not able to give the patient the sustained support he may require. The fact that most nurses are women, who in general play a more expressive role than men, that they are with the patient more constantly than the doctor, that they do not have the doctor's technical competence or authority, makes it particularly appropriate that they assume primary responsibility for expressive functions. Whether or not this expressive function of the nurse is formally recognized and sanctioned by the medical profession, the structure of the situation outlined above makes it almost inevitable that she will take the more expressive role.

So far we have been talking about the nurse-patient relationship and showing what the nurse contributes to the patient. Now let us ask what the nurse contributes to the doctor-nurse-patient relationship as a whole. Here also she has an expressive function, that of integrating the three-way system and making it operate as a harmonious whole. As we pointed out before, she does this by acting as a kind of intermediary between doctor and patient. Let us again quote nursing instructors in answer to this question: "What do you think is the main contribution the nurse makes to the doctor-nurse-patient relationship?"

> What the nurse is trying to do to a great extent is to act as an interpreter between the two. Say you have a patient admitted to the hospital and perhaps the nurse is the first to approach that patient. She introduces herself, shows interest in the patient, and lets the patient know who the doctor is, and if the doctor doesn't come shortly thereafter, she reassures the patient and lets him know the doctor will be around at a certain time or why he isn't there at any time.

> The nurse may take a protective attitude toward the patient and toward the doctor, and she is the one who would try to keep that relationship on an even keel.

> I think the first contribution the nurse makes is to support the doctor and help the doctor and help the patient to accept him trustingly and willingly. She helps to establish the patient's confidence in the physician, that's part of her responsibility.

It is essential for the best therapeutic results that the doctor-nurse-patient relationship be a harmoniously integrated one. The doctor as team leader is responsible for the major decisions regarding the patient's treatment, but if the patient does not trust the doctor or understand him his treatment may be less effective. It is upon the nurse that primary responsibility rests for establishing and maintaining a harmonious relationship between the two.

LIMITATIONS ON EXPRESSIVENESS

As Parsons and Fox and others have pointed out, there is clearly such a thing as going too far in gratifying and satisfying the patient in his immediate situation.[8] Too much support and tolerance for the patient's dependence and irrationality could be quite dangerous in that it could dispose the patient to become too attached to the sick role. Most nurses are probably familiar with the patient who "loves" the hospital, who literally dreads to get well. The optimum therapeutic result clearly depends on both expressive gratification and instrumental "discipline." There comes a point when the doctor (and sometimes the nurse) must say in effect to the patient, "You are not trying to get well, and I cannot approve of this kind of behavior or accept it."

The precise nature of the balance between gratification and discipline would depend upon the individual features of the case and the stage of recovery. While it is beyond the scope of this paper to deal in detail with this important problem of how much expressiveness is "too much," we will attempt to show how the possibility of the nurse's becoming overly expressive is reduced and controlled.

The key to this lies in the fact that although the nurse specializes in expressive functions, she also shares with the doctor the common therapeutic goal of getting the patient well. This common goal, which both creates and defines the coalition between nurse and doctor, sets limits on the nurse's expressiveness. It is part of the nurse's role as a member of the therapeutic team to recognize the therapeutic function of her expressive role and correspondingly to recognize that this expressiveness may become therapeutically contraindicated when carried too far.

Nurses are implicitly aware of this possibility. The following quotations illustrate that they recognize that expressiveness is good but also that it cannot be carried to a point where it interferes with their professional obligations to the patient.

> At the same time, you must not get so personally involved that you cannot be objective and still benefit the patient.
>
> I think relationships can get too wound up when you go as far as "mothering" them or "babying" them.
>
> If you get too close to them and too friendly to them, many of the things you want them to do they don't take seriously.
>
> My feeling is a patient can be interested in you and you can be interested in that patient and still you can think objectively.
>
> Many times you can get quite involved by returning to visit a patient. The patient can get too dependent on you.
>
> I think we as nurses have to help a young student very early understand how she can be professional and at the same time be a warm, likeable human being.

Over and over in these comments we notice that the nurse must remain "objective." Essentially this means that the nurse must recognize that her expressive role with the patient is not *just* a spontaneous "being sweet and kind" but that it also has a therapeutic purpose. This does not mean that the nurse has to be cold and calculating and "falsely" expressive, but rather that she be able to assess objectively the effect her behavior is having on the patient. This is not necessarily a contradiction. The nurse can genuinely care about the patient as a person and support and accept him, while at the same time she maintains a capacity to judge the effectiveness of her behavior.

We also notice that nurses often say, "the nurse must not become *too involved* with the patient." This observation points to the fact that the nurse, although she is expressive and does care about the patient as a person, is also a professional person sharing with the doctor the professional goal of getting the patient well. If she did allow herself to become overly involved with the patient, she could no longer be professionally effective. Obviously the nurse cannot allow herself to be completely crushed by the death of a patient, to fall in love with her patient, or to accept the diffuse obligations of friendship. For instance, if the nurse became too involved with the patient she might be "seduced" into not carrying out the doctor's orders because the procedure might hurt or upset the patient.

From a sociological standpoint, the very essence of "being professional" means that to the professional person (unlike the businessman) the welfare of his client is of primary importance. Because the professional person does have a competence which the client does not have, it is the role obligation of the professional always to act in the interest of his client. When we look specifically at the health professions, the professional role means that the doctor and nurse must do what is best for the patient. If the professional, then, allows himself to become too involved emotionally with the patient, he is no longer in a position to assess objectively what is best for the patient in terms of getting well.

The nurse, then, as a member of the health team, is a professional and is obligated to hold the welfare of the patient as of primary importance. As the expressive specialist on this team, it is her function to lower the tension level of patients and to keep the doctor-nurse-patient relationship harmonious. When she takes her expressiveness too far, by becoming too emotionally involved with the patient and allowing the patient to become too emotionally dependent on her, then this specialized function is no longer fulfilled. In the integrated case, however, her role as professional does not prevent her from being expressive but rather acts to control her expressive function for optimum therapeutic benefit to the patient.

SUMMARY

The nursing profession is seeking to define for itself and for the public the essential functions of the nurse. We have attempted to provide one general answer to this perplexing question. We have stated that the fundamental significance of the nurse's activities in caring for the patient is that these activities serve to give the patient immediate gratifications, and hence tension release, in his stressful situation of being ill and hospitalized. Her activities also serve to keep the relationship between doctor, nurse, and patient harmonious and integrated.

These functions are understood by the sociologist to be expressive functions, fully as important for the social system as the more obvious instrumental or technical functions of the doctor. We have tried to show that "being expressive," far from contradicting "being professional," is the nurse's specialized function as a professional person. We would suggest that, if the nurse is to become an associate of the doctor rather than a handmaiden to him, it will be in her capacity as expressive specialist rather than as a technical expert.

REFERENCES

1. Stewart, Donald S., and Needham, Christine. Operating room nurses' functions are studied. *Am. J. Nursing* 55:1347-1349, Nov. 1955.
2. Fagin, Claire Mintzer. *Study of Desirable Functions and Qualifications for Psychiatric Nurses.* New York, National League for Nursing, 1953.
3. ANA statements of functions, standards and qualifications. *Am. J. Nursing* 56:898-901, July 1956.
4. Parsons, Talcott, and Bales, Robert F. *Family, Socialization and Interaction Process.* Chicago, Free Press, 1955, p. 47.
5. Parsons, Talcott, Bales, Robert F., and Shils, Edward. *Working Papers in the Theory of Action.* Chicago, Free Press, 1953, ch. 4.
6. Lederer, Henry D. How the sick view their world. *J. Social Issues* 8(4): 4-15, 1952.
7. Rosen, George. *Specialization of Medicine.* New York, Froben Press, 1944, pp. 73-78.
8. Parsons, Talcott, and Fox, Renee. Illness, therapy, and the modern urban American family. *J. Social Issues* 8(4):31-44, 1952.

Additional suggested readings on other sociological analyses of aspects of the nurse's role:

Thorner, Isadore. Nursing: functional significance of an institutional pattern. *Am. Sociol. Rev.* 20:531-538, Oct. 1955.
Devereux, George, and Weiner, Florence R. Occupational status of nurses. *Am. Sociol. Rev.* 15:628-634, Oct. 1950.

The Role of the Hospital Nurse:
Is It Instrumental or Expressive?

JAMES K. SKIPPER, JR.

INTRODUCTION

In recent years increasing emphasis has been given to the application of the social sciences to patient care. For many practitioners and administrators this trend has been a severe challenge to traditional ways of thinking and of doing things. Since the nurse is in a pivotal position on the patient care team, this challenge has been particularly important for the nursing profession. In comparison with the medical and other paramedical professions, there has been a widespread acceptance of the behavioral sciences in nursing. Courses in sociology and psychology have been improved; related areas, such as communications and interpersonal relationships, have been added to the basic curriculum in one fashion or other.

But on the other hand, objective studies of actual nursing practice have shown repeatedly a trend away from the bedside, and the existence of a general "depersonalizing of nursing care. This is just one of many contradictions between ideal and reality on the patient care scene, but it is a particularly crucial one. For an understanding of this contradiction, we can turn to a basic unresolved question about the proper role for the nurse. To put it in sociologic terms, should the nurse take an expressive role in the patient-nurse-doctor triad? It should be made clear that no social scientist can resolve this question of what the nurse's role should be. That is a policy issue beyond the reach of social science. But "role" is a basic sociologic concept, and just what the role definitions *are* is a question of fact that can be answered by social research.

The sociologic literature points to two separate formulations of the

Specially prepared for this book. The author would like to express appreciation for the assistance of Raymond E. Sakumoto during the early stages of this research and to E. Gartly Jaco, editor of *The Journal of Health and Human Behavior*, for permission for extensive quotation from "The Functional Significance of the Nurse Role: An Evaluation," Spring, 1962, Vol. III, pp. 41-45.

nurse's role in the doctor-nurse-patient triad. The first maintains that the nurse's role is concerned with the instrumental function of "getting the patient well."[1] Thus Isadore Thorner wrote:

> . . . the pattern of expectations constituting the nursing role is characterized by disinterest, functional specificity, affective neutrality, universalism, and performance-oriented achievement.[2]

According to this school of thought, the hospital patient is regarded by the nurse and the doctor alike as simply a *case* to be cured, not as a *person*. It is not within the nurse's role to become involved with the patient emotionally or socially.

The other theoretic formulation of the nurse's role, as presented by Johnson and Martin, for example, recognizes that nurses contribute to the solution of the system's external problem of "getting the patient well," but contends that this need not be their primary task.[3] It is the doctor's role which has the instrumental task of giving the patient the technical assistance that he needs to regain his health. Yet, these instrumental activities create high levels of emotional tension in the patient, which threaten their effectiveness.* The nurse's role in this 3-way relationship is expressive, one of system integration, rather than mainly instrumental.[4] By her explanations, by willingness to listen and understand, by keeping the physical surroundings pleasant, and generally by providing comforting *care*, the nurse functions not so much to cure the patient as to maintain the necessary motivational balance while the patient is undergoing the technical processes designed to return him to health.[5] Therefore, the nurse must treat the patient as a *person* whom she cares about, rather than just some physical object.

Thorner's analysis was not intended to apply to all the highly diversified occupational roles that nurses might hold,[6] but just to the ordinary hospital nurse role in the doctor-nurse-patient social system. He assumed that the chief purpose of this system is the "full recovery of the patient." Given this system objective, he argued that the above pattern variables are functionally necessary. Several illustrations were presented in support of this line of reasoning. First, Thorner argued that nurses must treat patients as "cases" rather than as "persons." The nurse

> . . . caters to the patient's needs and, therefore, presents the most convenient "object of cathexis" on whom he may discharge his craving for response as well as aggressive impulses. [And since the situation also provides the nurse with] . . . the opportunity for

---

* See for example, the effect of preoperative tension on recovery from surgery in Rhetaugh G. Dumas, *et al., The Importance of The Expressive Function in Preoperative Preparation,"* in this book.

exploiting the patient's vulnerability . . . it is a functional prerequisite that all concerned take for granted that the exclusive
focus of interest is not the unique *person* but the abstract "patient." The chief obligation of the nurse, as of all the medical
profession, is to facilitate the expeditious transition of the patient
to the person.[7]

One exception to the rule is cited. "The therapeutic process 'requires'
as a condition of its effectiveness that the patient's functionally diffuse needs
for response and support be met in part. To this extent the patient must be
treated as a person."[8] Thus, nurses should treat patients as cases, except
when it is "therapeutically necessary" to treat them as persons.

Secondly, since patients often are demanding, unreasonable and irritating, and they suffer and sometimes die, the nurse, to keep from
collapsing under the strain, should not allow herself to become emotionally
attached to her patients.[9] Although functionally specific impersonality
must be the norm, an exception is again noted: ". . . the nurse is faced
with the problem of achieving a compromise between the functionally specific impersonality of her role and the therapeutically beneficial expression
of interest, warmth, kindness, and sympathy."[10]

Very closely related to emotional involvement in Thorner's opinion is
the expectation that a nurse should not marry a patient.

> Marrying a patient is disapproved because it implies that the nurse
> has taken advantage of the patient's vulnerability and placed the
> gratification of private interest and emotional expression above
> professional obligation and loyalty. It is prima facie evidence to
> the profession, regardless of mitigating circumstances, that dis-
> crimination has occurred among patients (contra universalistic
> expectations), that affective neutrality has broken down, and
> finally, that segregation of emotional relationships (other than
> what is therapeutically indicated) to the private sphere outside
> working hours has failed.[11]

Finally, Thorner states that the role elements of impersonality and
functional specificity, given certain conditions, make patients susceptible
to abuse.

> For example, when there is little or no possibility of full recovery
> as in the case of the aged sick or incurably insane and, when,
> consequently, the chief purpose of nursing and medicine is frus-
> trated, operation of the pattern variables may be twisted so as to
> render the helpless patient the victim of callousness and aggressive
> impulses on the part of doctors and nurses.[12]

Therefore, the system objective of "getting the patient well" should tend to
deny terminal patients the degree of care and attention accorded by nurses
to patients who have the probability of recovery.

Thorner's ideas came from observation as a patient in large private hospitals. The Johnson and Martin paper is, likewise, based on little quantified data. Although other interpretations of the nurse's role have been published, to this writer's knowledge no one has attempted to evaluate empirically these competing views.[13] This report does present some data and is essentially an overdue critique of Thorner's thesis.

DATA

In order to gain at least a cursory empirical view of the nurse's role definition, a self-administered questionnaire was given to 239 students and practicing nurses at one large metropolitan hospital.[14] Respondents were asked to indicate whether they agreed, disagreed, or were undecided about each item.

The responses to the items about whether nurses should treat patients as cases rather than as persons are presented in Table 1. In this table as well as the following 2, the percentage of responses that would fit more adequately the Thorner thesis are placed in parenthesis.

On each of the 4 items in Table 1, less than 9 per cent of the sample indicated that nurses should treat patients as "cases" rather than "persons," or be primarily interested in the physical recovery of patients. In fact, on each item at least 90 per cent of the sample disagreed.

The 4 items used to test the degree of emotional involvement are re-

TABLE 1. NURSES SHOULD TREAT PATIENTS AS CASES RATHER THAN AS PERSONS: PERCENTAGE OF RESPONSES. N = 239.

ITEM	AGREE	UNDECIDED	DISAGREE
A nurse should keep in mind that a patient is first and foremost a person who needs sympathy and understanding and not one who is simply ill physically.	91.6	7.6	(.8)
In her own mind a nurse should think of her patients as "cases" and not as persons.	(3.8)	.8	95.4
In her actions a nurse should treat her patients as "cases" and not as persons.	(2.9)	2.1	95.0
A nurse should only be interested in the recovery of her patients.	(8.8)	1.2	90.0

TABLE 2. NURSES' INVOLVEMENT WITH PATIENTS: PERCENTAGE OF RESPONSES. N = 239.

ITEM	AGREE	UNDECIDED	DISAGREE
A nurse should not spend much time listening and discussing with the patients their personal problems.	(9.4)	3.9	86.9
A nurse should be discouraged from establishing lasting friendships and associations with her patients.	(19.2)	18.0	62.8
A nurse should be personally interested in the problems of her patient.	68.2	6.3	(25.5)
A nurse should not become emotionally involved in the recovery of her patient.	(73.2)	5.0	21.8
Nurses should not be allowed to marry their patients.	(5.1)	25.9	69.0

ported in Table 2. The data here seem to indicate that warm and cordial nurse patient relationships are considered appropriate. However, almost three quarters of the sample indicated that nurses should not become involved emotionally in the recovery of patients.

The item concerning nurse-patient marriages is presented in Table 2. Thorner reported that every nurse whom he questioned disapproved of nurses marrying patients.

In sharp contrast, only 5 per cent of the sample agreed that nurses should not be allowed to marry their patients, while 69 per cent disagreed.

It must be explained that, from the wording of the question ("Nurses should not be allowed to marry their patients"), the respondents in the sample did not interpret this to mean marrying a patient during the time he is a patient in the hospital, but, on the contrary, marrying a former patient. This meaning became clear from several open-ended items used on the questionaire for other purposes to be reported at another time. Many replies indicated that marriages within the hospital between nurse and patient just "don't happen," and would be disapproved if they did; but a marriage between a nurse and one of her former patients is fairly common.

Table 3 presents the data in relation to what treatment should be and is given to terminal patients.

None of the 239 respondents indicated that nurses should give less attention to patients beyond the possibility of recovery. In fact, almost half the sample felt that nurses should give these patients *more* attention.

TABLE 3. TREATMENT OF TERMINAL PATIENTS: PERCENTAGE OF RESPONSES. N = 239.

DEGREE OF ATTENTION	NURSES SHOULD GIVE	NURSES GIVE	DOCTORS GIVE
Less attention	(...)	9.9	39.2
Same attention	51.9	37.0	36.5
More attention	47.3	50.8	22.7
No response	.8	2.3	1.6

These nurses, then, did not believe that patients with the possibility of recovery should be accorded preferential treatment. Yet, Thorner states that nurses' behavior is just the opposite. If it is, the situation must be quite threatening to nurses, and it is surprising that almost 10 per cent of the sample admitted that nurses do give less attention to terminal patients; and interestingly, almost 40 per cent see the doctor as the party giving less attention. This might be evidence that nurses feel guilty about not living up to role expectations and attempt to shift the blame to someone else.

SUMMARY AND CONCLUSION

To summarize, the data indicate that the nurses in the sample felt that patients should be treated as persons rather than as cases. Warm, cordial nurse patient relationships were approved; but close, personal, emotional relationships were not. The deviations from Thorner's hypotheses in these areas might be explained partially as being considered "therapeutically necessary." However, the fact that nurses did not look on nurse-patient marriages as strictly taboo cannot be accounted for in the same manner; nor can the fact that not one respondent admitted that terminal patients should be given less attention. Thus, in the very examples used by Thorner to illustrate his analysis, there appear to be enough exceptions to warrant modification of his theory. The data of this report indicate that the pattern of expectations constituting the nurse's role is not characterized completely by the variables of disinterest, functional specificity, affective neutrality, universalism, and performance-oriented achievement.

The job of constructing a more useful theoretic analysis of the nurse role is, of course, beyond the scope of this report. However, a closer look at Thorner's line of reasoning may be helpful in this regard as well as aiding in understanding the variations in the data of this report from his thesis.

1. Thorner, as a patient in a large general hospital, observed the be-

havior of nurses. From the actual behavior of nurses around him he constructed a theoretic explanation of how and why nurses act the way they do. Having to his satisfaction explained the behavior of the nurses whom he observed, he assumed that nurses believe that they should act in the way they do act, or more precisely in the way Thorner observed some nurses acting. Thorner, in postulating the pattern of expectations constituting the nursing role, left little room for differences between how nurses behave (role behavior), and how nurses think they ought to behave (role definition).[15] Certainly, there is enough evidence in the literature of discrepancies between expectations and actual behavior to warrant making this problematic in the case of nurses.

2. It should be understood that Thorner attempted to understand the nurse role in a doctor-nurse-patient social system only in terms of the system goal of "getting the patient well," i.e., the system's "goal attainment" problem. Thorner did not examine the nurse's role in relation to the other functional problems common to all social systems, that is "adaptive"— "pattern-maintenance and tension management" and "integrative."[16] Failure to take these other system problems into consideration may have led Thorner to an oversimplified analysis of the nurse's role. In other words, Thorner may have abstracted too little and ascribed too much importance to his abstraction to develop a systematic and accurate analysis of the hospital nurse role in all its various phases.

3. Furthermore, it would seem unwise in the case of any system to assume *a priori* the nature of the "goal attainment" problem, as Thorner did in the case of the doctor-nurse-patient system. This must be determined by empirical investigation. Even after having established the "goal attainment" problem by empirical investigation, it would not seem wise to assume that each role within the system necessarily contributes either equally or primarily toward it. A division of labor is quite possible. Thus, doctors may, in fact, be most responsible for the cure of patients, while nurses may focus their attention in other areas, e.g., patient care (as distinct from cure) and system administration.[17]

Finally, if one does find the external goal to be that of getting the patient well, and also finds that the nurse's role is oriented in that direction, the "therapeutically necessary" deviation from Thorner's thesis must not be underestimated. In recent years, the concept of "comprehensive medicine" has mushroomed. Today the idea that a patient is more than just an organism, that he is an individual acting and interacting in a social context[18] is commonly known if not totally accepted. We have begun to realize that his loves, hates, likes, dislikes, understandings, misunderstandings and fears, affect not only his attitudes toward medical care, but also his motivation to stay well, his very desire to live or die.[19] The fact that schools of nursing include courses in psychology and sociology is testimony to the influence of this concept of medical care on the education of nurses.

The results of this study show that nurses view their role as being more than strict adherence to instrumental tasks. They believe that they are required to participate in a variety of expressive tasks. However, the evidence is negligible that nurses do not also see an instrumental function in their role. Therefore, it may be concluded that neither of the aforementioned schools is justified in placing primary emphasis on one function, to the relative or total exclusion of the other.

Thus, on the basis of "what is" (as opposed to "what should be"), it is suggested that it might be most useful to view the nurse's role as a combination of both instrumental and expressive functions.

FOOTNOTES

1. Thorner, Isadore, "Nursing: The Functional Significance of an Institutional Pattern," *American Sociological Review* 20:531, 1955. Simpson, Ida Harper, *The Development of Professional Self-images Among Student Nurses,* unpublished dissertation, Department of Sociology and Anthropology, University of North Carolina, Chapel Hill, 1956.
2. Thorner, *op. cit.,* p. 532.
3. Johnson, Miriam, and Martin, Harry, "A Sociological Analysis of the Nurse Role," *American Journal of Nursing* 58:373, 1958, and in this volume.
4. Bales, Robert, "The Equilibrium Problem in Small Groups," *in* Parsons, *et al.* (eds.), *Working Papers in the Theory of Action,* Glencoe (Ill.), Free Press, 1953, p. 111.
5. Johnson and Martin, *op. cit.,* p. 375.
6. For a partial list concerning the nurse's role see the following: Corwin, Ronald, "The Professional Employee: A Study of Conflict in Nursing Roles," *American Journal of Sociology* 66:604-615, 1961; Devereaux, George, and Weiner, Florence, "The Occupational Status of Nurses," *American Sociological Review* 15:628-634, 1950; Habenstein, Robert, and Christ, Edwin, *Professionalizer, Traditionalizer and Utilizer: An Interpretive Study of the General Hospitals,* Columbia (Mo.), University of Missouri Press, 1955, pp. 373-377; Mauksch, Hans O., *The Nurse: A Study in Role Perception,* unpublished dissertation, Department of Sociology, University of Chicago, June, 1960; Saunders, Lyle, "The Changing Role of Nurses," *American Journal of Nursing* 54:1094-1096, 1954; Simpson, *op. cit.*; Schulman, Sam, "Basic Functional Roles of Nursing: Mother Surrogate and Healer," *in* Jaco, E. Gartly (ed.), *Patients, Physicians and Illness,* Glencoe, (Ill.), Free Press, 1958.
7. Thorner, *op. cit.,* pp. 531-532.
8. *Ibid.,* p. 532.
9. *Ibid.,* p. 534.
10. *Ibid.,* p. 534.
11. *Ibid.,* p. 533. It is not clear whether Thorner meant that nurses should not be allowed to marry patients, or whether the expectation extends even further to former patients.

12. *Ibid.,* p. 536.
13. See note 6.
14. The sample used was composed of both nurses and advanced student nurses. Since no important differences were found between the student nurse and nurse populations, the two were pooled together for the purposes of this analysis.
15. As used in this analysis, *role* refers to that set of norms, rules and expectations that are a function of the status of nurse, and prescribe how any person occupying that status ought to behave. The actual behavior of persons occupying the status of nurse is referred to as *role behavior.*
16. Parsons, Talcott, "General Theory in Sociology," *in* Merton, Robert, *et al.* (eds.): *Sociology Today,* New York, Basic Books, 1959, pp. 6-7.
17. See, for instance, Mauksch, *op. cit.,* pp. 130-141; and Johnson & Martin, *op. cit.,* pp. 373-377.
18. Wessen, Albert, "Medical Schools and the Sociologists," *Midwest Sociologist,* July 1959, p. 79, (now the *Sociological Quarterly*).
19. Porterfield, Austin L., "Social Knowledge in Medicine: An Editorial," *Journal of Health and Human Behavior,* 1:5, 1960.

Section 2

The Importance of
Communication

⚜ This section will examine the general nature of the communication process, and present papers which focus explicitly on exploring patterns of communication in the hospital setting. Special attention will be paid to communication between patients and nurses.

INTRODUCTION

The process of communication has been the subject of numerous studies in a wide variety of situations. These range from very small groups, to large bureaucracies, to the analysis of the mass media of communication, such as newspapers, magazines, radio, television, etc. It encompasses the work of writers in many different disciplines. The hospital as a social organization has not been immune from communication study, and a number of writers have noted the importance of communication with hospitalized patients. However, studies on the quality, the quantity, the significance and the functions of communication between hospitalized patients and hospital functionaries are rare.

The word *communication* is derived from the Latin word *communis*, which means *common*. When someone tries to communicate he attempts to establish a sort of "commonness" with someone else. He attempts to share his thoughts, attitudes, ideas, feelings, etc., with another person. As one writer has put it, communication is the "interchange of meanings among people." Conceived in this manner, communication is a basic social process. Through it interaction is possible. With it individuals are able to influence one another, carry on group activity and have social life. Communication is the key concept not only of this section, but also of this entire volume.

51

There are five essential elements of communication; a sender, a receiver, a message, a channel of transmission, and a response or effect. Any person may be a sender or a receiver in the communication process. A message may be on the cognitive level (logical thought) or on the affective level (emotional feeling). A physician who tells a patient that the medication he is about to apply may hurt a little is sending a message on the cognitive level. When the medication is applied and the patient says "Ow!" a message on the affective level has been sent. The method of transmission may be by word of mouth, as when a patient asks a nurse for a glass of water, or it may be in writing, as when a physician writes out instructions for the patient's care. A message may be, and often is, transmitted without the use of language altogether; that is, it is sent by nonverbal means. A patient sends a nonverbal message to the nurse when he waves to her as she walks past his room, or when he grits his teeth, or closes his eyes when she is giving him an injection. A nurse may transmit a nonverbal message to the patient by the very fact that she is wearing a white uniform, a symbol of her profession. Too often nurses forget that their smiles, frowns, body postures and even their touch transmit messages. As one observer has advised:

> Facial expression and gesture communicate particular qualities and traits. Tempo—the speed or slowness with which you move and work—suggests your temperament. At the bedside, your manner of speaking and your touch attract or repel the patient. Touch is instinctive. The clasped hand, tightening fingers relieve tension and instill courage. This kind of contact is telepathic—the physician communicates understanding, a desire to help. This language is universal, more meaningful than words. A pianist's touch communicates his interpretation of the score. The perceptive nurse communicates her feeling with equally sensitive hands.*

Patients often interpret the nurse's smile as an indication that the nurse likes them and is willing to care for them, whereas the frown is a sign of rejection. The brisk manner in which nurses sometimes enter and leave a patient's room sends a nonverbal message to the patient, which is often interpreted to mean: "The nurse is so very busy and overworked that I dare not bother her with my questions and trifling needs."

---

* Lockerby, Florence K., *Communication for Nurses*, St. Louis, C. V. Mosby Co., 1963, p. 107.

The fact that a message is sent in no way guarantees that it will be received at all, let alone by the receiver for whom it was intended. Patients often claim that they call and call for the nurse or physician but no one hears them. We are all too familiar with the case of a physician being paged, and paged, and paged on the hospital intercom system until everyone in the hospital except Dr. Brown knows that Dr. Brown is wanted in surgery.

A much more frequent occurrence than nonreception of a message is the situation in which a message is sent and received but not understood or else is misinterpreted. This gets at the very heart of the communication process. One of the main reasons we want to study communication is to learn how it achieves or fails to achieve the desired effects. We want to know what a certain type of communication does to certain types of people.

A number of factors are involved in understanding why messages sometimes are not sent as desired, or sent and misinterpreted. These factors may be thought of as barriers or obstacles to effective communication. To be effective, a message must be sent in a way in which it may be interpreted correctly by a receiver. For instance, an intern would find it difficult to elicit a case history in English from a Puerto Rican patient who understands only Spanish. Similarly, a physician would not be wise in using highly technical language to explain an illness to a patient with a very low level of medical sophistication. A nurse would not want to use the same message to a five-year-old to explain why he is not allowed to eat solid foods before his operation as she would to an adult. Note how important it is that a sender know something about the intended receiver of his message. In fact, one may generalize that the more a sender knows about an intended receiver, the better the sender will be able to tailor his messages accordingly. Too often as senders, we are guilty of failing to realize that a message which might be quite clear to one set or category of receivers, may be fuzzy to another category, and completely unintelligible to a third. We must always keep in mind that individuals of different age, sex, personality, socioeconomic and ethnic backgrounds may be interpreting our messages from different perceptual frameworks.

A second important barrier to communication is the senders' reluctance to make clear, sometimes even to himself, the full intent of his message. This occasion is likely to occur when a person may want to communicate something, but does not feel that it is socially expedient or acceptable to do so in the situation. For instance, in interviews with young nurses the following incidents were reported:

> I had been caring for Mrs. —— for about three days and I knew she was allergic to milk. So when Dr. Jones put her on an almost entirely milk diet I wanted to tell him I didn't think that was right. But then I thought, "well, that's not right—after all I am just a nurse. I shouldn't question the Dr. about what he does." So I just kept quiet and said "Yes Dr." It just about broke my heart that first day to bring in that milk and see her vomit. I finally told the head nurse.

In another case:

> Mr. Smith asked me this afternoon if I knew what was wrong with him. Well of course I knew he had had a heart attack, and I don't see any reason why he shouldn't know. But neither one of the attending physicians told him, because I was right there when they were in there this morning. All I could do was pretend I didn't hear and get out of his room in a hurry. Dr. Brown would have a fit if I told his patient anything.

Patients, as well as nurses, sometimes refrain from saying what they would like because of the mistaken belief that it would be inappropriate. For example, one patient told the interviewers:

> I wanted to tell the nurse that I needed the bedpan again, but I had called for it three times already in the last hour and it was always a false alarm. I was so embarrassed. This time I just held it for a while and suffered instead of calling.

This patient's reluctance to communicate her need is not rare; a number of studies demonstrate that hospitalized patients characteristically are restrained in their communications with physicians and nurses. They don't say exactly what they may mean or feel, because it does not fit their conception of what a "good patient" would do. We must remember that for many patients, being in the hospital may be an emotionally traumatic experience. Yet many of us have been taught since our early years that it is good to hide our emotions. We are expected to conceal fear, anxiety, anger and sometimes even affection. Thus many of us often are embarrassed and even ashamed at times when we show our emotions. This is especially true in the hospital. Nurses and physicians usually prefer patients who are stoical and hide their emotions. Patients try to conform to the expected behavior. On several occasions we have observed patients break down and cry and then apologize to the nurse or physician for not having conducted themselves properly.

In interviewing hospitalized patients we have been continually impressed with the latent hostility that exists toward the nursing and medical staff on the part of some patients, which never is communicated clearly and of which nurses and physicians usually are totally unaware. When the patient does not complain or make any specific requests, hospital personnel assume this means a "good" and well-satisfied patient. Too many times the patient's answer of "Well fine I guess," to the nurse or physician's question, "Is everything all right with you?" is interpreted at face value. No note is taken of the fact that there was a total lack of positive feeling in the verbal message, which may very well be an indication that things were anything but fine with the patient. Here the barrier to communication may lie just as much in the receiver as in the sender.

One of the most common barriers to communication is the tendency for receivers to interpret messages on strictly cognitive terms; that is, we take the words literally and tend to forget or disregard feeling states. For example, a patient who is feeling particularly lonely and has been unable to chat with anyone for some time may stop a nurse as she enters his room on some routine matter and ask her what the weather is like outside. His real motive may have nothing to do with the weather; he may simply be trying to communicate the fact that he would like someone to talk to for a while. If the nurse fails to understand the emotional overtones of this message and interprets the words literally, she might reply, "80°, partly cloudy, chances of rain two in ten." This of course would not be the response that the patient had hoped to get from his message and would probably do little to relieve his feeling of loneliness. A patient may be very anxious about the operation that she is going to have the next day and ask the nurse, "Is this a very difficult or dangerous operation?" This message may contain a real plea for reassurance and not just a request for information. If the nurse is not perceptive enough to realize this, she might reply, "Don't worry Mrs. Jackson, this is routine surgery." The intent of the nurse's message was well meaning, but it would probably do little to stem the patient's anxiety. Quite likely it could do the opposite. It could be received by Mrs. Jackson to mean, "My gosh! They are not taking any precautions. I am just being treated routinely." It always should be kept in mind that patients and staff may not always be viewing events in the hospital from the same frame of reference, that is, there may be a difference between the "medical" and "lay" definitions of the situation. What may be an entirely routine operation for the nursing and medical staff (as in the above example), may be a real crisis for the patient. On the other hand, what may be a "routine" ache or pain to the patient, may be an indication of serious illness to the staff. The fact that different interpretations of a situation may exist between patient and staff must always be taken into consideration.

To be able to be perceptive and sensitive to human feelings and to be able to reply to them adequately is not an easy task; it is an art that must be learned. There are no simple rules that may be applied to all situations. However, one authority* has suggested the following technics as being helpful in improving sensitivity to the needs and feelings of others:

> 1) Let the other person talk, even if it is small talk and seemingly unimportant; the very lack of significant content may give us an opportunity to detect the feeling behind the words. An increased sensitivity to voice, intonation, posture, and facial expression will help us understand what people *want* to say as well as what they do say.
>
> 2) Ask questions involving the word *feeling* rather than *thinking*.

In the example used above the nurse might have asked Mrs. Jackson how she felt about the operation and given her a legitimate chance to express her feelings fully. We should not forget that under the circumstances Mrs. Jackson might have felt quite embarrassed to blurt out that she was scared half to death to have the operation.

> 3) Mirroring or reflecting the feelings of others, without standing in judgment, is often helpful.

In other words, examining, reflecting, mirroring and talking with Mrs. Jackson about her feelings, and about her operation is a much more valuable technic than telling her she *should not* worry. In these writers' experience, only on rare occasions in or outside of the hospital have individuals been seen to stop worrying and become less anxious, just because someone stood in judgment and told them they should not worry.

Another very important barrier to communication remains: the lack of *feedback*. Feedback refers to the process by which a sender of

---

* Coleman, James C., *Personality Dynamics and Effective Behavior*, Chicago, Scott, Foresman & Company, 1960, p. 364.

a message is able to confirm that his message has been received. It also applies to finding to what degree the effect the sender had hoped to evoke has been realized. In the normal course of conversation individuals are communicating constantly back to one another. It is this return process which is the feedback. For instance, a physician may touch gently a portion of a patient's anatomy and ask, "Can you feel that?" The patient replies, "Yes but not very much" (feedback to the Dr.). "How about here?" "Ouch! that hurts!" (feedback to the Dr.). "I see; well that is fine." "What does that mean Doctor?" "That means that you have feeling in your leg, everything is going to be all right. The operation was a success" (feedback to the patient).

When feedback is either sparse or nonexistent, communication may be hampered severely, since there is little measurement of its effectiveness. It is dangerous to assume that because you have sent a message, it has been received and caused the response which you had intended. For instance, "good" nursing procedure requires that a nurse not only bring a patient's medication to him and ask him to take it, but also to *check and make sure* that he has taken it. A physician would be foolish to diagnose an illness, prescribe for it, and then not check on whether his directions had been followed and the desired effects achieved. This all seems very simple and clear cut, but in practice, hospital personnel often are guilty of not taking advantage of the opportunities for feedback which exist. Many times we have observed both nurses and physicians enter the room of a newly admitted patient, and in a very brisk, hurried and businesslike manner tell the patient that if he wants anything he should feel free to call on them. Then, when the patient responds more to the manner in which the message was delivered than the message itself ("They seem so busy and overworked I had better not bother them unless it is something very important"), it is assumed that because the patient does not call, he does not need anything. Often no one takes time to validate whether the message had the effect which they intended and that the patient acually will feel free to call if he does need something.

These brief remarks concerning the process of communication are far from being a comprehensive coverage of the topic, and they were not designed to be. Communication is much too broad a field to be given adequate treatment in a few pages. However, it is hoped that the framework and illustrations provided in this introduction will allow the reader to understand better some of the problems of communication which are discussed in the following selections.

This section begins with a selection by Skipper, "Communication and the Hospitalized Patient." It contends that communication has 2 primary meanings for the patients: information and interpersonal contact. A number of barriers to communication between patients and nurses and patients and physicians are described, foremost among which is the patients' perception that nurses and physicians are very busy and overworked and therefore, should not be bothered with requests for information, wanted services and complaints. In the final part of his paper the writer attempts to present some of the possible consequences of limited communication between patients and hospital functionaries. In so doing he derives 12 hypotheses which may be useful for further research.

The second article, by Aasterud, "Explanation to the Patient," is concerned with what the previous paper labeled the "information function" of communication. This paper deals with the role of the nurse in providing patients with explanations. Aasterud maintains that nurses are responsible for explaining their own actions to patients and also what she terms the "re-explanation" of information given to patients by other health functionaries. The problems of not explaining enough, the timing of explanations, the use of technical language, and the nurse's own social and cultural biases are given consideration. Aasterud points out that as yet no blanket rules for decisions concerning explanations have been set forth.

Dodge, in "Nurses' Sense of Adequacy and Attitudes Toward Keeping Patients Informed," also is concerned with informing patients about their conditions, care and treatment. However, in this study she assumes that communication is important to patients and that they do not always receive enough information from nurses and physicians. She investigates some of the factors related to nurses' willingness to keep patients medically informed. Her hypothesis is that nurses who have a feeling of confidence, personal adequacy and psychological strength will be more inclined to want to keep patients medically informed than nurses who rank low on these personality characteristics.

The Meyers contribution to this section, "The Effect of Types of Communication on Patients' Reactions to Stress," is a good example of an experimental study. Meyers sets up an experimental situation in which 3 different communication approaches with patients are compared. In the first approach the nurse is very careful to explain exactly what she is doing to the patient. In the second approach the nurse does not attempt to communicate verbally with the patient at all. In the final approach the nurse does not inform the patient of what she is doing to him, but does communicate with him about the weather (irrelevant to the procedure). In measuring the results of the 3 communication approaches on the patients, Meyers' data suggest that the first approach had the most beneficial effects.

In the selection "Talking With Patients" by Brian Bird, a physician, the value of talking and listening to patients is clearly, concisely and cogently presented. Dr. Bird points out that communication is an essential part of the therapeutic process, and that it involves careful listening and intelligent interpretation.

The next selection, by Elder, "What Is the Patient Saying?" is an excellent example of how an individual nurse senses a problem area in her own clinical experience and attempts to find answers to her questions through her own small scale research project. Elder demonstrates the importance of the nurses' ability to be able to interpret exactly what a patient really means in his communication. Her research shows that patients do not always communicate their needs clearly, especially in their initial contacts with nurses. She emphasizes the necessity of nurses' being able to view events in the hospital from the frame of reference of her patients.

Tarasuk, Rhymes and Leonard in their collaborative paper, "The Importance of Communication Skills for Effective Nursing," also are interested in the problem of accurate interpretation of patient needs. Their research highlights the fallacy of nurses' assuming the meaning of the behavior of patients without some "feedback" from the patients themselves. The authors' research efforts concentrate on the nurses' administration of pain medication to patients. One of the main conclusions is that patients' complaints of pain are often signs of other underlying problems that the administration of pain medication will not relieve.

The paper by Tryon and Leonard is another example of the product of collaboration between nurse and social scientist. Their work deals with the place of the patient in the therapeutic process. The question is posed whether it is better for the hospital work process for patients to be considered "non-persons," simply work products, or as persons and participants in the work process. The research presented is focused on the predelivery enema. The results of this experiment lead to the conclusion that patient participation in the work process may be functional for successful patient treatment and care.

In the last paper in this section, Gregg examines the meaning of "Reassurance." She demonstrates that it means much more to patients than the social bromides of "everything is going to be all right" and "there is no reason to worry." She suggests that nurses need to know quite a bit about their patients before they are able to tailor reassurance to individual patient needs. She also points out the necessity of allowing and assisting the patient to develop his own resources in achieving confidence and reassurance.

BIBLIOGRAPHY

Some of the concepts and ideas about the communication process used in this introduction were derived from the sources listed below. The reader interested in learning more about the general nature of communication is urged to pursue these sources as a convenient starting point.

1. Blau, Peter, and Scott, Richard, *Formal Organizations: A Comparative Approach,* San Francisco, Chandler Publishing Company, 1962, pp. 116-139.
2. Cherry, Colin, *On Human Communication: A Review, A Survey, and a Criticism,* New York, Science Editions, 1961.
3. Coleman, James C., *Personality Dynamics and Effective Behavior,* Chicago, Scott, Foresman and Company, 1960, pp. 207-210, 354-366.
4. Hartley, Eugene, and Hartley, Ruth, *Fundamentals of Social Psychology,* New York, Alfred Knopf, 1952, pp. 16-195.
5. Lockerby, Florence, *Communication for Nurses,* St. Louis, C. V. Mosby Company, 1963, pp. 96-147.
6. Schramm, Wilbur, "Mass Communication," in Paul Farnsworth (ed.), *Annual Review of Psychology,* Vol. 13, Palo Alto, California, Stanford University Press, 1962, pp. 251-284.

Communication and the Hospitalized Patient

JAMES K. SKIPPER, JR.

▉ This paper concerns communication in the hospital between patients and physicians and patients and nurses. It is divided into three parts: the meaning and function of communication to hospitalized patients; barriers to this communication; and some consequences of limited communication for the therapeutic process. The data were procured from a study that had as its goal the investigation of the patient role from the patient point of view.[1]

PROCEDURE

A sample of a patient population was interviewed using a semistructured and patient-oriented technic that allowed patients to express fully the range of their experiences. The patients in the sample included men and women between the ages of 40 and 60. All patients were Caucasian, American born, married, and had had previous hospital experience. Two major disease categories were included: cardiovascular, and gastrointestinal. A total of 132 interviews were conducted with 86 patients. The fifth day of hospitalization was the mean date of interviewing. All interviews were recorded verbatim and had a mean length of one hour.

This paper is a revision and a combination of three papers originally written by the author with Daisy Tagliacozzo and Hans Mauksch. These were published as: "What Communication Means to Patients," *American Journal of Nursing,* Vol. 64, No. 4, April 1964, pp. 101-103; "Some Barriers to Communication Between Patients and Hospital Functionaries," *Nursing Forum,* Vol. 2, No. 1, 1963, pp. 13-23; "Some Possible Consequences of Limited Communication Between Patients and Hospital Functionaries," *Journal of Health and Human Behavior,* Vol. 5, No. 1, 1964, pp. 34-39. The author would like to express his appreciation to Daisy Tagliacozzo, Hans Mauksch, *The American Journal of Nursing, Nursing Forum,* and *The Journal of Health and Human Behavior* for extensive quotations from these papers.

PART I. *The Meaning and Function of Communication to Hospitalized Patients.*

It is the thesis of this section of the paper that communication had two primary meanings for the hospitalized patients studied: (1) the securing of information, and (2) interpersonal contact. The securing of information seemed to serve instrumental functions, whereas interpersonal contact had both instrumental and expressive functions. *Expressive* refers to action concerned with direct gratification; *instrumental* refers to action directed toward a future goal.[2]

In any culture, illness brings with it a degree of fear and anxiety to the stricken individual. It also gives rise to changes in the behavior normally expected of the person. For instance, in our culture one who is ill has the right to expect that others will allow him to deviate from his normal role behavior because he is ill, and he also has the right to expect that he may become dependent on others. At the same time, he must accept the obligations to get well and to cooperate with those individuals who can help him to get well. These obligations often are referred to as the "illness role."[3] As a natural consequence of the concerns that accompany illness itself, the sick person desires information about his illness.[4] He also usually desires to be informed about his treatment plan. Without this information it is most difficult for him to take an active part in working toward his own health, and cooperating with those who are trying to help him. For the hospitalized patient the most reliable means of securing this information is communication with hospital functionaries, especially the physician.

During the interviews it was discovered that giving a "poor explanation" was *the* most criticized aspect of medical care. When questioned about what makes a "good doctor," almost 2 out of 3 patients (65 per cent) considered a "good explanation" of illness to be one of the most important qualities,* and 32 per cent emphasized that a "good doctor" should spend time answering patients' questions about their illness and treatment. Over two thirds of the patients indicated that they felt the physicians were obligated to give patients explanations of their illness. A full account of the nature and the extent of their illness, their progress toward recovery and their treatment plan seemed to have several functions for the patient. First,

---

* During the second phase of this study a mail-back questionnaire was sent to a large sample of patients. The sample consisted of all patients discharged from the hospital during a 60-day period in the winter season who were between the ages of 20 and 75 with the exception of practicing physicians, maternity, psychiatric and terminal cases. A total of (2,022) questionnaires were mailed and (1,294) were returned. One of the items included in the questionnaire concerned physicians giving patients explanations about their illness. Sixty-five per cent of the patients in this large sample indicated that they felt physicians should be expected to give patients explanations of their illness.

for some patients a "good explanation" seemed to have the effect of putting them more at ease, allowing them to be more relaxed and generally lowering their level of anxiety and tension.

"I have to have an explanation. I just could not live with it any other way. I can live with anything I can understand."

"If he could just tell me a little about what they are doing for me, the doctor I mean. If he could just let me in on it then maybe I would have some security."

"My physician has upset me. It drives me nuts . . . What's up? I don't know what's up. It's driving me crazy."

Secondly, communication with the physician allowed patients to know that he understood their illness and was using his skills to facilitate their recovery. This bolstered the patients' trust and confidence, and also helped them to cooperate with the physician.

(QUESTION: *What can be done to increase the patient's confidence in the doctor?*)

"I think doctors should tell patients the truth, because I think that builds a lot of confidence."

"I like them to tell me what's wrong with me and no beating around the bush. I feel I would cooperate much more with the doctor then."

"When I am told what I am supposed to do then I can help the doctor help me. Isn't that true for anybody?"

Finally, a "good explanation" of the nature and the extent of his illness allowed the patient to assess his "rights" more adequately. Patients characteristically had difficulties defining their "rights" in the hospital. Almost one quarter of the interviewed patients (23 per cent) admitted that they did not know what their rights were, and over 10 per cent stated categorically that they did not have *any* rights. Further inquiry revealed that for most patients, "rights" were determined by how ill the patient deemed himself to be, that is "the sicker I am the more I should get." Therefore, it was very important for patients to receive information about their illness.

(QUESTION: *What are your rights as a patient?*)

"Well, this is hard to answer. It depends on how sick you are."

"It depends on how sick you are. As I say, that I'm sure that when you are very sick, most of the care goes to you. If you are not sick you simply have to exercise some patience."

In addition to their concern with receiving information about their illness, patients also wanted to know about the technical and medical procedures that they were undertaking, the medicine that they were receiving, and generally what was going to happen to them, and when. In these matters, patients desired communication with both physicians and nurses. Information about these matters served several functions for the patient. For one thing, even though all the patients in the sample had had previous hospital experience, they lacked knowledge about technical medical procedures and found it difficult to foresee forthcoming events. Many times patients were taken by surprise and caught unprepared. At times anxiety and fear resulted from their lack of psychological preparation.

> "If they would tell you ahead of time, the house doctor or the intern will be in to give you a complete examination, you expect it. But I didn't expect it and that embarrassed me."

> "Certainly I would prefer being told beforehand. That way you can prepare for it. That makes a lot of difference in a person's attitude."

Patients often were preoccupied with safety factors in the hospital, and many were fearful of being neglected or made the subject of gross mistakes. Patients often related stories of previous hospital experiences of themselves or people they had known who had been wheeled to surgery instead of the x-ray department, had received the wrong medicine, or had not gotten their medicine on time.

> "You feel that something may happen to you if you do not get the things the doctor ordered on time and if they forget the medicine or give you the wrong medicine as it happened two weeks ago; you lose confidence and you feel you can't trust them."

Patients desired to secure information about what was supposed to be happening to them, so that they would have more control over the situation, and would be able to protect themselves better against errors and mistakes.

> ". . . I always ask questions because maybe they are doing the wrong thing."

> "If you don't watch them they will bring you the wrong medicine. You have to watch and take care of yourself to get well."

When an individual becomes ill, in addition to the expectations surrounding the "illness role," he is faced with another new set of rights and obligations when he becomes a patient in a hospital. These stem from the social organization of the hospital. Like any other organization, the hospital has certain rules and regulations, standard and accustomed ways of carrying out its functions of care and cure. These standard operating procedures allow hospital functionaries to carry on their jobs in a relatively predictable manner. Patients, of course, are expected to comply with established procedures and to exhibit appropriate forms of behavior. These obligations may be called the "hospitalized patient role." It must be recognized that the hospitalized patient role and the illness role are not one and the same. They do not call always for the same behavior. At times, the informally institutionalized illness role may be in direct conflict with the more formal role of the patient in the organization of the hospital. This conflict often results in a dilemma for the patient and places him under a great deal of strain. Although the patient entering the hospital may have some idea of what he may expect of others, and what they may expect of him, the interviews indicated that the hospital situation was not necessarily highly structured for all patients. Patients manifested a desire to learn and understand the "rules of the game." For instance: what do various nurses and doctors really expect of their patients? Which of the hospital regulations may be stretched a bit? Whom can one turn to for help with personal problems? How promptly will nurses answer my call? How does one identify the head nurse? This need for information appears to be more of a problem for patients in private rooms. In a multibed ward the new patient can talk with other patients. He has more of an opportunity to be initiated into the "rules of the game" and taught the reality of the hospital situation. As Barnes has described the typical ward:

> Patients have an almost uncanny knack of finding out exactly what is going on . . . Information is passed along a sort of secret "bush" telegraph and very little escapes their eyes. This seems to be true regardless of the type of ward or the type of illness of the patient.[5]

In the hospital under study a ward situation did not exist. Most patients were isolated from other patients, and the lines of informal communication were limited severely. Therefore, the hospitalized patient was very dependent on the more formal channels of communication with hospital functionaries:

> "Well, I think maybe a lot of patients coming to the hospital know very little about the hospital. As I mentioned before if the nurses can just explain things to you."
>
> (QUESTION: *Can a doctor help the patient in his adjustment to hospitalization?*)
>
> "Oh yes, by explaining to the patient the trouble there is in not having enough people around to help you. I think it is important to explain to the patient about his hospitalization."

Patients wanted to secure information with hospital functionaries through direct personal contact. However, personal contact also was desired by patients for other reasons than information. Many patients reported that the days passed slowly for them. There was little to occupy their time. Others felt extremely lonely and wished they "just had somebody to talk to." For this type of communication patients looked especially to nurses.

(QUESTION: *What is a really nice nurse?*)

"One that is willing to say a few words to you. After all when you are in the hospital it can get lonesome. I think it helps some people to have nurses that make occasional remarks whether it's about the weather or anything else."

(QUESTION: *What should a patient expect from his nurse?*)

"She should be ready to talk to the patient when she is around and ready to take a joke and joke back."

From the point of view of some patients, communications of this nature with the nurse are strictly expressive, i.e., concerned with direct gratification as an end in itself as contrasted to the more instrumental nature of the desire for information. This was illustrated nicely by the meaning ascribed by patients to the nurses' smiles.

"It just makes them [patients] a little more cheerful. It takes them out of the gloom."

"The patient feels that his day is a much better one when a nurse comes in with a smile. You feel things don't look so bad."

"If a grouchy nurse comes in the morning your day is ruined— I mean if she snaps at you."

However, this typically expressive type of communication also may be a means toward an instrumental end for the patient. For example, patients manifested a strong sense of obligation toward both the doctor and the nurse to be cooperative. They also felt obligated to be considerate, especially of the doctor, and not to be demanding. They also said that they should not be dependent, especially with the nurse. Although patients tried at all times to adhere to this hospitalized patient role, they often admitted that the sick patient is sometimes "not himself," and they expressed some anxiety over being rejected by hospital personnel (especially the nurse) for not being a "good patient." The kind, patient and tolerant nurse was able to indicate to the patient that his occasional deviations from being a "good patient" were understood and would not cause him to be rejected. It is interesting and important to note that in this case the nurse's smile may be more instrumental to the patient than it is expressive, for here it takes on an added symbolic meaning. For example:

"So when the nurse comes in here and she has a smile on her face, I know that she understands, and I know that she's willing to do anything."

"But a patient who really feels bad and needs assistance from a nurse, well, that really makes a difference. If the nurse is co-operative in that way and gives him a smile, or runs into the room once in a while it makes him feel good. She doesn't tire of that. She's not dissatisfied with the patient."

The possibility of rejection is closely related to a patient's preoccupation with safety, and must be discussed more adequately.

First, it must be understood that the most common belief expressed by almost every patient interviewed, was that both doctors and nurses were very busy, rushed and overworked, and really did not have enough time to take care of all their patients. Furthermore, patients were quite cognizant of the bureaucratic organization of the hospital with its complexity and impersonality. Some patients suspected that some doctors and nurses had little interest in their patients and were not as dedicated as they might be. A few patients insisted that some doctors were interested only in financial gain. These beliefs in combination with each other seemed to foster a fear in the patient that he must be on guard against being neglected or being the subject of gross mistakes that would hamper his chances of getting well.

The Meaning of Personalized Care

Even though many times patients were afraid for their safety in the hospital, there was relatively little doubt of the knowledge, the skills and the training of nurses and doctors. It seemed that patients, being laymen, found themselves unable to judge either the hospital or its functionaries on strictly technical grounds.[6] For instance, in defining criteria for evaluating nurses and doctors, "personalized care" was mentioned by 89 per cent of the patients for doctors, and 81 per cent for nurses—as compared with knowledge and skill, 57 per cent for doctors and 31 per cent for nurses. These percentages must be evaluated very carefully. It is not thought that they mean that the patients felt "personalized care" was a more important facet of total patient care than knowledge and skill. On the contrary, it is postulated that in the absence of being able to judge the knowledge and the skill of hospital personnel, patients used "personalized care" as a *sign*, or *indication*, that their doctors and nurses were technically competent, dedicated and had an interest in their patients. In other words, in this case, communications from hospital functionaries were not sought for direct gratification, but for the much more instrumental function of a sign of safety. Thus, it was the symbolic meaning that patients attached to the communication of "personalized care" which made it so important for them.

Communication of "personalized care" may take a variety of different forms. First, taking time to see and observe the patient was considered important.

(QUESTION: *What makes a good nurse?*)

"One who has got just a little above reading the paper and who observes the patients and sees if they look just right, and doesn't go by just what's written."

(QUESTION: *What else makes a good doctor?*)

"Coming down to see the patient as often as he can. When you're lying in bed here and your doctor doesn't come up all day long you feel like a piece of furniture. You know? The other way you feel that he's interested in you when he comes around to see how you are."

"I think that a doctor . . . whether he is a famous surgeon or not should spend a little time with the patient. I think the psychological effect helps immensely many times. And I think he is missing there."

Second, the manner in which nurses and doctors talk to and conduct themselves with patients has a profound effect on whether patients feel their doctors and nurses are dedicated and have an interest in them as "persons." For instance, consider these patient comments on nurses:

"Well, they don't have to come in and be a Pollyanna. I don't mean that, but they can give you a certain amount of assurance with the way they talk to you, the way they go about their work, the way they listen to you . . ."

"When nurses come in and introduce themselves and ask you how you are feeling, and that helps a lot. If somebody comes in there and just looks at you and walks out, it seems they're not part of you or trying to help you."

The same thing seemed to apply just as appropriately to the physician. For example:

"When a doctor comes into the room he should show you that he isn't coming in there because he has to, or that you're just another patient. Then you have the feeling that he cares, he isn't thinking of other patients, he is just thinking of you; and his mind is just on you."

"My old doctor made me feel like a new person . . . like part of the family not just as if it were a business. He made me feel at ease and comfortable and not reluctant to say what I feel."

SUMMARY OF PART ONE

The first part of this paper described the meaning and the function of communication between hospitalized patients and hospital functionaries from the point of view of a sample of patients in a large private urban hospital. It was discovered that communication had two primary meanings for the hospitalized patients; the securing of information, and interpersonal contact. Patients desired information about the nature and the extent of their illness, technical medical procedures, and what might be called the "general social organization" of the hospital. When received, this information tended to alleviate patients' fear and anxiety about their illness and what was going to happen to them, helped them to define and adapt to the expectations of hospital personnel, and met their need for a feeling of safety in the hospital. Interpersonal contact helped to stem patients' feeling of loneliness, aided them in defining their "rights" in the hospital, and contributed to meeting their need for personalized care. However, patients indicated that they were not satisfied totally with either the quantity or the quality of their communications with physicians and nurses. In the next section some of the barriers to effective and meaningful communication between patients and nurses and patients and physicians will be described and discussed.

PART II. *Barriers to Communication*

One of the most highly publicized stereotypes of nurses and physicians is that they are always very busy and overworked, and hardly have enough time to take care of all their patients. The hustle, bustle and fast pace of the hospital atmosphere seem to reinforce this belief with patients. This impression of hospital reality acted as an important restraint on patients' initiating communications with physicians and nurses. For instance, relative to asking questions of the physician:

"I have the feeling that I am afraid to take up their time."

And relative to attempting to talk with the nurse:

"If you want to tell her something, she won't listen to you. She is on her way out . . . and a patient senses that."

Patients were characteristically reluctant to complain about hospital services, since they felt that little could be done when personnel were "so busy."

"We wouldn't want to cause any trouble for any of the help, which a lot of times I don't think is their fault. I think sometimes maybe they are shorthanded, and that's one of the reasons."

Thus, one of the major barriers to communication between hospital functionaries and hospitalized patients was the patients' impression that the medical and nursing staffs were busy and overworked.

The patient's perception of the hospital work load was related to the strong feeling on the part of some patients that they had a moral obligation to other "sicker" patients who may need the personnel's limited time more than they did. (This feeling of obligation seemed to be much stronger among patients who had been unable to define how ill they were.) For example, one patient broke "doctor's orders" (which in itself is a strongly felt obligation) to stay in bed, rather than call a nurse and ask for a bedpan.

> "I got up and went to the toilet because I still could walk. I don't feel that you should call a nurse if you can do it by yourself."

Another patient commented on why she customarily refrained from asking nurses for services, in these words:

> "I mean undoubtedly there are some patients on this floor that are so much more in need of services than I am, and I just wouldn't."

Patients were often hesitant to ask questions, complain, or ask for services, because they feared negative reaction—especially from nurses. This too acted as a barrier to free communication of their needs.

> "I know that some hospitals are that way, the more you complain they shut the door and then you didn't see them."

> "I don't believe in asking so many questions. I don't want the people to get disgusted with you."

> (QUESTION: *You mean that you didn't get angry when they didn't bring you the bedpan on time?*)

> "No . . . you would just make yourself upset and also the nurse. The next time she would say: 'Oh well, why should I bother with her, let her wait.' "

In more than a few cases, patients expressed a degree of hostility and cynicism "about getting anything done in the hospital." This orientation was most characteristic of patients who were aware of the complexity and the impersonality of large bureaucratic organizations such as the hospital. These patients sometimes refused to ask for services "because it just would not do any good." For example:

> (QUESTION: *Why wouldn't you turn to the nurse for such things?*)

> "You probably should, but I wouldn't turn to the nurse because . . . I don't think that would probably get me any place."

> "I did ask one girl if they gave back rubs here. She said, 'yes, I will come back and give you one,' but she never did."

(QUESTION: *Why didn't you ask for it again?*)

"Well, what's the use?"

Patients frequently refused to ask nurses questions related to their illness because when they did, they rarely received satisfactory answers. Thus, nurses often were perceived as not having the authority to communicate this type of information to patients.

(QUESTION: *Do you ever ask the nurses for any information?*)

"Oh, come on now, this would be pretty silly. The nurse does not know anything. Nurses never give you answers."

"Well you have to remember that the nurse can't really do very much for you. She is only here to carry out the orders of the physician and some people forget that the nurse can't do much for them. She can't tell you anything."

Thus a feeling of futility, which seemed to grow stronger the longer the patient stayed in the hospital, kept patients from making their needs known.

Probably the most common barrier to physician-patient communication was simply the small amount of time that physicians spent with patients. During the physician's short—and from the patient's point of view, infrequent—visits, the patients were unable to find time to ask any questions. Or what was even more common, during the rush of the short visit the patients were unable to remember on the spur of the moment exactly what they wanted to ask. Several patients even attempted to keep a notebook of questions that they wanted to ask, so that they would be sure not to forget them when the physician came into the room.

"He (the physician) came over to me to talk and when I was just about ready to say something, he was on his way out. He did that every day. And I would rather have him come in once and talk for three minutes so I could ask him something rather than just come in and walk out."

"They say 'well, we will talk about it, next time.' And they come next time and they talk fast, they outtalk you; and they rush out of the room. When they are out of the room then you think, 'well I was supposed to ask him what he's going to do about my medicine, where is my shot, where is my pills . . .' "

"I have the feeling that I am afraid to take up their time, and I talk rapidly and forget half the things I wanted to ask him . . . I know there's pressure."

Thus, one of the patient's greatest problems in attempting to communicate with the physician was simply lack of time with him. As one patient put it:

> "They don't stand still long enough for you to draw a bead on um."

Sometimes a patient was able to corner his physician for a moment and ask him questions. But the physician's replies were in a jargon that was difficult for the patient to understand.*

> "And when they tell you something you very often don't understand it because it is said in such fancy language that it leaves a lot to your imagination."

> "You wait 24 hours before you see your physician. Then he puts his head into the door, comes perhaps and takes some candy, or he talks to you in a way you don't understand and then he goes out again."

On numerous occasions, patients perceived a great social distance between themselves and their physician, which left them in awe of his great power, authority and importance. This distance acted as an effective deterrent to communication.

> "Well, I think it's because he's a doctor, I'm sort of in awe of him or something."

> (QUESTION: *What is it about doctors that gives many people the feeling of awe?*)

> "I just don't know, it is because they are so important."

> (QUESTION: *Do you think you generally feel differently when you are talking with a doctor, than, say, a lawyer?*)

> "Yes."

> (QUESTION: *In what way?*)

> "Well, I think there is something awe inspiring about doctors."

Interestingly enough, some patients also felt status distance between themselves and white nurses, but this barrier to communication did not seem to be present in their relationship with Negro personnel.

> "I wouldn't ask any nurses, but I did ask a colored girl."

> "Well, with a colored girl you can ask them a question and they didn't think you are stupid. Now I would not open my mouth to the head nurse, because she might think I was stupid."

---

* For a more detailed discussion of the problem of the use of medical jargon with patients see the Samora, Saunders and Larson article, "Medical Vocabulary Knowledge Among Hospital Patients," in this volume.

In general, patients indicated that they were much less restrained and felt much more at ease in the presence of nonwhite personnel than they did with white personnel.[7]

PART III. *Consequences of Limited Communication*

One of the most universal complaints of hospitalized patients in western society (as well as the patients of this study), is that they do not have enough communication with hospital functionaries.[8] In the first part of this paper, the meaning and the function of communication to hospitalized patients were discussed. In the second part, some of the important barriers to communication between patients and hospital functionaries were reviewed. This final section will investigate some possible explanations for the limited communication between patients and nurses and patients and physicians, and also will explore some of the possible consequences of this situation for the therapeutic process.

One of the most important restrictions on patient communication is the gradual replacement of the old-fashioned open wards by private or semi-private rooms. This procedure may have the anticipated consequence of providing a more efficient arrangement for care and cure, in the sense of less noise and more privacy for each patient. It also may lower the possibility that functionaries will confuse one patient with another. However, the demise of the ward system also acts to restrict not only satisfaction of the patient's need for interpersonal contact, but also his desire to secure information about his illness, technical medical procedures and the general "social organization" of the hospital. It has had the effect of restricting patient involvement in ward affairs.[9] The ward patient had the advantage of being able to communicate with other patients and to observe the behavior of nurses and physicians as they worked in the ward with the others. As described in Part I, patients in private or semiprivate rooms often are reluctant to call functionaries and have them make a special trip just because they would like to ask a question, want some sort of service, or just would like to chat. This is true since so many of the patients perceive that nurses and physicians are "so very busy" with other (unseen) possibly "sicker" patients. In the ward the patient had more of an opportunity to communicate with functionaries as they came in and out performing their normal duties. In this way he was able to perceive it as more legitimate to "bother" personnel with his problems, since he did not have the restraint of feeling that he was causing them to make a special trip just for him.

Thus, the hospital without a ward system may severely limit patients' informal lines of communication. Hence we have,

Hypothesis I:
Patients in private or semiprivate rooms will have less opportunity to communicate informally with other patients and hospital functionaries, than will patients in wards.

Given the fact that patients desire communication in the hospital and that informal channels often are limited, one might question why physicians and nurses do not do more communicating with patients than patients seem to think they should. However, it should be understood that physicians, nurses and other hospital personnel are not totally unaware of patients' communication problems and their need for information and interpersonal contact. Certainly they do communicate with patients, and at times may recognize the importance of this communication.[10] Nevertheless, the structure of the modern hospital is not organized toward meeting patient needs for communication, but is dedicated to the more "action oriented" ends of caring for and curing patients. There is a failure to recognize that the patient is a participant in this process and that communication with him may be vital for the achievement of the ends of care and cure. As Barnes has remarked:

> General hospital personnel are characteristically action-minded. The very nature of their work demands action without much thought. Their whole approach to any kind of problem is to do something, and the telling seems to get forgotten in the doing.[11]

To a large extent, hospital functionaries seem to believe that they must have this attitude if they are to meet hospital goals. They reason that no matter how lonely a patient may be, or how badly he may want to know exactly what is causing the pain in his abdomen and how serious it is, taking time to chat with him informally and describe the nature and the extent of his inflamed appendix is much less crucial than taking his appendix out. Emphasis is placed on tasks that are directly instrumental to the physical care and cure of patients. There is little recognition of the patients' social and psychological needs and their relationship to his physical illness. Since many physicians and nurses are often busy and overworked, and since their performance as judged by hospital standards is not based on their skill in communicating with patients, it is not difficult to understand why hospital personnel may spend so little time in this activity. Any strictly expressive communication with patients is viewed often as time-consuming activity that may lead even to an emotional involvement with a patient. Giving information to patients about their illness and treatment may be seen as something that patients do not need and probably would not understand anyway. It also might cause an emotional reaction that would interfere with their physical care and cure, and at the very least takes the time of nurses and physicians away from the "more important tasks."[12]

Hypothesis II:

The greater the pressure on hospital functionaries to achieve the instrumental goals of physical care and cure, the less the probability that they will communicate with patients except when such communication is considered instrumental for physical care and cure.

Another major factor that may help to explain why hospital functionaries restrict their communication with patients is simply self-protection.[13] In spite of the many modern advances in medical science, there is still a great deal of uncertainty in the treatment of illness and disease. Failure to communicate with the patient tends to protect the physician from having to admit that he is uncertain about the correct diagnosis and treatment, or to commit himself and later have to admit his mistake. Thus, the more uncertain that medical personnel are about diagnosis and treatment, the less likely they will be to inform patients about their hypotheses.[14]

Keeping patients uninformed also allows nurses to protect themselves. If a patient is not informed about his care and treatment, he is hampered in evaluating whether the nurses are performing their duties adequately. As one patient stated:

> It is difficult for me to answer your question. I really cannot tell if the nurses here are good or not. I have never been able to find out what they are supposed to be doing for me. One day I get two baths. The next two days none at all. Sometimes I get my medicine every two hours right on the dot. At other times it comes about every two and a half hours. Is this somebody's mistake or is this the way the doc wanted it? Hell, I don't know. You never know because they keep things secret to themselves. You can ask them if you want, but they just give you a cute little smile and say everything is fine.

Thus if patients are not told what medications they are to receive, and exactly when they are to receive them, or when and if the nurse is required to take their temperature or blood pressure, or wheel them to x-ray, etc., they cannot judge as easily whether nurses are doing their job and they are receiving the proper care. By limiting the patient's knowledge of what care he is supposed to receive, nurses may safeguard themselves against patients' checking up on them.

Hypothesis III:

The greater the need of hospital functionaries to protect themselves from having errors and mistakes discovered in their performance of care and cure activities, the greater will be their restrictions on the communication of information about these activities to patients.

Another possible factor in explaining why physicians spend so little time in communication with patients is the fact that many physicians seem to receive little personal satisfaction from the interaction. Physician and patient often come from different social-cultural backgrounds, and the difference is accentuated by age, interest, experience and language.[15] On the other hand, many physicians tend to underestimate patients' level of medical sophistication and their ability to understand.[16] Hence, physicians may attempt to keep communications with patients as functionally specific and instrumental as possible.

Interestingly enough, the same thing does not seem to be equally true of nurses. There is evidence that communications with patients, frequent contact, "beside" nursing, and meeting patients' needs for "personalized relationships" are activities that many nurses find personally satisfying and in fact meet one of their important personal reasons for entering the nursing profession.[17]

Hypothesis IV:

The less personal satisfaction hospital functionaries receive from communication with patients, the less they will desire communication with patients.

Hypothesis V:

Nurses will desire to communicate more with patients than will physicians.

It must be pointed out, however, that nurses are rarely in a position to do what they may desire. Nurses are under great pressure to follow the rules and the regulations set down by the hospital and also to follow the instrumental care policy dictated by the physician.[18] Since a policy of extended communication with patients is not considered to be the most efficient policy by the physician and the hospital, nurses may not be able to satisfy their desire to communicate with patients.

Hypothesis VI:

The more the activities of nurses are controlled by hospital rules and regulations and the instrumental care policy dictated by physicians, the more will nurses be restricted from communicating with patients.

For the reasons stated above, hospital personnel may attempt to keep communications with hospitalized patients at a minimum. When this situation occurs, patients are less likely to receive information and have interpersonal contact with hospital functionaries.

Hypothesis VII:

The greater the extent of hypotheses II, III, IV, VI, the less probability that patients will receive information and have interpersonal contact with hospital functionaries.

CONSEQUENCES OF LIMITED COMMUNICATION

Having now examined some of the possible reasons for hospital functionaries' limited communication with hospitalized patients, it is necessary to examine the possible consequences of it.

Limited communication has the anticipated result of keeping the interaction of functionaries with patients on a strictly instrumental basis geared toward the main ends of the hospital: preserving and retaining the patient's physical health, and caring for him in the process. No additional time or effort is spent informing and explaining the reality of the hospital situation, the various therapeutic procedures, and the illness itself, let alone such time-consuming activities as comforting the patient and generally relating to him expressively. Second, not informing the patient about his illness and treatment protects physicians and nurses from encountering unmanageable reactions from those patients who would not understand and might cause difficulty for personnel. Moreover, it tends to guarantee that there will be no emotional reactions to the *knowledge* of illness that might hamper the patient's chances of getting well. However, as will be discussed shortly, this guarantee does not preclude the possibility that the patient will have an emotional reaction to *not having knowledge* of his illness and treatment. Finally, limited communication seems to have the anticipated consequence of safeguarding nurses and physicians from the possibility that patients will discover neglect and incompetence in their work.

Although the policy of limited communication may result in the anticipated consequences listed above, which may be functional for accomplishing the ends of efficient physical care and cure, it also seems to result in unanticipated consequences that may jeopardize the effectiveness of the total therapeutic process.

For instance, the staff's reluctance to communicate with the patient may cause the latter to be equally reticent. Patients are less likely to give personnel information that might be vital to their care and cure regarding new symptoms, lack of care and attention, needed services, etc., and of course, any "feedback" on mistakes discovered in their therapy. Just as important in this regard is the fact that limited communications with patients, especially about the nature and the seriousness of their illness, encourages the hospitalized individual to play the "good patient" role. When patients are not told how "sick" they are, or how serious their illness is, they are hampered in determining what their "rights" are in the hospital. This encourages even greater emphasis on the patients' already strong sense of obligation. Patients are more reluctant to make their needs known to functionaries and to pass on information that might be vital to their care and ultimate cure, because they do not wish to bother personnel, or to alienate them. Consequently, a barrier to the upward flow of communication is created in large part due directly to the restrictions on the downward flow of communication.

Hypothesis VIII:

The greater the restrictions on the flow of communication from hospital functionaries to patients, the greater the probability that restrictions will exist on the flow of communication from patients to hospital functionaries.

Not informing the patient about his illness may have the unanticipated effect of reducing his trust and confidence in the physician,[19] and also his willingness to cooperate with the physician.[20] Two quotations from patients interviewed illustrate this point.

(QUESTION: *What can a doctor do to increase the patient's confidence?*)

"Well, I don't know exactly. But this I can tell you for sure. With me I got confidence in a guy who will give it to you straight —the truth with no beating around the bush. And that goes for all them nurses they got around here too."

"When they let you know what is happening you can help them. But you can't cooperate with them when you don't know how. That is a fact."

This situation may be a hindrance to the therapeutic process in the sense that it may make it more difficult for functionaries to perform necessary physical care and cure measures.

Hypothesis IX:

The less communication between patients and hospital functionaries, the less the probability that patients will have confidence in hospital functionaries.

Hypothesis X:

The less communication between patients and hospital functionaries, the less probability that patients will be able to cooperate with hospital functionaries.

One of the most important reasons why functionaries make a practice of not telling patients about their illness and treatment is that they believe it would confuse and worry them and might make their condition worse.

Perhaps this does happen with some patients. However, there is considerable evidence that not informing the patient about his illness and treatment may have exactly the opposite effect. A degree of fear and anxiety over one's illness is quite normal. It hardly seems possible that this situation can be relieved by simply ignoring the patient's interest and desire for information. It is more likely that *not* informing the patient may have the effect of accentuating his fear and anxiety. Many times the unknown is a greater source of fear, if not greater, than the known.[21] Reactions of this nature occurred frequently in patients interviewed in this study. For example:

> "When the doctor doesn't tell you anything, then you know it's time to get scared."

> "If one of those pretty young nurses would just tell you in advance what they are going to do to you, then you would not have to be afraid every time someone comes into the room."

> "If I could just know what is wrong with me I could get a hold of myself."

Several studies of cancer patients tend to emphasize this point. Cancer is one of the very dreaded diseases today and receives a great deal of publicity. The chance of being afflicted with cancer seems to cause more fear and anxiety in individuals than from any of the other dreaded diseases.[22] Yet studies with cancer patients by Gerle and associates,[23] Aitken-Swan and Easson,[24] and Kelly and Friesen,[25] show that not only did the great majority of patients want to be told[26] and were thankful when they were, but the knowledge seemed to have a positive effect on their attitudes toward their illness.[27] In fact, Gerle reports that the patients who had not been informed had the most difficulties; they were more anxious and desperate.[28]

Hypothesis XI:
The greater the patient's fear and anxiety about the nature and the extent of his illness, the greater the probability that this fear and anxiety will not be reduced when such information is not communicated to him.

This type of situation in which patients are anxious and fearful over not knowing what is wrong with them, may lead to serious misconceptions about patients on the part of functionaries. If nurses and physicians firmly believe that information will cause the patient undue anxiety and fear, they are quite likely to take the patient's signs of fear and anxiety over not knowing the nature and the state of his illness as "proof positive" that the patient's condition is such that he should not be told. This may become a self-perpetuating process: the more that a patient worries about not being told, the more reluctant the personnel will be to tell him anything.

Another important misconception that may result from limited communication with patients lies in the functionaries' definition of "problem" patients. From the point of view of nurses and physicians, "good" patients are those who conform to the "good patient" role by restraining themselves, not asking questions and not demanding services, etc. Yet, in reality, it may very well be that it is the "good patient" who has the most problems, since it is more likely that it is his needs which are not being met. To a large degree those patients who cause the most "trouble" for doctors and nurses are the ones who make sure that someone is going to care for them.

Hypothesis XII:
The less communication between patients and hospital functionaries, the greater the probability that the functionaries will base their actions on misperceptions of the needs of their patients.

It must be kept in mind that the hypotheses presented in this last section were derived from the data of one study of the patient role, the author's personal observations and experiences in the hospital, and a survey of the literature concerning communication between patients and hospital functionaries. By no means should the hypotheses be considered tested, nor the analysis thought to be definitive. At best, both are in the first stage of development and must be subjected to further study, refinement and empirical test. Nevertheless, with these limitations in mind, it is hoped that this presentation will be of some heuristic value to those who are interested in a better understanding of the problems of communication in the modern hospital.

FOOTNOTES

1. This study was conducted by the Department of Patient Care Research, Presbyterian-St. Lukes Hospital, Chicago, Illinois, with the aid of a grant from the Commonwealth Fund. Hans O. Mauksch and Daisy L. Tagliacozzo were the directors of this project. The author would like to express his appreciation to them for their help in the preparation of this report.
2. Parsons, Talcott, and Shils, Edward, *Toward A General Theory of Action,* Cambridge, Mass., Harvard University Press, 1959, p. 75.
3. Parsons, Talcott, and Fox, Renne, "Illness, Therapy, and the Modern Urban Family," *in* Jaco, E. Gartly, (ed.) *Patients, Physicians and Illness,* Glencoe, Ill., Free Press, 1958, p. 234.
4. Barnes, Elizabeth, *People In Hospitals,* London, Macmillan, 1961, p. 15.
5. *Ibid.,* p. 88.
6. Freidson came to essentially this same conclusion in his study of subscribers to a prepaid medical plan in New York: Freidson, Eliot, *Patients' Views of Medical Practice,* New York, Russell Sage Foundation, 1961, p. 75.
7. This phenomenon may pose some interesting questions for nursing care, but

the data are slim in this area and much more research is needed before any type of definitive statement may be made.

8. See for instance: Barnes, *op. cit.,* p. 15; Burling, Temple; Lentz, Edith; and Wilson, Robert, *The Give and Take in Hospitals,* New York, G. P. Putnam's Sons, 1956, p. 355; Buck, R. L., "Socio-Cultural Stresses and the Physician-Patient Relationship," *Journal of the American Medical Association,* Vol. 170, 1959, pp. 1648-1651; Coser, Rose, *Life in the Ward,* East Lansing, Mich., Michigan State University Press, 1962, pp. 45-49; Galton, Lawrence, "The Best Medicine—Sympathy," *New York Times Magazine,* February 18, 1962, pp. 22, 72, 76, 78; Pratt, Lois; Seligmann, Arthur; and Reader, George, Physicians' Views on the Level of Medical Information Among Patients," *in* Jaco, *op. cit.,* pp. 222-228; Rothenberg, Robert, E., (ed.) "Author's Preface," *Understanding Surgery,* New York, Pocketbooks, 1955, pp. xvii-xviii.

9. Wessen, Albert, "Hospital Ideology and Communication Between Ward Personnel," *in* Jaco, *op. cit.,* p. 449. In the hospital under observation, the vast majority of accommodations were either one or two bed.

10. Skipper, James K., Jr., *The Social Obligations of Hospitalized Patients: A System Analysis,* unpublished Ph.D. dissertation, Department of Sociology, Northwestern University (1964).

11. Barnes, *op. cit.,* p. 16.

12. Miller, A., "The Patient's Right to Know the Truth," *Canadian Nurse,* Vol. 58, 1962, pp. 25-29; Barnes, *op. cit.,* p. 27; Kutner, Bernard, "Surgeons and their Patients: A Study in Social Perception," *in* Jaco, *op. cit.,* p. 390; Dodge, Joan, "Nurses' Sense of Adequacy and Attitudes Toward Keeping Patients Informed," *Journal of Health and Human Behavior,* Vol. 2, 1961, pp. 213-214.

13. See, for instance, Moore, Wilbert, and Tumin, Melvin, "Some Social Functions of Ignorance," *American Sociological Review,* Vol. 14, 1949, pp. 787-795.

14. Davis, Fred, "Uncertainty in Medical Prognosis, Clinical and Functional," *American Journal of Sociology,* Vol. 56, 1960, pp. 41-43.

15. Kutner, *op. cit.,* p. 392; Schaffer, Leslie, and Meyers, Jerome, "Psychotherapy and Social Stratification," *Psychiatry,* Vol. 17, 1954, pp. 83-93; Hollingshead, August, and Redlich, Frederick, *Social Class and Mental Illness,* New York, John Wiley & Sons, 1958; Mechanic, David, "Role Expectations and Communication In the Therapist-Patient Relationship," *Journal of Health and Human Behavior,* Vol. 2, 1961, p. 194.

16. Pratt, Seligmann, and Reader, *op. cit.,* p. 228.

17. Mauksch, Hans, *The Nurse: A Study in Role Perception,* unpublished Ph.D. Dissertation, Department of Sociology, University of Chicago, June 1960, pp. 57, 61, 155; Johnson, Miriam M., and Martin, Harry W., "A Sociological Analysis of the Nurse Role," *American Journal of Nursing,* Vol. 58, 1958, pp. 373-377; Skipper, James K., Jr., "Functional Significance of the Nurse Role: An Evaluation," *Journal of Health and Human Behavior,* Vol. 3, 1962, pp. 41-45; Skipper, James K., Jr., and Sakumoto, Raymond, "The Nurse Role: An Instrumental or Expressive Function?" *Canadian Nurse,* Vol. 59, 1963, pp. 139-142; Schulman, Sam, "Basic Functional Roles in Nursing: Mother Surrogate and Healer," *in* Jaco, *op. cit.,* pp. 528-537.

18. Abdellah, Faye; Beland, Irene; Martin, Almeda; and Metheney, Ruth, *Patient-Centered Approaches to Nursing,* New York, Macmillan, 1960, p. 39.
19. Kutner, *op. cit.,* p. 391.
20. Pratt, Seligmann, and Reader, *op. cit.,* p. 229, and Pratt, Lois, "How Do Patients Learn About Disease," *Social Problems,* Vol. 4, 1956, p. 29.
21. Lederer, Henry, "How the Sick View Their World," *in* Jaco, *op. cit.,* p. 249.
22. Levine reports that in a sample of 2,970 persons in 30 countries in the United States who responded to an interview about their degree of anxiety over various illnesses; it was *cancer* that evoked the greatest fear. Gene Levine, "Anxiety about Illness: Psychological and Social Basis," *Journal of Health and Human Behavior,* Vol. 3, 1962, p. 30.
23. Gerle, Bo; Lunden, Gerd; and Sandblom, Philip, "The Patient with Inoperable Cancer from the Psychiatric and Social Standpoints: A Study of 101 Cases," *Cancer,* Vol. 13, 1960, pp. 1206-1217.
24. Aitken-Swan, Jean, and Easson, E. C., "Reactions of Cancer Patients on Being Told Their Diagnosis," *British Medical Journal,* March 21, 1959, p. 783.
25. Kelly, W. D., and Friesen, S. R., "Do Cancer Patients Want to Be Told?" *Surgery,* Vol. 27, 1950, pp. 822-826.
26. *Ibid.*
27. Aitken-Swan, and Easson, *op. cit.*
28. Gerle, Lunden, and Sandblom, *op. cit.,* p. 1215.

Explanation to the Patient

MARGARET AASTERUD

Events that require explanation to patients are constantly occurring within the nurse-patient setting. Within the scope of her own functioning, the nurse is always responsible for the explanation of her own actions. In addition, she is frequently responsible for re-explaining information that has been imparted to patients by other members of the health team.

These three statements constitute the essence of the knowledge and beliefs on which, for years, the behavior advocated for the nurse in her role as "explainer to patients" has been based. The emphasis has largely been upon the need for such explanation; the type, extent, and timing of

Reprinted with permission from *Nursing Forum,* Vol. 2, No. 4, 1963, pp. 36-44.

the explanations has, more often than not, depended upon the personality and intuition of the individual nurse.

Expanding knowledge about the behavior of people under psychological and physiological stress is increasingly providing clues and working hypotheses which can aid the nurse in judging how much explanation is indicated and when it should be given. Incorporation of this knowledge into a rationale for certain nursing communications and the identification of factors which may block nurse-patient understanding will be not only profitable to the patient but stimulating to the nurse as she uses this knowledge in recognizing and responding to behavioral cues.

THE TYPE AND EXTENT OF EXPLANATIONS

A literal interpretation of a bed-fastened sign "N.P.O." as "nil per os" is meaningless to a person who has no knowledge of Latin or only a scanty recollection of it. Such an explanation is akin to the many situations in which a detailed interpretation is given to a casual question, or a factual description of an impending action is given without consideration of the level of understanding possessed by the person addressed. It is easy to forget that exact accounts of certain procedures are not of a sort to allay the apprehension of the person upon whom they are to be performed. Frequently, a general summary of what is to be done, the expected action of the patient during the procedure, and the approximate length of time it will require will be sufficient.

If the patient is informed that a particular radiologic examination will require restriction of food and fluids for eight hours and that he will be transported to the radiology department shortly after eight o'clock in the morning, he does not run the risk of being scolded for filling his own water pitcher, or of suffering the silence of those who have to wait for him to get ready in the morning. The element of surprise is further lessened if he knows that several films may be taken, and he will not be concerned when the total examination requires a substantial length of time. However, it would probably not be necessary to provide him with a great deal of technical information about the examination itself.

It must be remembered, however, that what may seem to the nurse to be a routine procedure, requiring a minimum amount of explanation, may appear in quite a different light to the patient. Before the nurse decides on the type and extent of explanation required, the patient should have an opportunity to express his views of the forthcoming event. His description may be grossly inaccurate, weird, or fanciful, but if communication does not start with recognition of his perception of the situation, the most careful of explanations may fail to assure him. For example, the person who believes that the administration of oxygen is reserved for those suffering from the most severe and terminal illnesses may become extremely apprehensive upon being told that oxygen is being given to him to "make it easier for you to breathe." His response may be a perfunctory, "I see," while his original fear and lack of understanding remain. Repeated assurances from different members of the health team may not contribute to relief of his anxiety until this source of fear is identified and eliminated, possibly by a more extensive explanation that had at first been contemplated.

However, the degree of apprehension felt by patients is not a completely reliable index to the amount of effort that should be expended on the explanations given them. Particular care should be taken in judging the type and extent of explanation given to patients who display a lack of concern about impending medical or surgical events. Intuitively, nurses often sense the unnaturalness of such unconcern and remark, "I don't think he knows what he is getting into." However, both physicians and nurses are usually relieved to find reinforcement of their own knowledge that the treatment is a "minor" one or, if it is an admitted "major" one, that it will proceed uneventfully. Accordingly, these unconcerned patients frequently receive a minimum amount of explanation about the event that lies ahead of them.

In the behavioral and psychoanalytical study of surgical patients by Janis, those patients whose preoperative behavior was one of unconcern displayed a significantly higher degree of emotional disturbance, anger, and resentment after the surgical procedure than did those patients who displayed moderate anxiety and apprehension in the preoperative period. The latter group seemed to have worked through in advance some of the impending unpleasant experiences and to have gained assurance from explanatory communications that stressed certain eventual benefits from the procedure.[1]

It *is* easy to under explain a procedure to a person who displays an attitude of sophistication regarding it, or who lightly dismisses the event as not being a cause for worry. In view of Janis' research, this is the patient about whom nurses should be especially concerned, not only as regards the scope of the nursing explanations but also in connection with the observations to be shared with the physician.

TIMING OF EXPLANATIONS

Judgment is required in deciding the appropriate time to explain to a person the event which will affect him in an uncomfortable or painful manner. Except for the desirability of informing the person in advance, there is, at present, no specific guideline about *when* explanation should be given.

In the case of a major event that involves changes in living patterns and sustained psychological or physiological stress, the person may require a period of time to plan adaptive changes and to work through his feelings. Information concerning the event itself or its anticipated sequelae might therefore be given to him fairly well in advance of its occurrence.

On the other hand, minor medical and nursing procedures are probably best explained just before their occurrence. Janis suggests that when patients are told in advance about a minor event, particularly one involving forcible intrusion of an orifice, the person has time to visualize it as a horrible ordeal. He states that it may be more difficult to reassure the patient after he has spent a great deal of time imagining what the threatening procedure might be like than it would be if he has remained unconcerned until the moment when the procedure is about to begin.[2] The person who is inordinately afraid of injections might suffer intensely during a long interim between the time he is told that an injection is to be given and the time when the nurse arrives to administer it. A catheterization or an enema may be built up until it looms as a major source of pain and discomfort, but be well tolerated if the nurse explains it just before institution and is calm, matter-of-fact, and supportive of the patient during the procedure.

Many nurses are aware of these feelings, perhaps again on an intuitive basis, and skillfully time their explanations accordingly. Others interpret the admonition "Explain what you are doing" to mean detailed descriptions made well in advance. For example, when a patient asks for more specific details, the nurse may yield to the temptation to "tell all one knows" and thus inadvertently add to the patient's anxiety by relating precautions taken in preparation for, or in the administration of, a procedure. An unexpressed reaction to such an account can be, "If there are those precautions, it must be dangerous." The patient may also be critical of those who, in the future, perform a similar procedure in a technically different manner.

An explanation made after an event occurs is less desirable, but is preferable to no explanation. A patient who is chagrined at finding dry toast and black coffee on his breakfast tray may be assuaged by the nurse who assures him, immediately after the arrival of the tray, that there has been no mistake in identity and that the frugal diet is a part of the test he is undergoing. Or, a statement to a person awakening from anesthesia that the incision is not as extensive as his bandage saves him from being frightened by the discovery that the bandage covers an area twice as large as he had expected. Certainly, an advance explanation would have been preferable, but an *ex post facto* explanation is better than none.

BLOCKS TO EXPLANATORY COMMUNICATIONS

The nurse may feel inadequate and frustrated in attempting to communicate with cultural groups other than her own. Because she may not be familiar with their conception of illness and health care, her explanations of certain aspects of care may be misunderstood or ignored. Frequently, cooperation on the part of the patient is interpreted as understanding when the assent was actually an attempt to please the physician or the nurse. This may be particularly true of persons from underprivileged and racially segregated groups.[3]

In many instances, explanations of events must be made in entirely nonmedical language. The transition from the use of technical to non-technical words and expressions is not always easy and may cause the nurse momentary confusion or self-consciousness, particularly if the explanation involves terms relating to eliminatory or reproductive functions.

Nurses are usually cognizant of a child's level of language understanding, and experienced pediatric nurses tend to make appropriate translations automatically. Too often however, it is assumed that the adult knows what is meant not only by accepted medical and anatomical terms, but also by unofficial abbreviations and medical jargon.

The patient who is known to be well educated or of above-average income and social status often has his understanding of health practices overestimated. Members of the health team assume that certain explanations would be "talking down" to him, and so they avoid making these explanations or do so in medically sophisticated language. Professional persons who have been hospitalized frequently have a poignant recollection of their inability to elicit simple and warm assurances from medical and nursing personnel because they were assumed to "know all about it."

The nurse must also take into consideration the viewpoints and biases she has derived from her own culture and personal experiences. A nurse whose background includes a family and community that placed value upon bearing pain stoically, and that treated most illnesses at home and reserved hospitalization for grave illness, may find it difficult to become concerned with patients who have "minor" complaints. She may be insensitive to or ignore some of the evidences of patient needs and therefore not provide explanation because of her culturally engendered expectations of behavior.

A degree of identification with the patient's problems may result in an increased sensitivity to and awareness of his needs for explanation and assurances. For example, a nurse who has personal and vivid recollections of an unpleasant hospital admitting routine is likely to spend more time explaining seemingly small items to a newly admitted patient and his family than would be spent by another nurse. However, the identification may be so strong that the nurse loses some of her potential usefulness. A nurse whose mother has undergone a radical operative procedure followed by a trying and family-disruptive convalescence may be unable to communicate on more than a superficial level with a patient who is to undergo a similar surgical intervention. Certain situations in which the nurse overidentifies with the patient may parallel Bird's example of the medical student who was unable to observe that the patient he was examining had a paralysis of an arm and a leg, his own father having recently sustained the same type of impairment.[4]

These variables among both patients and nurses emphasize the fact that decisions about the explanations that are given to patients cannot be based upon blanket rules or adages. Rather, they should be based upon knowledge of how people behave under stress, of how anxiety affects a person's ability to communicate, and of the influence of socio-cultural factors, and, in addition, on an assessment by the nurse of her own expectations.

REFERENCES

1. Janis, Irving, *Psychological Stress,* New York: John Wiley & Sons, 1958, pp. 398-406.
2. Janis, I., *op. cit.,* p. 387.
3. McCabe, Gracia, "Cultural Influences on Patient Behavior," *American Journal of Nursing* 60:1101 (August) 1960.
4. Bird, Brian, *Talking With Patients,* Philadelphia: J. B. Lippincott, 1955, p. 12.

Nurses' Sense of Adequacy and Attitudes Toward Keeping Patients Informed

JOAN S. DODGE

Patients constantly complain about the lack of information they receive from physicians and nurses regarding their conditions, their care, their treatments, and so forth. For various reasons, medical and nursing staffs (or at least individuals on these staffs) may feel it inadvisable to

Reprinted with permission from the author and the *Journal of Health and Human Behavior;* Vol. 2, 1961, pp. 213-216.

give too much information to the patient. They may feel it will only confuse and worry him. They may feel he is incapable of understanding any
but the most superficial aspects. Or they may wish, consciously or unconsciously, to preserve the notion that they, like the witch doctor of old,
are the sole possessors of great health-giving secrets.

Whatever the reason for not communicating to the patient, there is
increasing evidence that communication plays a vital role in patient care.
Research, such as that done by Janis[1] on surgical patients, suggests that
patients who are given relatively full explanations about *what* to expect
and *why* are less anxious about their operations. Although it is extremely
difficult, methodologically, to do a crucial test of the relation between
anxiety and speed of recovery, there seems to be little doubt that communication plays an important role.

THE RESEARCH QUESTION

The research question, then, becomes, What are the determinants of a
nurse's or physician's belief about importance of communication with the
patient? Reader's[2] work suggests that the physician's estimation of his
patients' medical knowledge might be a factor. Psychological research in
other areas suggests that the person who feels himself inadequate for
some reason or other is often less willing to communicate with others—
presumably because of a fear of exposing his ignorance. There may be no
actual inadequacy in the area under consideration. Rather, the important
factor seems to be a *generalized* belief in one's ability to meet the requirements of life.

To the person who feels inadequate, situations which require him to
tell what he knows are threatening, and he prefers to avoid them. Denying
their importance is the one way of avoiding them more easily. Generally,
people are not expected to do things that they do not believe in. By denying
the importance of communication, then, one can often avoid doing anything
about it.

The present research is based on this notion. We asked whether the
nurse who perceives herself as a psychologically strong or tough individual
differs in her belief as to the importance of keeping the patient informed
about what is going on from the nurse who perceives herself as relatively
weak. In light of existing evidence, we expected that the weaker nurse,

---

[1] Irving L. Janis, *Psychological Stress: Psychoanalytic and Behavioral Studies of Surgical Patients* (New York: John Wiley & Sons, Inc., 1958).

[2] Pratt, Lois, Arthur Seligmann, and George Reader, "Physicians' Views on the Level of Medical Information among Patients," in E. Gartly Jaco, *Patients, Physicians and Illness; Sourcebook in Behavioral Science and Medicine* (Glencoe: The Free Press, 1958), pp. 222-229.

feeling less adequate than the strong one, would be less likely to endorse communication.

PROCEDURE

The subjects were 126 registered nurses, licensed practical nurses, and nurses aides working in a 314 bed hospital for the aged and chronically ill. Each filled out a questionnaire designed to measure some of her attitudes toward herself, her patients, and patient care. Two sections are relevant to the present analysis: (1) the items relating to the nurse's expressed belief in the importance of keeping patients informed, (2) items measuring her attitude toward herself.

Attitudes toward communication were inferred from responses to four questions. Two of these concern beliefs about the doctor's role: (1) doctors should explain their patients' cases to them; (2) doctors should tell patients honestly if they do not know what is wrong with them. Two relate to beliefs about the nurses' role: (3) nurses should explain the reasons for doctors' orders to their patients; (4) a nurse should tell a patient honestly if she has done something wrong in caring for him. Subjects indicated how important they felt each was by checking the appropriate space on a five point scale. Alternatives ranged from, "This is one of the most important things for a doctor (or nurse) to do," to, "This is unimportant. It doesn't matter a bit to me."

Attitudes toward the self were measured by responses to sixteen pairs of antithetical statements separated by a six point scale. Subjects indicated which alternative they felt was more characteristic of them *and the degree* by checking the appropriate space on each scale. Four of these items were taken as measures of feelings of psychological strength or adequacy.[3] These are:

1. I do what is necessary regardless of the consequences; or the opposite, I let my feelings for others get in the way of what I have to do.

2. I never lack for excitement in my work, or the opposite, the daily routine of patient care is boring.

3. I always remain calm in an emergency, or, emergencies make me nervous.

4. It takes a lot to get me down, or, I get discouraged when things don't go right.

The subject's responses to these four items were summed and divided

---

[3] Responses to all sixteen items were intercorrelated and a factor analysis was performed. These four items were found to be highly loaded on the first factor to have (with one exception) minimal loadings on the other three.

into high, medium and low groups. The groups were, then, compared as to their feelings about the importance of keeping patients informed.

Analysis

In analyzing the data, we examined two factors in addition to psychological strength. We asked, first, whether the job category of the respondent had an effect; i.e., whether nurses, licensed practical nurses, and nurse aides feel differently about the importance of communication. Secondly, we asked whether the profession referred to was relevant; i.e., whether any difference was seen in the relative importance of communication for physicians versus nurses.

An analysis of variance technique, which permitted us to look at the effect of these three variables simultaneously, was used in making our comparisons. Tables of F values and means are available for any who wish to examine them, but are not included in this report.

The significant main effects were the level of psychological strength and the profession referred to. Nurses who scored high on psychological strength believed more in communication than did the medium group who, in turn, saw it as more important than low scorers did. Secondly, the total group believed communication a more important function for doctors than for nurses. It should be mentioned that the items referring to doctors were not identical with those referring to nurses. Since identical questions would probably have been meaningless in light of different medical and nursing functions, it was felt wiser to select communication situations which, for the nurse, would be analogous to, rather than identical with, those met by the physician.

When considered alone, the job category of the respondent was not related to belief in the importance of communication. Nurses, licensed practical nurses, and nurse aides felt it about equally important. However, when the joint effect of job category and profession referred to was examined, some interesting differences emerged. Whereas nurse aides saw no difference in the importance of communication for physicians and nurses, nurses and licensed practical nurses did. The largest difference was seen by the licensed practical nurses. Although they did not differ from registered nurses in their feelings as to the importance of communication by doctors, they felt it much less important for nurses to communicate.

The joint effect of the profession being referred to and the level of psychological strength is also interesting. The difference between strong and weak individuals was larger when nurses were referred to than when physicians were referred to. That is, although in both cases strong nurses attributed more importance to communication than weak nurses did, this difference was greatest when they were referring to communication by nurses. Thus, the level of psychological strength had a stronger effect when the nurse was concerned with the behavior of her own group.

INTERPRETATION OF FINDINGS

Do these data lend support to the hypothesis expressed earlier? Before answering that question, it might be well to point out the tentative nature of the data. We are still in the early stages of the study, and have not yet become aware of all the extraneous variables that should be controlled. Also, the sample being reported on, besides being small, may well be unique—not only because the nurses are dealing with a specific type of patient, but also because they chose to work with that type of patient. Finally although this in no sense exhausts the list, we have not yet collected data in any other hospital, and thus have very little knowledge of the generality of the findings. With these limitations in mind, we may see what the results might mean.

We hypothesized that the nurse who felt relatively weak psychologically would be less likely to endorse communication than the stronger nurse would. Our data lend support to this notion. Not only did we find differences related to feelings of psychological strength when considered by itself, but these differences were particularly evident when the subjects were dealing with nursing functions. There is no special reason for expecting large differences when people are discussing the behavior of others, except as one expects generalization of attitude. The threat to the ego occurs most strongly when the self is involved. Thus, in the psychologically strong group, there was almost no difference in expressed importance of communication for doctors and nurses. The difference increased in the medium group and reached its largest size in the psychologically weak group—the group which would be expected to feel the greatest threat.

The significant joint effect of job category and profession being referred to is also interesting here. The licensed practical nurse group saw communication as less important for nurses than either the registered nurses or aides did. It is conceivable that the licensed practical nurse may feel least qualified for the job she has to do. She has received more training than the aid has, but must also carry more responsibility—an ever increasing amount in most hospitals. In the hospital we have studied, her functions are essentially the same as those of the registered nurse. Yet her training is far from being as extensive. She agreed with the registered nurse in seeing communication as important for the doctor, but declined to see it as an important function for nurses.

Interestingly enough, aides saw no difference in its importance for doctors and nurses. This leads one to suspect that the aides as a group may not have considered that the term "nurse" referred to them, despite the fact that they are members of the nursing staff. If they had, one would, in light of the other findings, expect more differentiation between their expectancies for doctors and nurses.

In summary, we feel that these data provide support for the notion that willingness to keep patients medically informed is related to certain aspects of the self-picture—in particular, to a feeling of personal adequacy or psychological strength. Whether this is related really to behavior in communication is not yet known; but the hypothesis that it is so related is at present being explored. If consistent differences in behavior are found, we may have the beginnings of a solution to one of the most prevalent complaints of patients. We would then be armed with the knowledge that a key to fuller communication between nurses and patients is for the nurses to have a stronger conception of their own personal adequacy.

The Effect of Types of Communication on Patients' Reactions to Stress

MARY E. MEYERS

Any new event which impinges on an individual arouses tension and the person subjected to the stress employs various devices to assist in the reduction of this tension. Basic to the tension reduction is the need to attach some meaning to the event; to give it some cognitive structure. Because of underlying attitudes and personality differences, the matrix used in this structuring process differs for each person.[1] For some people, factual information or actual past medical experience may provide sufficient meaning. For others, the structuring they use may be based on stereotypes preconditioned from other sources, such as "parlor gossip," "old wives tales,"

Edited and reprinted with permission of author and Lucille E. Notter, editor, *Nursing Research,* Vol. 13, No. 2, Spring 1964, pp. 126-131. This study was supported by U.S.P.H.S. GM-06604-04, awarded to the School of Nursing, University of California, Los Angeles.

film fiction, or a vivid imagination that uses bits and pieces of all of the above.

The over-all experience of hospitalization, whether for medical or surgical reasons, involves many stressful or tension-producing situations for the patient and he reacts according to his past experience and his psychological orientation to the event.

An important and extensive investigation of psychological stress in patients undergoing surgery has been done by Janis.[2] He studied a series of hospitalized surgical patients through interviews and by daily behavioral records made by the hospital staff. He found that one group of patients manifested a low anticipatory fear level preoperatively which was based upon an optimistic denial of potential dangers and deprivations. A second group showing moderate fear he characterized as "part-time worriers" whose stress manifestations could be alleviated by mild sedatives and routine activity. Another group, the high anticipatory fear group, reacted in an exaggerated fashion by weeping, flushing, trembling, and even by making strong efforts to avoid the impending stress by seeking to postpone the surgery. He proposed that, for excessively fearful persons, reduction of the emotional excitement is essential so that the work of worrying can be done more effectively. He further states that when the individual is misinformed, corrective communication, realistic in nature, can lessen fear. He goes on to say that the high fear group probably would benefit most from a brief form of psychological treatment to assist the individual to gain emotional control. In normal persons, he indicates, certain types of information about a threatening experience may evoke fear reactions and suggests the giving of a communication which avoids "overdoses of fear-arousing material."

These findings are of great significance for nursing service and education. From a teaching and nursing standpoint, it is important to know how the stress of a new situation can best be reduced and what factors need to be considered to divert the patient's energies most effectively. Since nursing personnel and others committed to the care of the patients will certainly affect how a patient structures his environment, their attempts (or lack of them) to give the patient tools for this structuring are vital elements in helping the patient face a stressful situation.

It is the purpose of this study to explore the effects of three different conditions of communication on the impact and resulting cognitive structuring of an unfamiliar and moderately stressful situation.

METHOD

As a stimulus, a new procedure was designed to be done with the patient. It was expected that the unfamiliarity of the stimulus situation would produce a mild degree of stress. Since patients being studied were already being subjected to the stress of hospitalization, the procedure could not impede therapy of the illness for which the patient had been hospitalized. Thus the procedure was designed to begin a thinking process based on potential threat, yet was assumed to be sufficiently benign to avoid producing any physiological pathology. Specifically, the procedure was as follows:

> The investigator entered the patient's room carrying a covered tray which contained test tubes (one dry, one with tap water at room temperature) stick applicators, gauze, and an empty covered metal container. After identifying the patient by name and getting the patient into bed, if he was not already there, one of three conditions of communication was given. The inner aspect of the patient's forearm was exposed and swabbed with the tap water. The area was covered with gauze and at fifteen-second intervals the skin area was observed by lifting a corner of the gauze. This was done in such a way that the patient was unable to see the skin area. After one minute the gauze was removed, the area dried with a swab, materials used were placed on the tray and the tray was covered.

This moderately stressful, unfamiliar stimulus was presented to three different groups of patients. Each group, at the time the stimulus was applied, was given one of three different conditions of communication. These three conditions were (1) a "structuring" communication designed to explain the situation to the patient; (2) a "no" communication situation in which the patient was told nothing of what was going to happen to him; and (3) an "irrelevant" communication designed to distract or to divert attention from the designed procedure. Specifically the communications were:

1. Structuring communications.

> "I want to tell you exactly what I am going to do. I am going to take this stick (at this point the longer applicator was shown to the patient) and wet the cotton in this solution (the longer tube with solution was shown). I am going to spread the solution on your arm and cover the place with this gauze (gauze shown). I will look under it every so often. Then I will remove the gauze, dry the area with this (the smaller applicator was shown,) and put it in here (the smaller test tube shown). The procedure will not be painful." If the patient asked questions related to the procedure, the investigator said, "This is a routine test for allergy"; "This test will show whether you are allergic or not"; or "It is a routine test done on all patients."

2. "No" communication.

No communication was given. Comments or questions from the patient were ignored. If the patient became very demanding of some response, the investigator was permitted to say, "Just a moment, please."

3. "Irrelevant" communication.

"It's rather warm again today. I heard on the radio it will be around 90 degrees downtown. It isn't as warm in the Medical Center this year as it was last year. They put those outside shades on last Fall. They keep out a lot of the direct sun. I understand we will have air-conditioning soon, but they had to put the shades on first." This communication was given while the investigator went ahead with the procedure. It ended as the "timing" portion of the procedure began.

Following the application of the stimulus, the patient's reactions to the whole experience were elicited in a post-experiment interview.* These interview responses provided the basis for determining the effects of the three different conditions of communication, and the specific questions which the interviewer used will be described in the section on results.

SAMPLE

Seventy-two hospitalized patients were selected for study. The group included 37 females and 35 males. Ages of those studied ranged from 18 to 65, and the median age was 36 years. Both medical and surgical illnesses were represented among the patients. Because those classified by the institution as "seriously ill" were assumed to be coping with serious physiological stress, they were excluded from the study. Those patients who were disoriented or otherwise unable to respond lucidly were likewise excluded.

Patients selected for the study were assigned to three different groups so that each group had approximately the same age and sex distribution as follows:

Group I, which received the "structuring" communication, included 13 females and 10 males. Thirteen of these subjects were below the median age of 36 and 10 subjects were above it.

Group II, which received "no" communication, included 11 females and 11 males, with 11 of them in the younger group and the other 11 in the older group.

Group III, which received the "irrelevant" communication, included 13 females and 14 males, with 12 in the younger and 15 in the older group.

---

* The interviews were conducted by the author and another registered nurse trained and supervised by the author.

Due to the subject matter of the "irrelevant" communication, the weather imposed one restriction on the assignment of the subjects. On the warmest days, the patients that were available were assigned to Group III to insure a sufficient population in that group.

RESULTS

The post-experimental interview focused on the patient's subjective response as to what he thought was going to happen to him, his recall of what did actually happen, his feelings during the procedure, and his recall of items of equipment on the tray, including his subjective measurement of lengths of swabs, tubes, etc. and his description of other items on the tray. Analysis of these responses provided five scores. These were: an accuracy score, a blood-needle score, an overestimation score, an underestimation score, and a talkativeness score.

1. **Accuracy Score.** The accuracy score was derived from the subject's responses to the question, "Could you tell me what was on the tray?" The patient could score anywhere from zero (that is, the subject remembered nothing about the tray) to nine (that is, correctly identified all items on the tray) as follows:

> There were six items on the tray: one 3" applicator, one 6" applicator, one 3¾" test tube, one 6" test tube, one 4" x 4" piece of gauze and one covered container. The subject received one point if he mentioned both applicators, one point if he mentioned both tubes, and one point each if he recalled the gauze and the container. The patient was also asked to describe the size of each object he recalled except for the container.* The remaining five points were given for correct identification of the size of the first five items described above with one point for each correct identification.

Since the highest number of points actually scored was six, those receiving 3-6 points were considered to be "more accurate," with those receiving 0-2 points considered to be "less accurate."

Analysis of the accuracy score is shown in Table 1. Neither sex nor age affected accuracy but the condition of communication did, and this difference was significant, by chi square test, at the .05 level.

---

* The investigator using a metal strip calibrated to 12 inches (on one side only), held the uncalibrated side toward the patient. He was asked to indicate on the "strip" what he thought was the length of each item. The investigator could observe the exact length from the calibrated side. In tabulating the data related to lengths of applicators, it became necessary to make an arbitrary assignment when only one stick was mentioned. In these instances a 4½" or under measurement was tabulated as a description of the 3" applicator; 4¾" and over as describing the 6" applicator.

TABLE 1. RELATION OF ACCURACY OF RECALL TO CONDITION
OF COMMUNICATION, AGE, AND SEX*

| SUBJECTS | ACCURACY SCORE | | | | TOTAL | |
| | MORE ACCURATE (3-6 POINTS) | | LESS ACCURATE (0-2 POINTS) | | | |
	N	%	N	%	N	%
Group I (Structuring)	16	70	7	30	23	100
Group II (No)	13	59	9	41	22	100
Group III (Irrelevant)	9	33	18	67	27	100
Total	38		34		72	

* The difference due to condition of communication was significant, by chi square test, at the .05 level.

Seventy per cent of the patients who received the "structuring" communication were more accurate in their recall, whereas the "no" and "irrelevant" groups showed much lower percentages (59 per cent and 33 per cent respectively). The finding that such a large percentage of patients who received the "structuring" communication were more accurate than those receiving "no" communication or the "irrelevant" communication shows that those who were told exactly what was to happen to them were able to accept the situation on its own terms, that is, to see it for what it really was. In other words, they were able to focus on actual details because their attention was not diverted to the concentration on only one part. Their perception was not confused by the need to bring past conditioning from "old wives' tales" and "parlor gossip" into the situation, nor was it confused by thinking of the investigator's rationale for giving no communication or for changing the subject. They were able to look at the situation more realistically, that is, as part of the whole.

2. **Blood-Needle Score.** To see whether those who were told what was going to happen to them tended to be less tense, i.e., more comfortable, as measured by the mention of the words "blood" and/or "needle," a second score was developed. This score, a "blood-needle score," was derived from responses to the question, "What thoughts ran through your mind while I was doing the procedure?" Anyone who used either the word "blood" or "needle" was classified in the "used term" group. Those who did not were classified in the "did not use term" group.

Analysis of the blood-needle score is shown in Table 2. Neither age nor

TABLE 2. USE OF THE TERMS "BLOOD" OR "NEEDLE" TO DESCRIBE
ONE'S THOUGHTS DURING THE PROCEDURE*

| | BLOOD-NEEDLE SCORE | | | | | |
| SUBJECTS | USED TERM | | DID NOT USE TERM | | TOTAL | |
	N	%	N	%	N	%
Group I (Structuring)	4	17	19	83	23	100
Group II (No)	9	41	13	59	22	100
Group III (Irrelevant)	14	52	13	48	27	100
Total	27		45		72	

* The difference due to condition of communication was significant, by chi square test, at the .05 level.

sex showed a significant difference but the condition of communication did, and this difference was significant, by chi square test, at the .05 level.

While a small percentage of the "structuring" communication group (17 per cent) mentioned blood and/or needle, much larger percentages of the "no" and "irrelevant" communication groups did at least one of the words (41 per cent and 52 per cent respectively). The finding that more subjects in the groups receiving "no" communication or the "irrelevant" communication included the use of these words in describing the thoughts that ran through their minds may indicate that they were tense and uncomfortable, their thought processes tending to recall previous "discomfort" situations. This was evident in the responses of those receiving "no" communication or the "irrelevant" communication. The subjects in these groups tended to relate the present event to a past experience with a rather typical response being, "I was just thinking that we had just gone through a session with this left arm and I thought—oh, no, here we go with this arm. Most lab tests do stick you, so I was just waiting." In contrast, those who were told what was to happen to them focused their thoughts on the immediate situation which they described by making such responses as, "I was just wondering what you were doing this for."

CONCLUSION

In teaching students of nursing in a baccalaureate program, questions relating to the biological sciences are fairly easily answered and substantiated. It is in the area of the psycho-social justification of a suggested approach that teachers of nursing experience some difficulty. Theories in these fields are numerous but it is in the application of these theories to a specific patient situation that the justification becomes "shaky" and questionable. In most approaches by the nurse to a new situation for the patient, the usual instruction is "explain to the patient." The alert student will respond with "What shall I tell her?" "How specific shall I be?" "Do I tell the same thing to all patients?" "What governs my approach?" "What is meant by 'explain'?"

In thinking of the specific function of the professional nurse as a "maintenance specialist," that is, "maintaining or re-establishing a moving state of equilibrium throughout the health change process," answers to the above questions pose questions also to the teacher of nursing.[3] Since tension may result from a disturbance in equilibrium and knowing that any new situation arouses tension, on what basis does the nurse best plan her intervention to relieve or minimize this tension? What does she need to know and take into consideration before she attempts to approach the patient?

From time immemorial, nurses have accepted "pat" instructions as "gospel" or as facts to be unquestioned. Study of these is essential so that, if in fact they are justified, we can incorporate such proven information in our plan to provide the kind of nursing care which will relieve or minimize tension and allow the patient to conserve his energy needed for defense or adaption.

Questions, by students, related to "explain to the patient" led to the preceding study, inasmuch as the answers to questions raised were not accessible except from general, theoretical responses.

Having studied what occurs in the thought processes of patients subjected to a mild degree of stress, it is easier to expand on the instruction to "explain to the patient" because now it is clear that for tension to be reduced or minimized, patients need to have the means provided to cognitively structure, that is, to give meaning to, the events which happen to them. Discomfort can be relieved. To deprive patients of knowledge of what is to happen to them is to increase tension which may limit their ability to structure mild or more stressful situations in the future.

In addition to the necessity for communicating specific information regarding the situation, the response to the patient needs to be governed by a more intimate understanding of the individual's personality in which the factors must be known as to how the person learned to deal with stress and how this governs (influences) his reaction to the present stress.

In summary, less tension is created when the patient is given specific information upon which he can structure the event of impending stress. It is essential to keep in mind that how he has learned to cope with stress from past experience will influence to a large extent the way he handles the stress; but regardless of the fact that he may be overfearful or denying as a result of his personality, communication is important. Since tension is produced by distracting communication, this type of approach is the least desirable and in terms of tension reduction, it would be better to say nothing at all. To tell the patient exactly what is going to happen to him (by structuring the communication) is most desirable. It decreases tension and can make the patient more comfortable during stressful events throughout hospitalization and/or illness.

If we are concerned with patient-centered nursing and are probing the area of the psycho-social justification of a suggested nursing approach, we may conclude that the favorable response on the patient's part to the structured "communication" type approach is related to the fact that he is no longer a depersonalized patient, being treated in a routine way. Rather, he is being treated as a person of intelligence whose cooperation is being sought by his nurse. If a measure of the stress a patient feels upon hospitalization is related to the deprivation he experiences, then it follows that the "communication" approach will negate or at least minimize some of the stress inherent in hospitalization.

REFERENCES

1. Krech, David, and Crutchfield, R. S., *Theory and Problems of Social Psychology*. New York: McGraw-Hill Book Co., 1948.
2. Janis, I. L., *Psychological Stress*. New York: John Wiley and Sons, 1958.
3. Johnson, Dorothy E., The significance of nursing care. *Amer. J. Nurs.* 61:63-66, Nov. 1961.

Talking With Patients

BRIAN BIRD

If one wants to learn something, he must be prepared to listen. This, in fact, is the main object of talking; to get the patient to talk, to hear from him, to listen.

*   *   *

Accordingly, the aim of talking with a patient is to find out not only about his immediate symptoms, but about him—his strengths and his weaknesses, his experiences throughout life, and his reactions to them. If the illness is to be understood fully, what must be learned is the kind of defenses the patient has had at his disposal, how they were developed, how strong they were, and where and why they broke down; all this in addition to learning what currently harmful events have happened to the patient and what infectious or noxious agents have invaded him.

To learn only the latter—the immediate causes of illness—is to learn only the final steps in the history of disease. Admittedly that is the urgent thing to do, and it is also the easiest; but in most illnesses it is no more than elaborate first aid and is not of lasting importance.

*   *   *

Another point in talking with the patient about his past history is that it is not enough simply to learn item by item, those past medical events. The essential thing in that regard is to learn what each of those past events did to him, how he reacted to them, even how he used them. One illness commonly predisposes a patient to another; it weakens his defenses. But not always. Sometimes one illness will act as a defense against another illness or will be used to defend the patient from some worse situation.

*   *   *

Another general aim in talking with patients is to learn the pattern of the patient's illnesses so that through this knowledge his future can at least be predicted and possibly even changed. If the circumstances leading up to or surrounding a certain attack of illness are known, it is possible

Reprinted with permission of the author. These brief excerpts were taken from pages 11, 3, 5 and 7 of the book *Talking With Patients* (Philadelphia, J. B. Lippincott Co., 1955), a classic manual on the subject. The book is highly recommended.

that by avoiding such circumstances a recurrence of the illness may be avoided.

What Is the Patient Saying?

RUTH G. ELDER

A young nursing student in the psychiatric setting was heard to say, "I'm so glad to be going back to the general hospital where patients tell you what they want when they want it and that's all there is to it!"

How often do we take it for granted that patients in general hospitals can clearly communicate their needs with little or no help from the personnel? The numerous requests, questions, and comments from patients that we hear as we make rounds, respond to the executone, and give treatments and medication would seem to indicate that patients are able to make their needs known. But is this true?

THE MOTIVATING INCIDENT FOR THE STUDY

An experience on a surgical unit focused my attention on the patient's initial communication to nursing personnel. While I was working with one patient, I heard another patient in the room—a young woman with a puzzled frown who was sitting up in bed—ask a nurse when her operation was scheduled. The nurse told her it was scheduled for the "day after tomorrow" and then went on her way. A few minutes later, I was surprised to hear Miss X ask the identical question of another member of the staff. She received a similar answer. Almost on the heels of this brief encounter, her physician entered the room, and she asked the same question of him. Apparently she had asked him this before because he said, "Now don't you worry about a thing. I've told you it's the day after tomorrow and there's nothing to worry about." He, too, left.

Puzzled and concerned, I then approached the young woman only to be greeted by the same query. I responded by sharing with her my puzzle-

Reprinted with permission from *Nursing Forum*, Vol. 2, No. 1, 1963, pp. 25-37.

ment, telling her that I had heard her ask the same question of a number of people and that I felt that somehow their answers did not seem to satisfy her. I wondered what it was she really wanted to know. She looked extremely miserable as she said, "Yes, I know that's what I've been doing, but . . ." her voice trailed off. As I carefully encouraged her and clarified the words she was using, it gradually emerged that she was extremely frightened of the proposed operation on her leg. She had been hospitalized a few months before, following an accident in which she had received head injuries, and for a few days had been "out of her mind." She vaguely remembered the terror of this period, but more important, she had the feeling that the same thing would happen again after the operation on her leg. No wonder she was so frightened! As she talked and we outlined the vast differences between these two hospitalizations, she seemed to relax; she heaved a deep sigh and smiled for the first time since I had begun observing her.

After telling Miss X that I would see her the next day, I went to the head nurse to report what had occurred. The nurse broke into my narrative to tell me that this patient was "crazy." She had been asking everyone the same question about her operation; obviously she was confused and didn't remember the previous answer. I wasn't to let her upset me. I agreed that I, too, had wondered if the patient was unable to remember what had been told her and recounted my experience of that morning. The nurse immediately commented sympathetically and expressed her amazement at how "mixed up" Miss X was about the operation.

Then I spoke with the physician, who said that he knew something was worrying Miss X but had had no idea that that was what it was. After hearing my story, both the nursing personnel and the physician rallied to the patient's support, encouraging her to relate her doubts and misgivings about the operation and explicitly outlining what she might realistically expect.

I continued working with this patient throughout her hospital stay. Her progress presented many interesting facets, but the aspect that I wish to examine here is her initial communication to the staff—her questions and her furrowed brow. Both the nurses and the physician had observed this behavior and had come to a conclusion about its meaning. Their actions from this point on did not seem to be helpful to Miss X. Yet each had had thoughts evoked by Miss X's behavior which, if directly utilized to gain more information about how the patient was thinking and feeling, might have been of benefit. For instance, the nurse might have asked Miss X if she realized that she had asked the same question several times before. Or, if the patient sounded confused to her, she might have attempted to sort out with her exactly what it was that was confusing in the situation. Then both she and Miss X would have been at least one step closer to finding out what was so upsetting. By the same token, the doctor might have asked

Miss X what was worrying her, instead of attempting a blanket reassurance. One thing was certain: this patient was not communicating clearly and she certainly needed some help to do so.

THE STUDY OF SIXTY NURSE-PATIENT CONTACTS

As I became more intrigued with patients' communications, I began to examine more closely their initial communication to the nursing personnel. I was particularly interested in their verbal and non-verbal behavior as a nurse approached them. I wanted to determine how clearly or adequately this behavior expressed their state of comfort or discomfort, or their need for nursing assistance. To collect data of this type I became a nurse participant-observer, working with patients on a semi-private, surgical unit. This was not rigidly controlled research, but rather a beginning, exploratory study. My sample was made up of patient contacts similar to those the nurse on the floor was encountering. All patients to whom I responded, whether they were directly assigned to me or not, were included in the study. Some patients were encountered more than once, but only the first interaction on any day was included in the sample. In all, the study included a total of sixty contacts with forty-one patients.

As I came in contact with patients, I noted their verbal and non-verbal behavior and then responded to them in accord with some aspect of the thoughts, feelings, or questions that their behavior evoked in me. This response was made in an exploratory and non-judgmental manner so that the patients were encouraged to confirm, deny, or elaborate upon my perception of their behavior or situation. The ensuing interaction was directed toward a mutual understanding of their present condition and their areas of discomfort or distress. If they were experiencing discomfort, I then focused on ways to alleviate it or to enhance their ability to cope more adequately with their current concerns, using whatever nursing skills were required. The data thus collected included (1) the verbal and non-verbal behavior manifested by patients as the nurse observer approached (overt behavior), (2) the state of comfort, discomfort, concern, or distress revealed by patients during the nurse-patient interaction (aspects of covert behavior), and (3) the type of nursing assistance that the patients required to attain a more satisfactory adjustment to their current situation if they were experiencing some degree of distress.

THE FINDINGS OF THE STUDY

The results of the study offer implications for nursing practice as well as ideas for further research. First and foremost was the finding that the patients in this study did not adequately communicate their needs for nursing assistance as the nurse initially approached them. In forty-seven of the sixty contacts, the patients expressed no aspect of their needs clearly in their presenting behavior. In an additional eleven contacts, the patients did not express their needs fully. Over 40 per cent of these patients had received either "routine morning care" or "routine evening care" immediately prior to their contact with the nurse observer—a fact that offered further support to the hypothesis that patients do not communicate their needs clearly or adequately to nursing personnel. Presumably, if the patients had been able to express their needs for nursing assistance clearly, they would have been met during the evening or the morning care period.

In the eleven instances in which the patients did express their needs in part, an interesting phenomenon occurred. Each of these patients requested some concrete item of physical assistance, such as a bedpan, an adjustment in the height of the bed, or a glass of water. As I met these requests satisfactorily, other needs emerged. The patients tended to move from expressing needs which involved concrete help to the expression of those which are frequently categorized as emotional. Some of the patients were confused and apprehensive about their illness or treatment to the point where they were experiencing severe emotional tension, yet they initiated communication with a relatively minor request for assistance.

One of the patients in this group had already acquired the title of "demander," although she had been in the hospital for only a few hours. As I passed her room she called to me, "Nurse, will you put down this window? I'm in a draft." She was a thin, middle-aged woman, with a pale, pinched, birdlike face and restless, fluttering hands. Before I finished adjusting the window, she asked if I would find out when her doctor was coming to see her. I later learned that she had just asked this question of the nurse who had given her evening care. Instead of immediately going to find out, I wondered aloud if there were some particular reason for her wanting to see him. With this slight bit of encouragement, she poured out her tale of how she happened to be in the hospital, of the scheduled operation, of her many fears and concerns about what was going to happen to her. I encouraged her to talk. Many of her fears were unrealistic, based on misconceptions and misinformation about hospital procedures in the postoperative period. I carefully clarified with her what she might expect and the specific questions she had yet to ask her doctor. As she talked, her facial expression changed, the muscles around her mouth and eyes seemed to relax, and her hands quietly came to rest. She verified my impression that her excess tension was abated by commenting on how anxious she had felt before and how much better she felt now. Like many patients, this woman was unable to say directly to any of the nursing personnel, "I am so anxious, frightened, and confused about this operation scheduled for me. I need desperately to talk to someone and see if I can't get a few things sorted out." Instead, she manifested her intense anxiety by requesting small individual items of care or service from the staff.

In the forty-seven contacts in which patients were not clear in communicating any aspect of their need as the nurse approached them (including thirty in which the patients' behavior was coded as "non-verbal only"), the patients followed a variety of patterns when their behavior was explored. Some needed physical assistance first, and then as they became more comfortable through this means, began to discuss their concerns, worries, and fears. Others reversed this pattern; only as they began to feel some relief from their pent-up emotions did they seem to become aware of specific areas of bodily discomfort. For example, a man who was suffering from severe postoperative gas pains angrily berated the staff and complained about the service he had been receiving. I listened to him and expressed my concern for his discomfort, and we gradually clarified his misunderstandings about the physician's orders and his plan of treatment. He responded to this discussion by relaxing, releasing flatus, and then feeling relief from pain.

In most situations, however, there was no clear-cut demarcation between the two types of approach—physical and emotional. As I was bathing perspiring bodies, changing damp, wrinkled linen, adjusting bandages or dressings that were either too tight or too loose, massaging aching backs, and helping patients to shift into more comfortable positions, I was also listening and responding to their reactions to their current situations. It was difficult, if not impossible, to ascertain which specific intervention, response, or action met a particular need. In other words, it was impossible to separate *psyche* from *soma*.

A second finding of my study was that the form of behavior initially exhibited by a patient was not a reliable basis for assessing his degree of discomfort. The thirty patients who were experiencing severe discomfort at the beginning of my contact with them manifested a wide range of observable behavior. The largest single group (fourteen patients) said nothing, but their tense facial expressions and contorted body positions indicated that something was amiss. At the opposite extreme were those who at first glance seemed relaxed and comfortable, sitting quietly in their beds and appearing to observe the passing scene. Some patients initiated interaction with requests, others asked for information, and still others merely made a comment—for example, "I find it difficult to sleep in hospitals." One man was steadfastly pacing the hall, head down, hands behind his back. With all of these patients an investigative approach was essential to find out how severe their distress was and how they could be helped to relieve it.

IMPLICATIONS OF THE STUDY

As I have stated, my main finding was that the patients in this study did not communicate their needs for assistance adequately. Is this a universal phenomenon, or was it peculiar to this ward milieu? Descriptions of patient behavior in nursing literature indicate that this finding is not atypical of other settings, other classes of patients, or other parts of this country.[1, 2] Nevertheless, further study is needed to ascertain the degree to which the findings are replicated in other settings and the effects that such factors as age, social class, and racial origin have on a patient's ability to communicate clearly.

The reasons patients do not communicate more clearly are probably multiple and varied and involve cultural, psychological, and physiological factors. Initially, both patient and nurse are strangers to each other. In our culture, we hesitate to reveal our thoughts and feelings and more intimate personal needs until we have a sense of trust in or safety with the other person involved. One patient expressed it this way: "It's sort of a sizing up of the nurse. What is she going to be like with me? Can I talk to her and is she going to try to understand, or is she going to make me feel like an idiot? Or is she in a hurry; will she have time?" This patient went on to say that he could do this "sizing up" in a minute in some cases. "It isn't so much what she says as how she says it . . . how she looks at you. Does she really hear you and really see you, or is she thinking of something else?"

In addition to the possible effect of this cultural factor, some patients are only vaguely aware of what is making them feel uncomfortable. They do not really know what assistance they really need. Occasionally medications interfere with the patients' ability to think clearly, or the disease and recovery process may leave them little energy for assessing their situation realistically. They frequently require a nurse with considerable skill in responding to the nuances of their verbal and non-verbal behavior before the immediate sources of distress can be identified and the specific means to alleviate it provided.

Those of us who have been patients ourselves may recognize another factor which can enter into the situation. Even persons who pride themselves on their communications skills and who are familiar enough with hospitals not to have the extra burden of strangeness find that the stress of hospitalization, illness, or uncertain diagnosis renders them astonishingly inept at expressing themselves. Anxiety can interfere with a patient's ability to communicate, although he may know within himself exactly what he wants to say.

The ward social system may also have an effect on patients' communications. Even though it is acknowledged that it is desirable to meet patient needs, it is obvious that in many hospitals the primary focus of the administrative and ward personnel is on the general management of the unit, on "getting the work done." Moreover, there are few concrete rewards by way of status or financial recognition for those who might be interested in developing their skill in working more effectively with patients.[3] Consequently, the very structure of the work situation discourages patients from communicating clearly. Frequently we hear nurses criticizing the physician who hurriedly makes rounds, leaving the patient little opportunity to air his concerns. Not as many nurses seem aware that they do precisely the same thing. Patients realize it, however, as is indicated by their frequent comment, "The nurses are so busy."

Is the nurse really so busy that she does not have time to respond effectively to patients? On the unit on which I made my study, she was. She was involved in a multitude of nursing, administrative, and organizational tasks. As one nurse expressed it, "I don't even have time to get that medication to him within a reasonable period after he asks for it, let alone stop and talk." This is one aspect of the problem. Reorganization must occur in our hospitals if the nurse is to be freed to respond to the needs of patients and develop the potential of her staff to do likewise. Yet lack of time is not the total answer, as research by Aydelotte and by New, Nite, and Callahan has so dramatically demonstrated. Both of these studies indicate that even when the nurse does have time, she does not use it in direct patient-care activities. In the New study, patients expressed no increased satisfaction with nursing care as the staffing pattern increased, contrary to expectations.[4] Aydelotte found no improvement in patient welfare with increases in staffing.[5]

No doubt effective nursing care does require more time at specific stages in a patient's illness and hospitalization. However, this factor may be balanced by the time subsequently saved. To answer a patient's light every few minutes may require a great deal of time and energy on the part of both nurse and patient. If some extra minutes of exploration are allowed when the call light first flashes, other trips may not be necessary, and the satisfaction of both the nurse and the patient may be increased. Many nurses who worked twelve-hour shifts learned through experience that a few minutes spent with patients in the evening saved many minutes later in the night. Relaxed, satisfied patients meant fewer sleeping and pain medications, fewer post-operative catheterizations, and fewer complications, as well as greater satisfaction for all concerned. It appears that the old adage, "a stitch in time saves nine" can be applied to the nurse as well as to the housewife. It is an adage worth testing by research.

In any event, the time, though short, must be utilized effectively. If patients do not express their needs adequately on initial contact, it is the nurse's responsibility to initiate activity toward the discernment of need. Clarity of purpose and skill in communicating are fundamental to this end. The nurse must have access to the patient's frame of reference, taking into consideration his perception of his plight and his feelings, concerns, and desires before she acts or even assesses the situation with any degree of validity.

In initiating activity, the separation of patients' needs into physical and emotional categories can lead to several dilemmas. One is illustrated by the nurse who attempts to investigate a patient's emotional needs and considers that the only way to fulfill this function is through interviewing techniques and verbal interaction. Her efforts may be doomed to failure if her patient's first concern is with matters which require physical activity on her part. On the other hand, the nurse who limits herself to physical activities may find her efforts ineffective with patients whose discomfort is primarily caused by their reactions to their illness, treatment or environment.

Despite inaccuracy and inadequacy of the patient's presenting behavior as an index of his total need, it has an essential place in the establishment of a free flow of communication. Ruesch[6] notes that "cooperative abilities begin with the acknowledgment of the participants' perceptions of each other; this marks the opening signal for subsequent communicative exchanges." If the nurse responds to the patient by expressing aspects of the perceptions, thoughts, or feelings evoked in her by his initial behavior, several objectives are accomplished immediately. The patient has the impact of a nurse who actually sees him, is aware of him, is interested in him, and is implicitly or explicitly asking him to verify, correct, or elaborate on her perceptions. He is thus encouraged to reveal what he is experiencing, thinking, or attempting to communicate in the situation. His responses, verbal and non-verbal, stimulate new thoughts and feelings in the nurse, aspects of which she may continue to express or utilize in an effort to understand with the patient his present situation. This ongoing communicative process sets the stage for nursing as a cooperative endeavor.

REFERENCES

1. Van San, Genne, "Patients' Problems Are Not Always Obvious," *American Journal of Nursing,* April 1962, p. 59.
2. McCabe, Gracia, "Cultural Influences on Patient Behavior," *American Journal of Nursing,* August 1960.

3. Brown, Esther Lucile, *Newer Dimensions of Patient Care,* Part II, Introduction and Chapter I, Russell Sage Foundation, New York, 1962.
4. New, P. K.; Nite, Gladys; and Callahan, Josephine M., *Nursing Service and Patient Care: A Staffing Experiment,* Community Studies, Inc., Kansas City, Missouri, November 1959, pp. 73ff.
5. Aydelotte, Myrtle K., *An Investigation of the Relation Between Nursing Activity and Patient Welfare,* State University of Iowa, 1960.
6. Ruesch, Jurgen, and Kees, Weldon, *Nonverbal Communication,* University of California Press, Berkeley and Los Angeles, 1956, p. 82.

BIBLIOGRAPHY

Brown, Esther Lucile, *Newer Dimensions of Patient Care,* Part I and II, Russell Sage Foundation, New York, 1962.
Orlando, I. J., *The Dynamic Nurse-Patient Relationship,* G. P. Putnam's Sons, New York, 1961.
Peplau, Hildegard, *Interpersonal Relations in Nursing,* G. P. Putnam's Sons, New York, 1952.

An Experimental Test of the Importance of Communication Skills for Effective Nursing*

MARY B. TARASUK · JULINA P. RHYMES ·
ROBERT C. LEONARD

INTRODUCTION

One of the key concepts in the behavioral sciences is communication. The ability to symbolize experience and to communicate it through space and time, dramatically separates man from other animals and is the source of his social organization. In turn, his social organization is the basis of man's dominance over the rest of nature. Despite the basic necessity of communicating with others, the process can be extremely difficult; yet strangely enough, very often little attention is paid to the development of communication skills.[1]

When we are mindful of communication as a technic, we soon find out that we do not know as much about it as we thought we did. Certain

---

* Specially prepared for this book.

questions arise—for example, can communication skills be taught, or are they a matter of personality that some people are just born with and others are not? How do communication skills fit into nursing? Are they as important as the other skills, based on the biologic sciences, that the nurse learns? Which is more important: to be able to perform a procedure or to be able to talk to the patient? When a patient complains of pain, is it more important to be able to communicate with that patient or to know how to administer the prescribed pain medication?

Our hypothesis is that communication skills are as essential for professional patient care as any of the procedures and technics used by nurses. In this paper we present data from a clinical experiment applying this idea to the administration of pain medication. We conclude by arguing that skill in communicating with patients has basic elements that can be identified and taught. For the situation we studied, communication skill seems especially important for the diagnostic phase of the nurse-patient interaction. Administering pain medication automatically without first finding out the nature of the patient's "pain" is often useless and perhaps at times harmful.

THE EXPERIMENTS

The research was conducted in a large urban teaching hospital attached to a university medical center. In this hospital all pain medications were administered by a single medication nurse on each floor. Thus, all communications from patients that were interpreted as meaning "pain" were channeled to one person. The research nurse arranged with the medications nurses to take every other one of the complaints received herself and to go along as an observer for the others.[2] In this manner, the "control" patients were taken care of by the medication nurse who happened to be on duty, and all the others were nursed by the researcher. The pilot experiment included 10 patients in each group. The research nurse made process recordings of all interactions. The replication was conducted the following year and incorporated several refinements, including the services of an assistant who observed and recorded the interactions and their outcomes for both groups of patients.[3] In the time available for the second experiment it was possible to include 9 patients in the experimental group and 10 in the control group.

It might be useful to make clear at this point that the experimental nursing was conducted under relatively ideal conditions, by a nurse who had special education in communication skills. In addition, this situation was one in which she felt, from previous clinical experience, she could get better than ordinary results. She was free to spend as much time as she desired with any patient. In contrast, the control patients were cared for by regular staff nurses who had all the usual duties of their position. This does not in any way invalidate the results of the experiment, since the question concerns the effect of talking with the patient and not what conditions are necessary so that the nurse can talk to the patient. But under these contrasting conditions, what were the differences in outcome for the patients?

All the control patients were given pain medication. In contrast, only 31 per cent of the experimental patients received medication. In other words, in over two thirds of the cases the experimental nurse decided that the patient's complaint did not really mean "pain" in a sense that would indicate medication as the appropriate course of action. Since the two groups of patients were composed in a way designed to make them comparable, this suggests that most of the medication received by the control patients was not needed.[4]

Whether or not medication was used is, of course, not really an indicator of the nurse's effectiveness but rather is part of her nursing action. In fact, however, the experimental approach did result in faster relief of the patient's complaints and in more complete relief. Relief was measured by the patient's response to a question, such as: "How is your pain now?" as well as by such nonverbal cues as facial expression and color, posture, nervous movements and so forth. These indicators of relief were recorded and later placed on cards which were rated by judges who did not know which kind of nursing approach the patients had received. Recordings were made immediately after the nursing action and then one half and one hour later. The great majority of the experimental group had immediate relief, before the nurse left the room, whereas almost none of the control patients did so (Table 1). Furthermore, 25 per cent of the control patients never received any relief from the nurse's action (medication), whereas only one of the patients judged as not relieved was in the experimental group.

Even more important in some ways than speed is the degree of ultimate relief. In the second experiment the data were collected in a way that permitted the judges to rate the degree of relief into three

TABLE 1. EFFECT OF NURSING APPROACH ON RELIEF OF PATIENTS'
COMPLAINTS (SPEED OF RELIEF)

		EXPERIMENTAL GROUP	CONTROL GROUP
Speed of relief	Immediate	14	2
	Later	4	13
	None	1	5
	N =	(19)	(20)

categories: "marked relief," "some relief," or "none." Although all the control patients received pain medication, none ever achieved "marked" relief, and two patients (20 per cent) received no relief at all. The results of the experimental nursing approach were in sharp contrast; almost all experimental patients received "marked" relief (Table 2). It is worth pointing out that some of these experimental patients did receive medication. Thus even when medication was the action chosen, it was more effective when the experimental approach was used. All of these differences are statistically significant at the .01 level.

These results, if representative, suggest a great lack of communication between nurse and patient. The results are not too surprising, however, since in the control cases the nurse was seldom observed even attempting to find out exactly what the patient's complaint meant. Let us now examine some details in the differences between the control and the experimental nursing approaches. First, consider this illustration of the care received by the control patients.

TABLE 2. EFFECT OF NURSING APPROACH ON RELIEF OF PATIENTS'
COMPLAINTS (DEGREE OF RELIEF)

		EXPERIMENTAL GROUP	CONTROL GROUP
Degree of relief*	Marked	8	0
	Some	1	8
	None	0	2
	N =	(9)	(10)

* Verbal and also nonverbal behavior of patient before and after treatment was recorded on cards and degree of "relief" was determined by independent judges. At half hour intervals each patient was asked, "How is your pain now, Mr. (Mrs.) . . . . . . ?" This data available from the second experiment only.

A Control Group Case

> Mrs. D, a pneumonia patient, was lying flat in bed. To the observer her facial expression appeared drawn. The patient said: "My chest is uncomfortable." The nurse decided that the patient needed what the doctor had ordered, a pain medication. Without saying anything to the patient, the nurse gave the medication. Half an hour later it should have been taking effect but the patient told us: "I still have the headache and this pain in my chest." An hour later she said: "This pain in my chest is very bad."

In this case, there is no evidence that the nursing activity was effective. Although the patient got "just what the doctor ordered," it was probably not what she needed; and the nurse's decision to give the medication turned out to be quite possibly a mistake. Now, it would be wrong to claim that nurses should be infallible, but it would be equally wrong to fail to learn from our mistakes. In this case the medication did not relieve the patient's distress.

We do not know for sure what this particular patient needed to be relieved of her discomfort or just why the medication did not do it. However, it may very well have been that it was not really the chest that was bothering her. If the nurse had spent a little time exploring this possibility with the patient, she might have avoided wasting medication and time and also discovered what the patient actually needed to be relieved. But in the control group, none of the nurses attempted to find out from the patients anything about the nature of the complaints. Even when the complaint was relayed indirectly, through a third person, the nurses automatically prepared the medication without first seeing the patient. It is interesting to note how these medications were administered. Every nurse in the control group engaged in, at best, only minimal communication with the patient. Without exception the nurses limited their conversation to remarks such as: "Here are your pills." "Do you want it in your hip or your arm?" "Turn over, please." One nurse walked into the room, administered the medication and walked out without saying anything at all. In general, then, there is very little to be said about the communication skills exercised by the nurses of the control group, because there was not much communication. What little there was tended to be a very instrumental type. Neither the nurses nor the patients had much to say. Again, it should be underscored that we cannot generalize about current nursing practice from a single study of this kind. However, we do not believe that the interactions we observed are at all unusual in present-day nursing practice.

The control patients thus were typically left with the complete responsibility for communicating their needs clearly to the nurse. For many reasons this may be too difficult for the patient.* By contrast, the experimental approach used in this study made a deliberate effort to make sure exactly what the patient's complaint meant. To illustrate the approach and how communication skills were brought into play in order to diagnose the situation accurately before acting, consider the following case.

An Experimental Case

The research nurse was notified by the medication nurse that a patient had complained of pain. As had been previously agreed, it was the research nurse's turn to take care of the patient. As nurse and observer entered the room, they saw a young woman lying on her back in bed with her eyes open. The patient initiated communication by looking toward the nurse and saying:

"I have pains all over." The nurse walked to the bedside and said:

"Oh? I'm sorry—where is the pain?" (Two elemental communication skills are already illustrated in this interaction; (1) giving support and recognition by saying "I'm sorry," and (2) exploration of the patient's behavior in an attempt to determine just what was meant by "pains all over." This proved to be immediately fruitful in changing the nature of the complaint.) The patient looked up at the nurse and said:

"It's just my neck, it's so sore." (The nurse might have decided at this point that pain medication was indicated for a neck pain, but instead she explored further the patient's complaint.) The nurse touched the patient's neck and asked:

"Does it hurt here?" The patient nodded that it did and the nurse began massaging the patient's neck and asked:

"When did it start being sore?" The patient responded:

"Just a little while ago—I can't sleep because there's so much noise in here." (Notice that the complaint has shifted again, this time completely away from "pain" to noise and inability to sleep. The nurse might have gone on asking about "pain," or she might have decided to do something about the noise. And she might have decided at this point that sleeping medication was indicated.) Instead, she replied to the patient:

"Yes it is really noisier than usual tonight, but is there something I can do to help you to sleep—you seem to me to be so

---

* Cf. Skipper's "Communication and the Hospitalized Patient," especially Part II, in this section of the volume.

sleepy?" (Notice again that "support and recognition" is given the patient's complaint about the noise. And again "exploration" is used, rather than assuming that medication was needed for sleep.) The patient responded quickly to the nurse's question concerning what might help her sleep by saying:

"Could I please have the bedpan? I've had to go for so long now, and I can't get up myself, and everyone is so busy, I don't want to be a bother." (Again, we have a shift in the source of the patient's discomfort. This time the patient seemed to have clearly communicated a need, and the nurse gave her the bedpan.) The nurse might now have assumed that this was all the patient needed, but instead she checked by asking:

"Now, is there something else I can do for you?" The patient replied:

"Oh, no, that's fine, now I can sleep." The patient appeared much more relaxed, turned on her side and smiled. (The nurse seemed to have plenty of reason to conclude that the patient's distress had been relieved. But instead she continued to be skeptical of what the patient had said even though posture and facial expression corroborated the statement of relief.) The nurse replied to the patient's assurances of comfort by saying:

"That's fine, by the way, how's your neck now?" The patient continued to smile and said:

"Oh my neck isn't sore anymore—the rubbing made me feel wonderful." The patient closed her eyes. A half hour later, she was snoring and at the end of one hour was still snoring. This case was classified as complete immediate relief.

Did the experimental nurse have some secret ingredient in her personality that made her more effective than others? Perhaps—we have no way of knowing from the data of this study. But more important, we do know that her approach to patients' complaints was different and we have described that difference. She used a deliberative nursing process which assumed that in order to do what a patient needs, the nurse must first know what that need is.[5] This is obvious, but what is not so obvious is that determining what the patient needs is far from a simple matter. Very often a patient is unable to communicate the need clearly. His use of the word "pain" may be different from the way that medical personnel use it, and it may be different for patients from different cultural backgrounds. Furthermore, the kind of action to relieve the pain that will be acceptable to patients may vary.[6]

It turned out in the experimental case that the patient's original complaint did not at all indicate pain medication. In fact, what she needed was a bedpan. We cannot help wondering how a patient's initial communication could be so far from indicating what was really needed, but other studies verify the regular occurrence of such a situation.[7] Whatever the reason for the misleading character of the patient's initial communication, this case points up the difficulty that the nurse may encounter in helping the patient to communicate his distress. By using her perceptions and exploring them with the patient, by noticing and responding to nonverbal messages from the patient as well as verbal ones, and by being sensitive to every shift in the nature of the complaint, the research nurse finally managed to uncover the fact that the patient was being kept awake by the need to void. Several times the nurse might have assumed that she had at last found the source of the distress. Each time she might have assumed that she now accurately understood the patient's meaning and made a decision about the appropriate action. But instead, she continued to check the validity of her decision with the patient. Finally, after the patient clearly and unequivocally communicated the need for a bedpan, and received it, the nurse checked the accuracy of her final diagnosis by finding out how the treatment had affected the patient. Every experimental patient's complaint was handled in this way. Of course, in some cases the nurse decided that the patient needed pain medication, but this was only 31 per cent of the time, as compared with 100 per cent in the control group.

What may have been the difference between the control and the experimental approaches that produced the greater effectiveness of the experimental nursing? The control approach, without exception, made assumptions about the meaning of the patients' behavior without obtaining feedback from the patients themselves. The nurse responded by making judgments about what the patients needed without really hearing or seeing what their behavior may have been communicating to her. In each case, the control nurse carried out a routine technical procedure and focused her behavior on this procedure rather than on the patient. Her approach was stereotyped, lacked spontaneity, and was not always appropriate for her patient in that particular situation. None of the control nurses made use of their communication potential to be of help to the patient.

On the other hand, the research nurse made a deliberate attempt to establish meaningful communication. She picked up subtle verbal and nonverbal messages from the patient and responded to them directly. She tried not to make assumptions about the meaning of the patients' behavior, but fed back to the patient her own perceptions, thoughts and feelings. By doing this she helped him to communicate correctly what he was experiencing.

SUMMARY

Communication skills are as important as any other skills that the members of a helping profession such as nursing must acquire. Professional practice is a social process and as such is basically a matter of communication. This truth is not always recognized, because of the extensive reliance on the biophysical sciences by practitioners in health professions. At the same time, there is a tendency to assume that research into practitioner-patient communication is either impossible, not necessary, or else not important enough. But it is the poorly educated nurse who does not know that the patient may be trying to communicate by a complaint of pain something far different than what the word usually means to herself and her colleagues in the medical culture. It is the ineffective nurse who does not know how to find out the particular meaning of the message for the particular patient. No matter how great the technical competence or the knowledge of basic pharmacology and physiology, it is all useless when pain medication is administered to a patient who does not need it.

In our study, patients were observed who had made complaints that were interpreted by the staff as meaning "pain." We then observed the subsequent activities of nurses who responded to the complaints. We found that more often than not, the nurses made hasty, inaccurate judgments about the meaning of the patient's message and responded automatically with p.r.n. medications. We also found that the patient was not always relieved, even though pain medication had been given. We compared this nursing approach with a different one and found that many times the complaint did not mean what we ordinarily regard as pain, and the patient was relieved without the use of drugs. The experimental approach not only used less medication, but also increased the speed and the thoroughness with which the patient was relieved. In addition, relief seemed quicker and more thorough even when medication was used.

It should be emphasized that the important point of these results is not what nurses are presently failing to do; it is instead the promise implicit in the demonstration of what nurses *can* do on their own initiative and with their own special skills and opportunity for communicating with the patient. Thus, it is easy to see that the results of this study, if supported by further research, very strongly support the importance of communication skills for effective patient care.[8]

FOOTNOTES

1. As an exception, see Lockerby, Florence K., *Communication for Nurses,* St. Louis: C. V. Mosby Co., 1963, Second Ed., Chapter 4.
2. A similar procedure was used in the second experiment, except that different floors were taken for the two groups in order to avoid "spillover" from one treatment group to the other. R. A. Fisher's classic design for experiments calls for strictly random assignment of subjects to groups so that all the uncontrolled background variables can be taken into account by the statistical test of significance. Probably the differences in our groups are random, but the possibility of a bias in the composition of the two groups has to be taken into account in interpreting the results.
3. Acknowledgments are due Professor Donald B. Trow for his contributions to design of the first experiment. Professor Ida J. Orlando contributed to both experiments. For the full report of the master's study see: Bochnak, Mary A., "The Effect of Automatic and Deliberative Process of Nursing Activity on the Relief of Patient's Pain: A Clinical Experiment," Yale Medical Library (June 1961). See also the popularized report by Bochnak, Mary A., Rhymes, Julina P., and Leonard, Robert C., "The Comparison of Two Types of Nursing Activity on the Relief of Pain," in *Innovations in Nurse-Patient Relationships,* New York: American Nurses' Association, Monograph No. 6 (1962). The assistant for the second experiment, Mrs. Rhymes, was doing her field work for the research methods term paper in the same Master's Degree program.
4. This difference in the amount of medication received by the two groups is statistically significant beyond the .01 level. This probability figure means that there is less than one chance in 100 that this result is due to the experimental group's being composed of a different kind of patient rather than due to the experimental nurse's approach to the patients.
5. Orlando, Ida J., *The Dynamic Nurse-Patient Relationship,* G. P. Putnam's Sons, 1961.
6. Zborowski, Mark, "Cultural Components in Responses to Pain," *Journal of Social Issues,* 8, 1952, pp. 16-30. Also reprinted in Jaco, E. Gartly (ed.), *Physicians, Patients and Illness,* Glencoe, Ill., Free Press, 1958, pp. 256-268.
7. Elder, Ruth G., "What Is the Patient Saying?" (the preceding paper in this book); Orlando, Ida J., *op. cit.,* pp. 23-29.
8. But the very importance of these implications dictates caution in generalizing from this one study. In order to give a basis for judging our conclusions, and an idea of how the experiment might be repeated, we have included details of our research methodology. In a refined replication of these experiments, Barron seems to have found similar results, except that the reduced

use of medication may not apply to postoperative patients. (Barron, Mary A., "The Effects Varied Nursing Approaches Have on Patient's Complaints of Pain: A Clinical Experiment," unpublished Master's Report, Yale School of Nursing, June 1964. On the other hand, one recent experiment suggests a very considerable social-psychological component in the determinants of postoperative pain. (Egbert, Lawrence D., M.D., "Reduction of Postoperative Pain by Encouragement and Instruction of Patients: A Study of Doctor-patient Rapport," *New England Journal of Medicine,* 270, April 16, 1964, pp. 825-827.) See also Crowley, Dorothy, *Pain and Its Alleviation,* University of California Press, 1962.

Giving the Patient an Active Role

PHYLLIS A. TRYON · ROBERT C. LEONARD

THE THEORY

In the course of an ordinary day, a person plays many roles in our modern society. As parent, spouse, student, teacher, employer, employee, or citizen, a person is involved in different networks of obligations and is rewarded in different ways for fulfilling those obligations. A person is motivated to take on one or the other role by the expectation of certain rewards, but in order to receive those rewards he must perform the role in the appropriate way. And in order to perform his duties he must have the appropriate knowledge, skills and other resources. As Parsons has pointed out, when a person is permitted to take the "sick" role, he is not held responsible for his incapacity and is excused from the regular performance of his other roles.[1] And he has the right to expect care and treatment. At the same time, the person in the sick role is obligated to try to get well, to seek professional help actively, and to cooperate with those offering the help. Thus, when a person seeks medical help it is because he thinks he has a medical problem that he or his family is unable to handle, and he expects the medical practitioner to help him. In seeking this help he takes on yet

Specially prepared for this book. We gratefully acknowledge *Nursing Forum,* Alice R. Clarke, Editor, for use of some previously published material. This work has been supported partially by USPHS Grant NU00060. We would like to acknowledge comments by Rita J. Simon on an earlier draft. Observing and interviewing for the research was done by Mary Brodish, R.N., and Avril Sutin.

another role. He becomes a patient. What is the appropriate behavior in his role as a patient? Does being a patient mean that he sits back and lets the nurses take care of him and the doctors make him well? Or does he continue to have some responsibility to take care of himself and to get himself well?

These are questions that concern every person who becomes a patient and every practitioner who works with patients. The professional's answer tends, in practice, to add up to a very passive role for the patient. Of course, in becoming a patient one admits to a need for help. But does one necessarily also admit inability to make any decisions or take any part in planning or execution of that help? The patient usually is treated as though this were so, with "routine," "doctor's orders," or "the nursing shortage" as the excuse. Our theory is that *if a patient is approached as a person with the ultimate power of accepting or rejecting the proposed care, then the effectiveness of that care is increased and both patient and staff satisfaction is increased.* Administration of one nursing procedure, the predelivery enema, was taken to test this theory. The potential value of active patient participation is recognized by nursing educators. For example, Fuerst and Wolff[2] say:

> The relationship of the nurse to the patient should be one of *mutual planning and consent.* It is disastrous for the nurse to assume an authoritarian role and place the patient in a position of a recipient of care which he may neither understand or want.

Of more direct relevance here, Wiedenbach explicitly predicts greater effectiveness for the predelivery enema if acceptance and cooperation is elicited by the nurse.[3] The experiments reported here were designed to test this hypothesis.

EXPERIMENTAL DESIGN

R. A. Fisher's basic design for experiments was used, with two treatment groups. As eligible patients entered the maternity unit, they were assigned randomly to either the control or the experimental group. All private and nonprivate patients with a doctor's order for a soap enema were eligible except those scheduled for Caesarean section. In the pilot experiment the research nurse, a certified nurse-midwife, gave the experimental treatment, and the control was provided by the usual hospital staffing, which turned out to be about 15 different graduate and student nurses. In the second experiment the research nurse gave both treatments.

In contrast to much social research, it was relatively easy to make many of our dependent variables objective. But even so, subconscious observer bias was still possible, especially since the observer had an investment in the hypothesis. The best prevention for this is "blind" measurement, in which the observer does not know which treatment the subject has received. Adequate control over observer bias often can be provided by a specially trained observer who is not involved in giving the treatment being tested. In the first experiment all measurements were recorded by the research nurse. In the second experiment a full time nonparticipant observer was hired in order to increase accuracy and completeness as well as increase our confidence in the objectivity of the data. With the variables that permitted, blind observation was used in the second experiment.

THE NURSING APPROACH

The hypothesis requires varying the nurse's approach so that the patient is given an active role in the experimental group. A first step, then, was developing a way of administering the procedure to establish the necessary climate of mutual planning and consent. The general idea of a nonauthoritarian, patient-centered approach is, of course, current in nursing.[4, 5] Thus the problem was one of developing specific application to the procedure in question by trial and error with a series of cases. The salient results of that exploratory phase of the study are illustrated by case material in an earlier paper.[6] An underlying assumption of the experimental nursing approach is that the patient wants to help herself. This means, then, that the nurse's purpose is to facilitate the patient's own efforts to obtain whatever the patient feels is needed rather than to impose on the patient her own assumptions about what is needed.[7] If a procedure is required because of hospital policy or doctor's orders, then it is the nurse's responsibility to elicit the patient's understanding and acceptance before administering the procedure. This can be achieved by exploring the patient's thoughts and feelings about the proposed procedure in order to uncover adverse reactions and identify possible ways of relieving them.

In the first experiment the many different nurses giving the control treatment were not instructed, but rather carried out the procedure in their usual manner. The research nurse gave both treatments in the second experiment, in order to establish greater control over this variation. This required making up explicit guidelines for the two approaches and many trial runs until the research nurse was able to shift her approach in the specified ways. The guide for the control treatment was based on her own previous experience as well as the nursing approaches observed in the first experiment. The control approach was specified as follows: (1) Present the idea of having the enema as a fact of doctor's order, e.g., "Are you ready to have your enema now?" or "I have an order to give you an enema."

(2) No exploration of the patient's response but instead; (3) Use persuasion and stereotyped reassurances such as, "You are doing fine," "It won't hurt" or "It is good for you." (4) Give only those explanations and directions necessary to carry out the procedure and; (5) Try to administer the enema unless absolutely refused (this did not happen). The experimental approach was based on the earlier research and was specified as follows: (1) Present the idea of having the enema as a fact of doctor's order; (2) Explore the patient's response to the idea, e.g., "You don't sound too happy about it" or "How do you feel about having it?"; (3) Base further nursing action on how the patient is experiencing the situation by, (a) further exploration to guarantee accurate diagnosis of patient's feelings, (b) if indicated, offering modifications to make it acceptable, (c) consulting with the doctor if the enema is in no way acceptable, (d) give enema only when the patient consents to it. In general then, the control approach could be characterized as task-centered and directive, whereas the experimental approach was centered on the patient's definition of the situation and was nondirective. The expectation was that this approach would result in more active participation in the procedure by the experimental patients.

PATIENT ACCEPTANCE

The key to increasing procedure effectiveness is to gain active patient cooperation and acceptance. In both experiments the enema was accepted much more often and much more freely by the experimental group than by the control group. In analyzing the patient response, explicit verbal acceptance was indicated by statements such as, "You can give me the enema now." Statements such as, "I don't mind them," or "I expected to have one," were scored as implicit acceptance. Doubtful cases were classified in the direction opposite to the hypothesis. In the pilot experiment all of the experimental patients verbally accepted the procedure, while at most only 72 per cent of the control patients did so. This difference is not surprising, since none of the control nurses asked the patients' permission or explored their feelings about the procedure. In the second experiment similar differences occurred. Ninety five per cent of the experimental group definitely accepted the procedure, whereas only 70 per cent of the control group did so.

EFFECTIVENESS OF THE PROCEDURE

We already have seen that the experimental approach resulted in greater acceptance of the enema. Acceptance is, however, just an intervening variable in our experiment, since we are concerned ultimately with how well the enema does what it is supposed to do. The indicators of effectiveness for both experiments were (1) amount of fluid intake, (2) fecal return, (3) fluid return. In the first experiment all measurements were by the research nurse. In the second experiment they were evaluated by a nonparticipant observer.

Fecal Return. In both experiments "ample" fecal return was more often observed in the experimental group. Fecal return is the most subjective of all the indicators in this study, even though evaluation was done as objectively as possible. But since it is the criterion on which the effectiveness of the cleansing enema is most often evaluated, it is felt to be important in this study. Statistically significant differences in the predicted direction were obtained. By this most commonly used measure, the experimental approach resulted in a more effective procedure.

Fluid Intake and Return. In the first experiment the evaluation of fluid return was literally guesswork, but the difference was still in the predicted direction. In the second experiment a procedure was devised so that the fluid intake and return could be measured accurately to the nearest 50 cc. The mean percentage of fluid was calculated for the two groups. The experimental group expelled an average of 105 per cent of the fluid intake, in contrast to only 87 per cent in the control group. This difference is significant at greater than the .005 level using the "t" test. In other words, as predicted, the procedure was more effective for the experimental group.

PATIENT SATISFACTION

In the second experiment, patients were interviewed before their discharge. Two cases in each group were discharged before the interviewer could get them. Almost all the patients reported being "very satisfied" about the hospital, the doctors and nurses, and about labor and delivery. This was equally true of both experimental and control group patients. However, on specific questions about the enema we found some differences in the expected direction. None of the experimental patients reported feeling uncomfortable about it, but 22 per cent of the control patients said they were.[8] They also were asked, "Was the nurse who gave it to you helpful, indifferent or not helpful?" None of the experimental patients responded with anything but "helpful"; 17 per cent of the control patients said "indifferent." These differences probably would have been even greater had we provided a greater range of response.

CONCLUSIONS AND IMPLICATIONS

Should the patient's role be active or passive? On the one hand, it is an obligation of the sick person to do everything possible to get well as soon as possible. But on the other hand he is encouraged by the hospital environment to be passive. When a person becomes a hospital patient he finds others doing *to* and *for* him whether he wants them to or not. He finds a lack of participation, a loss of the usual control he has over his environment.* Things which he ordinarily does are done by others. He is no longer supposed to wash himself or get his own food, even though he may well be capable. His experience with nursing will discourage him from taking initiative if the preponderance of his contacts with nurses are either nurse-active, patient-passive or nurse-guide, patient-obedient.[9] Like the doctor, the nurse often continues her active role beyond the point of necessity. She does things for the patient when he is quite capable of doing for himself, at least with some guidance. For example, a nurse was bathing a patient scheduled to go home and obviously able to bathe himself. Perhaps this nurse kept the patient in his passive role because she felt that she did not earn her salary unless she did *for* him. Some nurses do *to* or *for* rather than *with* their patients because it takes less time. It may be easier to do a colostomy dressing for the patient than to tell him how to do it. Other nurses may not allow the patient a more active role for fear of getting "involved." Getting involved may mean that the nurse is afraid that the patient will present a problem that she cannot handle, or one she thinks that she isn't supposed to talk about. For instance, the nurse may become quite upset when the patient asks a question about "condition." "Condition" is the doctor's province. The nurse is afraid of saying the wrong thing and sidesteps this question, making sure that she will not be put on the spot again. She knows that she has not helped the patient, but she retreats with the excuse that there is a nursing shortage and she just doesn't have time. The patient is not encouraged by this to either ask for information that might help him to help himself, nor to offer information that might make the nurse's efforts more effective. Is it any wonder if patients do not work with those helping them? That they do not communicate their problems and feelings about their care?

Wilson notes as "one of the most interesting current developments in nursing," a move to reverse the habit of staff directiveness and to increase patient participation.† In the study reported here, the patients reacted favorably to a more active role. Although the interaction was initiated by the nurse, patients were able to initiate further interaction to express their needs more clearly. For instance, one patient asked the experimental nurse

---

* Cf. Skipper, "Communication and the Hospitalized Patient," especially Part I, in this section of the volume.

† Wilson, Robert N., "The Social Structure of a General Hospital," *The Annals of the American Academy of Political and Social Science,* March 1963, p. 70. Also in this volume.

to put away some clothing before her husband came in. Five other people had seen this patient, three of them nurses. The patient might have asked any one to put the clothes away, but each had some specific purpose in seeing her and did not make her feel free to ask them or to interrupt them. Since the experimental nurse was interested in how the patient felt about the procedure, she assumed that this nurse was interested in her and that the request would not be an imposition.

When the patient participates in planning for his care, he assumes some responsibility for the outcome or the effect of that care. When he participates, he is able to use more effectively the health resources offered him. When a particular course of action is suggested, he knows why it has been suggested and is able to express his feeling about it. If he questions the advisability of a particular procedure, his reasons are heard and given consideration. Care is administered with the patient's understanding and consent. He is not merely the object of care and treatment, but is a partner in planning for his recovery.

There is still much confusion about the proper components of the patient role, and whether or when it should be active or passive. We conclude that the patient who assumes an active role contributes to the effectiveness of his care. However, being a patient is unfamiliar to him. He takes his cues from those around him. When he is encouraged to ask questions, to express his feelings, and to participate in planning for his care, the behavior expected of him becomes apparent. If he is discouraged from expressing himself and taking part in his care, he will assume that the proper role is passive and will not be as able to take responsibility when this is desirable. An active patient role requires more of the patient. It also requires more involvement of those working with him. But the outcome in both effectiveness of care and satisfaction of patient and practitioner makes the added investment worthwhile.

FOOTNOTES

1. Parsons, Talcott, "Definitions of Health and Illness in the Light of American Values and Social Structure," in Jaco, E. Gartly (ed.), *Patients, Physicians and Illness,* Glencoe, Ill., Free Press, 1958, p. 176. (Reprinted from *The Journal of Social Issues,* Vol. VIII, No. 4, 1952, pp. 2-3, 31-44.)
2. Fuerst, Elinor, V., and Wolff, Luverne, *Fundamentals of Nursing.* Philadelphia: J. B. Lippincott, 1964, p. 40.
3. Wiedenbach, Ernestine, *Family Centered Maternity Nursing.* New York: G. P. Putnam's Sons, 1958, p. 223.
4. Abdellah, Faye, G.; Beland, I. L.; Martin, A.; and Matheney, R. J., *Patient-Centered Approaches to Nursing.* New York: Macmillan, 1960.
5. Orlando, Ida Jean, *The Dynamic Nurse-Patient Relationship.* New York: G. P. Putnam's Sons, 1961.

6. Tryon, Phyllis A., "The Effect of Patient Participation in Decision-making on the Outcome of a Nursing Procedure," *American Nurses Association Monograph #19,* 1962.

7. Wiedenbach, Ernestine, *Clinical Nursing a Helping Art.* New York: Springer Publishing Co., 1964. See also this same author's "The Helping Art of Nursing," *American Journal of Nursing,* Vol. 63, November, 1963, pp. 54-57.

8. They were asked first, "How did you feel about having the enema?" Their responses to this open-ended question were recorded, and then they were asked, "What sort of experience was it—comfortable, fairly comfortable, fairly uncomfortable, or very uncomfortable?" No patient chose to say it was "very uncomfortable."

9. Szasz, Thomas S., and Hollender, Marc, "A Contribution to the Philosophy of Medicine—The Basic Models of Doctor-Patient Relationship." *A.M.A. Archives of Internal Medicine,* Vol. 97, 1956, p. 585.

Reassurance

Dorothy Gregg

🖎   A nurse walked into a patient's room and found her looking very forlorn and upset. This was their conversation.

NURSE: Oh, come now, Mrs. Carson, nothing could be that bad! You look like you have lost your last friend!

PATIENT: The doctor just told me that it will be impossible for me to get well if I don't have the operation. I'm so mixed up—I wish I knew what to do.

NURSE: There is only one thing to do, and that is to have the surgery! You haven't a thing to worry about. You have the best surgeon in town. He has done hundreds of operations just like yours.

PATIENT: You don't understand—I have confidence in my doctor's skill—it's—well—.

NURSE: Most people are a little scared when they think about having an operation. Remember when you had your first baby several years ago

Reprinted with permission from the *American Journal of Nursing,* Vol. 55, No. 2, 1955, pp. 171-174. In preparing this paper, Miss Gregg consulted Ewald W. Busse, M.D., Chairman, Department of Psychiatry, Duke University School of Medicine, and Betty Van Huben, Instructor in Psychiatric Nursing, University of Colorado School of Nursing; she acknowledges their help.

while I was working on OB? You had the longest and hardest labor of anyone on the ward, and I never heard a whimper out of you! I was so proud of you! You were the best patient in the whole hospital! After what you went through, this operation should be a picnic, and this time you'll be completely unconscious from the anesthetic. You won't feel a thing.

During this conversation the nurse probably was sincere in her desire to reassure the patient, but she was not aware of what constitutes reassurance. She may not even discover that she has failed, but she will probably wonder why the patient talked more freely to someone else than she did to her. If we attempt to see how the patient felt in this conversation, maybe we can make some guesses about what she experienced.

Mrs. Carson's reaction to the nurse's first comment might have been: *I feel very upset, and she can see that I am upset. Why does she say, "nothing could be that bad?" How could she possibly know? And losing friends has nothing to do with how I feel. This is worse than losing friends—what a silly remark!*

Such cliches frequently are used socially to reduce the danger of an unwanted "scene" and to preserve social equanimity. What happens most often is that they reduce the importance of the other person's feelings. In this situation they failed to convey to the patient that the nurse understood the concern that she has perceived in the patient. Webster defines reassurance as a "restoration of confidence." There was little in this opening to the conversation that restored Mrs. Carson's confidence.

The patient's feelings about the nurse's second comment might have been: *I tried to tell her that I was mixed up. It is hard for me to explain to another person how I feel, and she didn't even let me finish! Maybe she doesn't care how I feel. Now she thinks I am frightened about the operation. I guess she wouldn't know what it's like to be afraid of something bigger than an operation! She tells me there is only one thing to do—if life were only that simple! Why does she have to tell me what to do? I didn't ask for that! What does she mean—"I haven't anything to worry about"? I wonder what she would do if she had my little boy? She doesn't even know what I'm worried about! Maybe that's it—maybe she doesn't want to know —maybe she is afraid to know. I guess I really shouldn't bother other people with this. No one could possibly understand how I feel. What is this about the surgeon? Does she think my doctor isn't good enough? Why else would she be so eager to tell me he is good? I have confidence in him—well—I think I have—.*

This is one possible outcome of jumping ahead of a patient's expression of her feelings and guessing at what she is trying to say. The guess can easily be wrong and, furthermore, it conveys that the patient is not important enough to the nurse for her to care what the patient has to say. A second error in the nurse's approach was that she immediately started telling the patient what to do. This action was based on the assumption that the patient couldn't make a decision for herself and that she wished the nurse to make it for her. Erroneously, the nurse believed that she was helping the patient when she told her what to do.

In addition, in an attempt to allay unknown fears, she made another guess that the patient was not sure of her doctor's skill, and in so doing, she was in danger of creating doubt. If the nurse is fortunate, the patient may be able to perceive that the nurse is anxious and has made a false assumption regarding her own fears, but there is the possibility that an anxiety-ridden patient may not be capable of such perception at the moment, so she takes the cue from the nurse to worry about her surgeon's skill.

Regarding the nurse's third response, the patient may have felt: *She didn't let me finish—she must think I am stupid because I can't talk without stumbling over my words. There she goes on about the operation again. She just can't understand! There is just no point in talking with her! What is this about the way I behaved at the birth of my baby? If she only knew —I was so scared I couldn't whimper—but she was proud of me! That very baby is my biggest problem! What is she saying? Does she mean good patients don't cry? I guess I'm supposed to be brave and silent, and here I am telling her about being so mixed up! Is she afraid I'll make a scene? Oh, what's the use? How could anyone understand about John? She says I won't feel a thing—maybe I won't—maybe I really won't!*

Twice the patient tried to express to the nurse how she felt and as she hesitated and searched for words, the nurse became anxious and guessed at her problem, thereby cutting off the patient's chance to talk about what was bothering her. The nurse further expressed her own anxiety when she unwittingly told the patient how she expected her to behave by holding her past performance up to her as an example of behaving as a "good" patient should. She also conveyed disrespect for the patient in her present disturbance by telling her that the coming episode would be "a picnic." The implication was that she blamed the patient for her present distressed behavior. It is rarely comforting to an anxiety-ridden person to be told that she will be unconscious, for in her apprehension, she may look upon this as simply another situation in which she will be "out of control."

Later in the day, another nurse entered the same patient's room to prepare her for the night. Mrs. Carson smiled a greeting, but initiated no further conversation. She seemed preoccupied, and her face was tear-stained. The nurse began to rub her back.

NURSE: It seems hard for you to relax tonight. You must have had a difficult day.

PATIENT: Yes.

(silence)

NURSE: Would you like to tell me about it?

PATIENT: It would seem silly to you. It's so hard to explain——. If I thought I could make it home, I would leave——. No one understands.

NURSE: I would like to try to understand if it will help you.

PATIENT: They say I have to have an operation, and I'm so scared and mixed up. They think it's the operation that scares me, but—oh, well—I don't know how you could understand. I'm such a mess!

(silence)

NURSE: It's hard to talk about it.

PATIENT: Yes—If I weren't around maybe he could get someone who would really help John. I just don't have the patience any more—maybe I never did! (pause)

NURSE: Could you tell me who John is, and who could get someone else?

PATIENT: John is my oldest child. He has cerebral palsy. He is a sweet little boy but he needs so much care, and you have to be so patient with him, and I'm just not. Since I've been sick we haven't been able to send him to his special school. My medical bills stand in the way of his chances to get help, and when he is home all the time—well—I guess I get impatient with his troubles, and I'm always scolding when I know he can't help it. My husband has the burden of both of us. He is so kind to the boy, and so patient with me. They would both be better off without me. I shouldn't have the operation.

NURSE: Are you saying that you may not live if you don't have the operation and that this would be better for John and your husband?

PATIENT: The doctor said I can't expect to live long without surgery. (thoughtful silence) I guess I really am silly—that would be kind of like suicide, wouldn't it? (crying) Now you know how mixed up I am! I guess I am a little crazy—worrying about John and the money and everything. (sobbing)

NURSE (hands patient a handkerchief): It's such a tough problem that you would just like to escape from it.

PATIENT: Yes, but I don't really want to die. I can't really say that my husband would be better off if I died. He would be all alone with our little boy. What a coward I am! What would he do all alone? And Johnny—he needs me even if I'm not much of a mother. If I just knew what to do! If I could just be patient like other mothers!

NURSE: All mothers get angry and impatient with their children sometimes.

PATIENT: I do get angry at the other children, but I don't feel so bad when I jump on them.

NURSE: It's more difficult with John, because he has special problems.

PATIENT: Yes. I feel so helpless with John. I guess if I knew how to work with him better I wouldn't be so impatient.

NURSE: There is a specially trained person on our staff who works with children with cerebral palsy. She might be helpful to you and John, and if you feel you would like to talk with her, it can be arranged.

PATIENT: Yes, I would. I used to talk with John's teacher, and that helped a lot, but since he hasn't been in school I haven't seen her. We must get him back in school soon. We will have to borrow money for the operation; that is why his schooling has to wait. I wish there were some way to pay for both at the same time.

NURSE: There are also people on our staff who are trained to help with financial problems. Maybe one of them could help you make a payment plan for your operation so it would not be such a burden to you.

PATIENT: Could my husband and I both talk to them before I have the operation? I would want him to see the person with me.

In this conversation, the nurse recognized the patient's distress, as the nurse in the first episode did. Contrary to the way her colleague responded, however, she did not derogate the patient by making light of her feelings. She made an opening for the patient to communicate her distress, which the discouraged patient fenced off by a simple "Yes."

The nurse's next question, "Would you like to tell me about it?" opened further the opportunity for the patient to speak. To be helpful, this question would have to reflect the nurse's sincere interest and warmth for the patient. If it were a curious probe without real interest in understanding the patient better, the patient would probably be able to detect it as such. This is only one of several similar kinds of openings. For example, one might use, "Tell me what happened," or further identification of feelings might be attempted to encourage expression, such as, "It must have been pretty upsetting." The nurse observed that the patient had a need to talk with someone, but at this point she needed a little help to feel that the nurse would actually accept her.

Next, the nurse attempted to convey to the patient that she wanted to try to understand her, even though the patient thought that it was impossible. The patient gave three clues to the fact that it would be difficult for her to feel accepted enough to talk about her problem: (1) she expected nurses to think that her distress was silly; (2) she said that her feelings were hard to explain; and (3) she wished to escape the whole issue by going home. The nurse made the inference that the patient's confidence might begin to be restored if she could be assisted to work out her problem for herself.

The nurse's second inference was that the patient might experience further distress, perhaps to the point of devastation, if she were allowed to escape from working with her difficulties.

The patient's first step in having a successful experience in problem-solving is to feel accepted and understood, so she can feel free to talk about all the facets of her problems in order to view them clearly in making her decisions. The nurse created a feeling of acceptance by what she said and did as she listened to her. By listening with sincere interest, by identifying the feelings that the patient was expressing and by seeking clarification when meanings were not clear to her, the nurse conveyed that she was trying to understand.

The nurse's statement, "It is hard to talk about it," was an attempt to identify and accept the patient's feeling of half-wanting and half-not-wanting to talk "it" over, and to show that she accepted the turmoil that the patient felt.

As the patient started to work with her problem, she made opening statements that were not quite clear. When the nurse sought clarification by asking, "Could you tell me who John is . . . ?" she accomplished two things. First she conveyed that she was really interested in knowing exactly what was being said, and secondly, she helped the patient communicate more clearly. Issues sometimes can be perceived more adequately as they are described to another person. If the factors involved in a problem are clear, accurate identification of the problem is possible.

The nurse's question, "Are you saying that you may not live . . . ?" was also a clarification maneuver, using a slightly different method. The nurse picked up something the patient said and tried to help her re-examine it to see if she really meant what she was saying. There are a variety of clarification-seeking responses that might have been used. For instance, "What do you mean?" or "Why shouldn't you have the operation?"

When one uses any "helping measure" there is the possibility that he is using it to serve his own purpose rather than that of the person he is helping. If the nurse uses a clarification maneuver to help the patient look at her meanings more clearly and use her own resources to reformulate her concepts, the patient experiences a feeling of confidence that comes when a problem is successfully resolved. However, if the nurse uses the clarification maneuver to achieve a sense of power in manipulating the patient and thus to raise her own feeling of prestige, her patient may feel foolish for approaching her difficulties as she did. She will not be reassured about her own strength, but she may feel more helpless and inadequate than she did before, and become more anxious and less able to solve her problems rationally.

Within an accepting relationship, a patient is able to take the next step in problem-solving. Mrs. Carson took a second look at what her death would mean. As she realized somewhat more clearly what she had been thinking, she became self-condemnatory. She expressed her feeling through crying and by saying that she was "mixed up" and "crazy." The nurse's behavior conveyed that it is all right for her to feel and act upset. She sympathetically realized with her that hers was a difficult situation. This acceptance made it possible for the patient to explore and express her feelings further, and perhaps to uncover more facets of the problem.

The nurse made several responses that identified the patient's feelings. This helped the patient look at the feeling herself and identify what she actually felt. Secondly, they helped her realize that the nurse saw the feelings too, and did not dislike her or blame her for having them. Thirdly, the nurse identified feelings that Mrs. Carson had in common with other mothers which helped her realize that she was not an unusual, bizarre, or bad person. In other words, these responses conveyed to the patient that the nurse could accept what she was saying and understand what she was feeling. This made it possible for the patient to look at her feelings more realistically and to express some of her other feelings that were difficult for her to accept.

The nurse would be of little value to her patient if her role stopped here. The purpose of exploring and examining feelings is to help the patient see how they relate to her problem and to make it possible for her to identify her problem. Mrs. Carson identified her problem as being an inadequate mother to a child with special needs. As she was helped to express and clarify her feelings, she replaced her nonrational thinking of death as a solution with a more constructive approach. She began to consider making plans for the care of her child with the assistance of someone else, and she began to take steps to work out her financial problems.

Talking things over is helpful only if new insights are gained, insights that were not present when the situation was being mulled over alone. The nurse uses techniques in her interpersonal relationship that convey acceptance, ask for clarification, and identify feelings and issues to help her patient get all of the parts of a problem examined. This examination includes a survey of the facets that make up the problem, identification of the problem, the choice of possible solutions, and the recognition of factors that are involved in possible outcomes. Whether a problem is great or small, the nurse's role is not to make choices for the patient, but to help him arrive at a solution after considering all the factors involved.

To return to Webster's definition that reassurance is "a restoration of confidence," a patient experiences this restoration when his "mixed-up" and indecisive feelings disappear and his thinking becomes clearer. He can then discard the nonrational solutions made in panic and begin to work toward a realistic outcome.

Frequently the patient will need the aid of specially trained persons to deal with certain problems or facets of problems. The nurse needs to know who is available on the health team and in what ways other services can be useful to patients. She also needs to interpret these services skillfully to the patient. Concrete help, such as finding a resource person to help with a financial problem, is not always a part of the reassuring process. Also, one cannot assume that simply referring a patient to a source of aid suffices as a reassuring experience, for it does not replace the necessary emotional reassurance.

Essentially, then, the technique of giving is very difficult to separate from the total interpersonal process of the nurse-patient relationship. In the examples we have cited of nurses' conversations with patients, we have suggested that patients feel reassured when they are helped to use their own skills to work with problems that seem overwhelming at the outset. Patients probably feel reassured when someone is willing to listen and to value them as persons, accepting what they say without condemning them for expressing what they feel. As a part of this, there is probably a feeling of reassurance when a patient feels that the nurse's actions, feelings, and words indicate her respect for him.

There are other elements in the problem of reassuring people that command our attention. There are times when a person is so anxious that reasonable problem-solving is not possible at the moment. Reassurance for this person requires a different approach. In moments of great apprehension it is usually comforting not to be left alone. A child is comforted by the calm presence of his mother when he runs to her terrified, and finds that the terror is not duplicated in her. As the mother comforts the child by holding him and saying she will not allow him to be hurt, his terror is reduced, and eventually he begins to talk about the experience that frightened him; thus the problem-solving process begins. This is similar to many situations with adult patients. During labor or just before electrotherapy or surgery, for example, the adult experiences reassurance by having someone with him whom he knows and trusts. The reassuring person may be a member of the patient's family, a friend, or a churchman; in the hospital, this person is often one of the members of the health team—most frequently, the nurse.

Correcting a false expectation or a misconception by giving correct information can be a reassuring measure if the patient has an opportunity to discuss the issue adequately with someone he trusts. A patient's apparent efforts to seek information are not always an attempt to get the facts, however. For example, when a patient who is about to have an electrotherapy treatment asks the nurse, "How many patients die from this?" he is usually not seeking a factual answer. More likely, this is a "front" question that tests to see if the nurse will respond with understanding. Behind this "front" the patient may be feeling, "I'm afraid I am going to die, and I need to tell you how afraid I am!" If the nurse responds with a factual answer, she conveys that she does not understand his underlying fear, and the patient will usually refrain from pushing the matter further. She has not given the patient the opportunity to express his feeling and what she expected to be reassuring has become a blocking measure. On the other hand, when information is needed but is withheld, a situation is produced that is far from reassuring. A patient experiences reassurance when he is given authentic information, by someone he trusts, when he needs it.

Reassurance is also experienced when a limit that is reasonable is set with fairness. There are always a few necessary limitations on one's behavior, at any age and in any situation. In illness, patients are sometimes unable to set their own limits without help. It is reassuring to a psychiatric patient when a nurse enforces a limit that prevents him from damaging himself or others. It is reassuring to a patient when the nurse sets some necessary limitations on the behavior of those around him as, for example, when she observes that visitors are disturbing to him, and tactfully helps them terminate their visit. It is also reassuring to a patient to be oriented to the limitations and the expectations of the hospital setting.

A patient is reassured by his trust in those who are in the "helping" role—trust in both their interpersonal and functional abilities. The patient observes the nurse's competence in administering technical procedures and hygienic measures, and when he perceives that these are done well, he is reassured. He is aware of the clinical and administrative judgments that concern him directly and indirectly. When he feels that competent people are making these judgments, he is reassured. Verbal reassurance cannot substitute for functional competence, nor for sincerity and warmth of feeling toward people.

It is not uncommon to hear professional people attempting to reassure patients with the social "bromides," such as, "Everything is going to be all right" and "There is no reason to worry." These are of little value to a person in trouble. They are false reassurances because they lack a rational operating principle and do not provide the opportunity for the person to experience reassurance. The urgings to "cheer up" or "buck up" are equally useless to the person in distress. Another kind of false reassurance, the frank falsification or lie, can be quite devastating when the patient discovers the falsehood.

A common misconception is that it helps to change the subject when a patient starts to talk about something that is disturbing, either to himself or to the listener. This maneuver only prevents the patient from working a problem through, and it betrays the listener's lack of acceptance. A similar measure is to stay away from, or leave, patients who are upset, in order to avoid a "scene." In this situation, the patient experiences isolation and loneliness; he is rarely reassured.

Reassurance involves all of nursing. It is an element of every procedure and every personal contact with patients. Its effectiveness depends on a basic philosophy of respect for another person. Reassurance is experienced by a patient when he finds that he is respected and understood by the nurse who assists him to recognize and develop his own resources and thereby restore his confidence in himself.

Section 3

The Patient's View
of His Situation

INTRODUCTION

One of our basic propositions is that an individual's definition of his situation is a major determinant of his behavior in that situation. Of special importance is the individual's understanding of what other people expect of him in that situation. For example, the hospitalized patient's feelings about his treatment or condition and his understanding of how he should behave is a major determinant of how in fact he will behave. This can even be true for behavior that is widely thought to be completely determined biologically. For example, there is evidence to indicate that vomiting, elevated blood pressure, response to a nursing procedure such as an enema, and verbalized pain, as well as many other physical signs and symptoms are strongly affected by how the patient is defining the situation. In the previous sections we have seen evidence to support this general proposition and illustrations of how through social interaction with the patient, it is possible for those responsible for his care to increase the effectiveness of that care by the appropriate kind of communication *with* the patient. Communicating with the patient calls for finding out what he is thinking about his condition and his treatment and care. One of the essential steps in the nursing process is diagnosis before prescribing or carrying out a nursing activity. This means that an essential first step before any nursing action is to find out how the patient is defining the situation.

Failure to take the patient's point of view into account is one of the major sources of breakdown in staff-patient communication. In Section 1, Esther Lucile Brown suggests that perhaps the only way medical and nursing students would really learn to appreciate the patient's point of view, would be to be forced to spend a period as a patient in the hospital (page 14). Our first selection in this Section provides a vicarious substitute for actual experience as a patient. In "Orientals Are Stoic," Tao-Kim-Hai eloquently describes the long series of unintentional insults and rudenesses finally leading to his bitter outburst in which he demands of his helpless surgeon why the hospital does not take care of its patients' mental welfare as well as their physical welfare and why the nurses do not treat their patients as human beings. No doubt there are many reasonable explanations for the way that the staff handled this patient. But of most interest here is the fact that none of them made a successful attempt at any point in the course of this patient's hospitalization to learn his perception of his situation—*even after his outburst!*

In the next paper, Henry Lederer, a psychiatrist, reviews the range of reactions that persons may have as an illness becomes diagnosed, treatment begins, and as finally a transition is made back to health in the convalescent period. In the next selection Paul Brauer makes a similar review of possible thoughts and feelings about terminal illness. In his discussion Brauer includes a discussion of the situation from the family's point of view. The next article was written by the widow of a patient who died in a large metropolitan hospital. "A Way of Dying," gives a brief but powerful glimpse of the situation from the patient's point of view, as well as from his wife's. Notice that after his second operation and after the doctor had told him that they would do for him what they could, the patient said, "There you are, they just don't care." What was needed most then, sedatives or understanding? In the next piece, by a psychologist, we read the astounding account of how through a series of ludicrous misunderstandings a Navaho Indian became diagnosed, "psychotic." Again, when someone finally was able to understand this patient's point of view, his behavior became quite understandable.

The personnel who came in contact with the Navaho subject of Jewell's article believed that the man did not "have contact with reality." But it is necessary to understand that what is "reality" or "rational" for one person may not be so for another. "Reality" is relative. It depends on your point of view. A person who is doing something that seems "unrealistic" might very well have a "rationale" for his action that makes it seem very realistic to himself. There are many words in our language for this. For example, we can call it "rationale," "frame of reference," "value-orientation," "ethos," "point of view," "perspective," or "culture." Although each of these words often is used in other ways, they all can be used to refer to the way that a person gives meaning to his experience, the system a person uses for defining life's situations. We emphasize in this book the term *culture*.

People who share the same culture tend to define the same situation in the same way. And since an individual's behavior in a situation is guided by his definition of that situation, we get "cultural variation" in patterns of behavior. If you know the culture that a person comes from, then to some extent you are able to predict what his behavior will be in various situations. This is, of course, the basis for social organization. If we could not predict the behavior of those we are working with, our actions could not be coordinated. What a person in a helping profession must realize is that cultures vary. Of particular relevance for the health professions are variations from culture to culture in conceptions of health and appropriate behaviors for the ill person and the healer. In "Anthropological Perspectives on Medicine and Public Health," Benjamin D. Paul emphasizes the importance of culture to the health professions. Note especially his discussion of how a cultural gap between practitioner and patient can complicate communication between the two and thus reduce or prevent the effectiveness of the health worker. He illustrates these principles from the experience of American health workers around the world. He then goes on to comment on the existence of "sub-cultural variation" within any particular nation or group. He notes as one source of subcultural variation, the "status gap."

In the next selection, Barbara Baumann reports differences between medical students and patients in their conceptions of what it means to be healthy. As Baumann points out,

> . . . persons may fail to respond to measures designed to improve their health because they fail to perceive the measures as related to their conception of health. When such a difference in conception goes undetected in the interaction between physician and patient, each party may find the other's attitudes incomprehensible, and, in consequence, an unnecessary strain may be imposed on the doctor-patient relationship.

In other words, failure to find out how the patient is defining the situation may result in the practitioner's failure to achieve his purpose.

From open-ended interviews with patients and medical students, Baumann discovered three dimensions along which the meaning of *health* seemed to vary. These dimensions might be called feeling, knowing, and doing. For the patients, health tended to have more meaning as a matter of feeling or doing. Being "healthy" was for them a matter of "feeling good" or activity, the ability to perform one's normal roles in life. In contrast, the medical students were much more symptom oriented—for them the meaning of health was more a matter of knowing and recognizing medical symptoms. This can be seen as an example of an important cultural difference that probably always exists between medical practitioners and their patients. For this reason alone, if there were no other cultural differences between practitioner and patient, cultural variation must be an important variable to take into account in attempting to improve professional practice through an improved understanding of the patient's point of view. Nurses share the culture of the hospital; the patients do not; hence, there is always at least one cultural barrier to any successful attempt to communicate with the patient. Baumann goes on to point out (in Table 5) further evidence indicating how this divergence of the medical practitioner from the patient increases as the student progresses in the medical school. As the student becomes more and more socialized into the medical culture, his definitions of health increasingly diverge from the patient's definitions. No doubt a similar process occurs in nursing school. Baumann goes on to note that the relative importance of different dimensions of the meaning of health depend on education and religion of the patients. And, of course, the difference between the patients and the medical students might be seen as an occupational difference. In general, "background characteristics," or "status variables," such as income, education, religion and occupation are important indicators of "sub-cultural variation" and hence are important to the health practitioner as potential barriers to effective understanding of the patient's definition of the situation.

In our final selection Tagliocozzo reports some interesting data from interviews with patients giving their perceptions of the nurse. This data, collected by social scientists, supplements and elaborates on the perceptions of the nurses presented in a more particular and individualistic and less systematic way by the patient who wrote the article opening this section.

It is one thing to say that understanding the patient's definition of the situation is important for effective patient care. It is another thing to stipulate the conditions that make it possible for those responsible for the patient's care to communicate effectively *with* the patient. In the next section the social context within which patient care takes place is analyzed with special reference to conditions that produce barriers to effective understanding of the patient's point of view.

Orientals Are Stoic

André M. Tao-Kim-Hai

Reprinted by permission;
Copr. © 1957 The New Yorker Magazine, Inc.

The most peaceful moments of my first stay in an American hospital came just after my operation. Bandaged, half doped, faintly aching, I lay flat on my back between smooth, clean sheets and hazily reflected that nothing is more annoying than a fresh incision with fresh stitches in one's abdomen except, of course, two fresh incisions with fresh stitches in one's abdomen. The thought, for some reason, made me chuckle, and the chuckle made me more than intellectually aware of the incisions—the result of that morning's operation for double hernia. But even pain did not quite touch me, and in the euphoria of ether intoxication I felt at one with the whole world, whose center for me was this New York hospital. I did not expect then that only a few days later I would commit there the most unpardonable sin for an Oriental (I am Vietnamese)—that of losing face through one's own bad behavior. But lose face I did, and to this day I wonder whether my shame was caused by the hypersensitivity of an ethnic minority group reduced to one specimen, or by my secret desire not to be treated as a foreigner in my wife's native land, or by my old, ill-suppressed Oriental prejudice against being openly pushed around by women, or simply by the fact that I had never been a hospital patient before and was hopelessly unprepared for the efficient, cold-blooded, and frequently, it seemed, nonsensical routines that are so familiar and so irritating to most convalescents. I still don't know, in short, whether my behavior was a display of just indignation or a childish tantrum.

I had a nurse, of course, after my operation—a woman whose white hair was ineffectually covered by a ridiculously small white bonnet, and who fluttered around my little private room with concentrated energy and, I am sure, efficiency. Despite a few minor differences, she reminded me of a Sister of Charity whom I had known twenty-eight years earlier in the Vietnamese town of Soctrang. My brother and I referred to this nun between ourselves as the *ange de charité*—a cliché we employed with no hint of irony because we knew she worked without salary and because the two huge, triangular white wings of her coif flapped over her shoulders angelically whenever she moved. On her flat chest she wore a black wooden cross with a worn metal Christ on it, and from her belt swung a long, heavy rosary. She was gentle and cheerful, as we imagined angels to be, although she sang in a French strongly tinged with a Marseille accent, which we some- how felt was not the true tone of angels. Did my New York nurse speak French? I was too weak in the hours following the operation to find out, and too weak even to try to identify her accent, which might have been that of Brooklyn. She was plump and there was none of the selfless gentle- ness of the nun about her. But a nurse is a nurse, I told myself, and therefore an angel. With this reassuring conclusion, I closed my eyes and sank back into the fog of ether, thinking about how poorly my childhood had prepared me for modern medical care.

I was born in a small village on the banks of a canal, among the rich rice fields of South Vietnam. According to local standards, my father was a wealthy man, for he owned over a hundred and twenty hectares of rice fields, and our family lived in an enclosure containing a tile-roofed master house and several thatch-roofed outbuildings for farm hands, domestic servants, water buffaloes, and agricultural implements. This was an inviting world for a young boy, and I enjoyed it in an active, almost headlong fashion, collecting a vast assortment of cuts and bumps along the way. Whenever I hurt myself I would cry to get my mother's attention. She would come at once to scold not me but the object that hurt me, and then would rub my bruise or wash my cut with rain water, as the case might be (we had no clinic in our village, and no arnica or mercurochrome in our household), and tell me to forget about it. Then she would carry me across the yard to my favorite old water buffalo, and I would have an extra ride on his back all around our compound, to inspect the sparrow nests under the eaves of our red tile roof, to pass in review the dwarf coconut palms along the wide ditches where our barges were moored, or to pick hibiscus flowers from the hedge that separated our compound from the communal canal. Or, if it was raining, my mother would lay me in a hammock and swing it gently with one foot while she sat in a wicker chair beside me and read me passages from ancient stories that were full of heroes who suffered with equanimity—including a general who had a broken arrowhead removed from one arm and the wound cleansed with rice alcohol while playing Chinese chess with his free hand.

My older brother was, in his small way, another example to me. If he had a toothache, he would hold a spoonful of rice alcohol in his mouth—a Vietnamese remedy based on the principle of fighting pain with fire—without whimpering. He would even challenge me, in sign language, to one of the innumerable games Vietnamese children have played for generations, and, leering at me derisively over his mouthful of fire, beat me, no matter what the game. The fact that he was incapable of comment or small talk only added to his importance.

After my father's death, in 1910, my education fell temporarily to my mother and to one or another of her younger brothers. Maternal Uncle Number Three was a true scholar, whose philosophy was based on a mingling of native tradition, Taoism, Confucianism, and Buddhism. Along with my letters, he taught me our fundamental Vietnamese beliefs—among them the concept of man's three souls. The Superior Man, he often told me, pays little attention to his vegetative soul, restrains his animal soul under all circumstances, and strives to develop his spiritual soul as much as possible, in order to distinguish himself from cabbages, eggplants, coconut palms, cats, dogs, pigs, and water buffaloes. This uncle had a vegetative soul plagued by a number of minor tropical diseases—malaria and various skin eruptions—but he sternly refused to take notice of its sufferings. He classified his internal troubles into two categories—those caused by an excess of internal heat, to be treated with rhinoceros horn, and those caused by a deficiency of internal heat, to be treated with ginger. The first medicine is prepared by patiently rubbing a rhinoceros horn—from which the rhinoceros has been detached, of course—across the rough inner surface of an earthenware bowl containing cold water. When the water becomes milky, you drink it until your fever subsides. The second remedy is no more than a hot infusion of fresh ginger sweetened with rock sugar. You drink it until you feel warmer, which is very soon. My uncle had no quarrel with other local medicinal products, such as deer antler, dried bumblebees, tiger bones, ginseng, orange peel, and mint, but he saw no reason to implicate his life with them when he had a rhinoceros horn stored in a tin box and ginger growing in his own yard. As for surgical operations, he considered them sins against filial piety. Were they not mutilations of one's body, which was a precious gift from one's parents and not to be tampered with under any circumstances?

The concessions he did make to illness were rare and grudging. He bore his skin diseases without even scratching. He would drink rhinoceros-horn water and bathe himself with it from time to time, although he expected no rapid results. My mother used to bathe our mangy dogs in creosote diluted with water, and she urged my uncle to try the same cure for his skin troubles. "Of course, it must hurt a little," she said, "but it does the dogs a lot of good. You, Little Brother, have the same vegetative soul that dogs have, so why don't you try it?"

Little Brother resented this reminder of the least of his three souls. He was also an adult Vietnamese and only human, and was therefore suspicious of the creosote because it came in a bottle with a French label. But to prove to his elder sister that he did not shy away from pain he bathed himself once or twice with her dog medicine, proving simultaneously that it did not hasten the purging of his blood.

Malaria made him more cooperative with his vegetative soul. In some uncanny fashion, he knew when he was about to have a malarial seizure, and he would prepare his mat and his concoctions beforehand. As soon as he started to feel the chill, he would drink the ginger, lie down on his mat, and shake lamentably. After a time, the chill would pass, and there would be a little lull. Then the fever would seize him, and he would drink rhinoceros-horn water and perspire profusely for a while—a long while, it seemed to me. When the fever subsided he would sit up, give me a quizzical smile, half of apology and half of pride, and prepare himself a pot of Chinese tea while smoking one of the conical cigarettes he made out of black Vietnamese tobacco and the same coarse white paper I made kites with.

When I went off to a boarding school run by a group of Christian Brothers, I encountered another way of dealing with physical miseries. The *très cher Frère Infirmier* in charge of the school's infirmary was a fat man with a big red beard, and big blue eyes made bigger by thick lenses, who spoke French and Vietnamese with a Breton accent and who believed in Western medicine and Christian purgatory. Armed with a bottle of iodine and an applicator, he could make the smallest wound feel like a major abscess, and he classified our cuts and bruises as deserving, according to their size, one hundred days, two hundred days, or three hundred days of deliverance from purgatory, provided the patient offered his pain as a sacrifice to the Almighty and did not cry or whimper. Any rise in body temperature—checked with the *cher Frère's* oral thermometer—was followed by the administration of castor oil. The patients stood at attention in a row, and the *Frère Infirmier*, a huge bottle of castor oil in one hand and a teaspoon in the other, passed slowly down the line like a fatherly colonel, explaining to neophytes that they would receive three spoonfuls of the stuff, each worth one hundred days' remission from purgatory if the medicine was bravely offered to God. Sometimes a spoonful of castor oil, through no fault of the recipient, refused to stay down. The *Infirmier* would continue his distribution as though nothing unusual had happened, but he would keep the unfortunate boy after the others had been dismissed, to console him for his medicinal and spiritual loss.

As I lay now on my hard hospital bed and tried to remember the exact appearance of the *Infirmier's* face, my half-closed eyes were struck by a strong electric light switched on over my head. Another face, tanned and kind, seemed to be floating above me. I made an effort to focus on it, and recognized it as that of my surgeon. Behind him was a group of internes.

"How're you doing?" the surgeon asked me in a gentle voice.

"I'm doing all right, Doctor," I answered.

He uncovered me by pulling down the sheet and pulling up my hospital gown. My belly was warm, his fingers were cold, and at the best of times I am ticklish. The result was that I winced, and my face must have shown an inexplicable hilarity. The internes converged on me, watching me seriously. The cold fingers poked; I wiggled and giggled involuntarily. The soft voice asked "Does it hurt?" I answered "No," partly because my flesh was still numb and partly to reassure him that my wiggling was not due to pain. The internes looked on with intense gravity, from which I surmised that I was a rare sort of hospital patient, to be observed with special attention. The examination went on like this for some time, until at last the surgeon covered me again and departed with his solemn retinue.

I had full confidence in my surgeon and liked him, although many of our earlier encounters had been marked by this same kind of foolish misunderstanding. I must admit that at our first meeting, in 1948, I had disliked him. I had joined the United Nations staff in New York in 1946. Two years later, at the conclusion of a routine physical examination—the U.N. has its own clinic and its own staff of doctors giving regular physical checkups to all members of its Secretariat—a charming French-speaking woman doctor told me that she wanted me to see the specialist on hernia. "Just to make sure, you know," she added reassuringly. That was how I met my surgeon. He was nine years younger then, still under thirty, and perhaps a little less gentle than he is now. I was far from patient with him, not because of my youth, since I was already forty-three, but because I spoke little English and he knew no French. When he asked me to uncover my middle, I started to explain to him in my slow English that I had never noticed anything wrong. He cut me short with an impatient "Yes, but—" and plunged a long, firm finger into me. "Cough!" he commanded. I didn't feel like coughing, but I tried to oblige. "Louder!" he snapped. I did my best. He poked harder, and I began to giggle.

"There's nothing to laugh about," he said, and my blood pressure rose several points. After all, I was much older than he (in Vietnam he would have had to call me *ông*, which literally means "grandfather"), and we were of equal rank in the U.N. But my limited English prevented me from making a properly acid retort.

After a few more pokes, the doctor straightened up and asked, "How long have you had this double hernia?"

His tone was an accusation, as if I had known of the hernia all along and had willfully concealed it on my medical questionnaire. But again my English wouldn't come, and I could only answer him with a phrase I had learned from comic strips—"I dunno."

"Why don't you know?" he fired at me.

Nobody had asked me such a question since the days when I was a *soldat de deuxième classe* in the French Army. Sensing my rising temper at last, he tried to make me feel at ease. "You must be a real tough guy," he said.

This was no better. I had heard the epithet "tough guy," but I had always translated it to myself as *"mauvais garçon."* Again he must have seen my anger and incomprehension, because he modified his statement. "You don't pay much attention to minor pains, do you?"

After that, we got along better. He told me that there was no hurry about an operation, but I must come to him for an examination at least once a year. So for the next seven years I dutifully reported to his office, where he would poke and I would jump, and the operation would again be postponed, because, he told me, it was only the beginnings of a hernia. Last year, however, I informed him of my decision to retire from the U.N. and to move to Hawaii, and he said that the time had come for surgery. I was not getting any younger, he told me, and I might not find such good hospital facilities away from New York. My wife voted with the doctor, and I reluctantly agreed. I did not then know what was in store for me.

One afternoon late last winter, I presented myself at the hospital, where my wife and I waited patiently and endlessly for a nurse in the admitting office to grant me an audience. At last she produced questionnaires and began to ask me a series of questions that reminded me of my first encounter with the Gestapo, in Marseille in 1943. My difficulties started with the very first questions: "What's your first name? What's your last name?"

Being intellectually scrupulous, I wanted clarification on what she meant by first and last. "First is what comes first. Last is what comes last," the bureaucrat-nurse said with infinite weariness.

My trouble was that we tradition-bound Vietnamese have been more reluctant than the Chinese to Westernize our way of writing our names, even when we live in a Western country, by reversing our usual order of family name first and given name last. My Vietnamese name is Tao-Kim-Hai, the family name, Tao, coming first. But when I became a French citizen in 1929, I was required by law to add a Western given name in front of my old name. Thus my full name, André Marie Tao-Kim-Hai, now contains two first names first, then my family name, and then two first names *last*. After much explanation on my part and bored impatience on the nurse's part, my names were written down, but I reduced the name Marie to the initial M, in order to avoid confusing the nurse as to my sex.

"Country of birth?"

This was easy, or so I thought, and I answered without hesitation, "Vietnam."

The young lady held her pen poised but refused to write. "Never heard of it," she said, as if I had just invented a new country.

Vietnam is not a new country. Its first king is thought to have died in the year 2879 B.C. Perhaps an American lady, even a professional and educated lady, cannot be expected to know Vietnamese ancient history, because the name of the country has changed several times. But how about Bao-Dai, Ho Chi Minh, Ngo Dinh Diem, Saigon, Hanoi, and Diên-Biên-Phu?

"Is it in China?" the nurse asked.

Now, that is a question calculated to drive any Vietnamese wild. The Vietnamese respect China as the seat of a very honorable culture, but they cannot forget the thousand years of war between China and Vietnam. Historically, ethnically, geographically, and politically the lady was wrong, but I drew a deep breath and held my temper. It took me a long time, but eventually the nurse passed me, not *cum laude*, and turned me over to a male attendant, who turned me over to a cashier to pay in advance for private nurses. Finally, I was allowed to go to my room.

The room was small but comfortable and well located, with a balcony and a view over the city. When my sister-in-law was in the Soctrang hospital in 1929, she had a whole suite to herself on the ground floor, surrounded by a hedge of blooming hibiscus. Here in New York there was no blooming hibiscus but a hedge of dirty buildings, with a few skyscrapers in the background. Nevertheless, my room cost at least twenty times as much as the suite in the Soctrang hospital and at least twice as much as the room I had occupied in the Waldorf-Astoria in 1945. At that price, I decided, I could expect good service, some comfort, and a certain measure of privacy. I changed my business suit for pajamas and a robe, said good-bye to my wife, and eased myself comfortably into the one armchair and started to read.

The door opened suddenly and a voice boomed "Hi, André!" It was a Catholic priest, plump and jovial, complete with prayer book and stole. "How about Confession and Communion?"

I had told the admitting nurse expressly that although I was a Catholic, I did not want a priest, but here he was. He seemed a bit disappointed when

I told him that it was not to be a serious operation, that I expected to survive, and that, anyway, I did not take death as seriously as many other Christians do. I tried to talk religion with him, but he did not seem particularly interested, and left after a few minutes.

Almost immediately, another man came in. He pointed an accusing finger at me and said with what I took to be a Middle European accent, "You have tuberculosis. You have venereal disease. You have—" There was not the slightest interrogative inflection in his voice.

"Who are you?" I interrupted.

"The anesthetist," he answered.

"*Parlez-vous français?*"

"*Oui,*" he said, and resumed "*Vous avez la tuberculose. Vous avez des maladies vénériennes. Vous avez—*" as affirmatively as ever.

During that first afternoon in the hospital, many other unexpected and unknown visitors came in, always without knocking, without introducing themselves, and without stating their business—except for the man who came to rent me a television set. I was both annoyed and amused, assuming, rightly or wrongly, that all this was the normal routine of an American hospital.

There is nothing to report about the next morning, except that a man came in to prepare me for the operation and a nurse popped in to give me a hypodermic, the significance of which I did not realize until I woke in the afternoon and discovered the incisions in my abdomen.

That evening, when I was fast asleep, somebody again turned on the light above my head. I looked at my watch and found that it was a few minutes after ten. Two young male internes and a young woman interne were sitting in chairs tilted back against the wall and looking at me. I recognized them as having been in the group that had visited me with the surgeon that afternoon. They smiled at me and I smiled back at them. We talked. One interne said that he had been surprised when I giggled during the surgeon's examination in the afternoon. "Orientals are stoic," he stated sententiously.

I decided that by "stoic" he meant tough, in the way my surgeon meant it when he said I was a tough guy, and I took it to be a compliment. But I wondered about "Orientals" and asked him for his interpretation of the word.

"Chinese, of course," he said.

I asked him if he thought the whole Orient—whatever geographical limits he gave to that word—was peopled by Chinese. To my astonishment, he said that he took it for granted that I was Chinese, and anyway, all yellow people were the same. I asked him if he thought all white people were the same. I saw that he was embarrassed, and I was aware that it was

I who was embarrassing him. I tried to put him at ease—as if I were a host in this room, and not a man who had just had an operation and was hoping to be allowed to sleep—with the story of my adventure with some Canadian broadcasters.

A few years back, I told the interne, I had received a telephone call from Ottawa inviting me to go there as the guest of the Canadian Radio-diffusion and read a few pages of French text for a film sound track.

"Don't any of you in Canada speak French any more?" I asked.

"Yes, but we want somebody from the Orient to do it."

"What's the text?" I asked.

But it was a long-distance call, and they didn't want to go into details. I was glad to visit Canada at somebody else's expense and get paid for it besides. I flew to Ottawa, had an excellent French lunch, and was shown the film, which was about India, and I read their text aloud into a micro-phone. I read it in my own French accent, which had grown out of twenty-two years' residence in France, out of my study of French diction, and out of several years spent as an habitué of the Club du Faubourg, where Parisian orators discuss everything from Paul Valéry to colonialism. When I finished my recording, despair was on the faces of my Canadian hosts. I sensed that I was a complete failure, and said I was sorry.

A French-Canadian said, *"Mais c'est de la Comédie-Française!* Couldn't you read French with an Oriental accent?"

"Which Oriental accent?" I replied. I explained that I did not know any of the dozens of languages spoken in India, any more than I knew Japanese or Chinese or Laotian or Cambodian or Malay or Siamese or Burmese, or whatever languages they speak in Afghanistan, Tibet, and Inner and Outer Mongolia. All I knew was Vietnamese, and my Vietnamese friends had told me that I spoke Vietnamese with an American accent, whatever that might be.

At the end of this story, the internes dropped the subject of race and tackled me on Oriental religions. I had a hard time explaining to them that neither Taoism nor Confucianism nor Buddhism is a religion in the Western sense of the word. They shrugged, and one of them said, "Tell us about Oriental food." But here again I had to say that I could find no common denominator for a Japanese *sukiyaki*, a Korean *pulgogi*, an Indo-nesian *nasi goreng*, a Siamese *mee kraub*, and an Indian curry. And so they left. They had not been unkind, but I had a feeling that they were dis-appointed by my inability to give them any general ideas and unhappy because they were no longer sure of the general ideas they had had.

My real troubles started the next morning. Around five, a nurse came into my room and propped both doors wide open. I had never been awakened so early in my life except once in Oxford, where an English maid woke me before dawn to serve me early-morning tea. Here, in the New York hospital, my nurse served me an early-morning thermometer, without asking my consent or cooperation. I resolved to be patient, however, and tried, unsuccessfully, to go back to sleep. Around seven o'clock, I thought it was late enough to ask for a special favor, and I rang. Ten minutes later, a nurse in her late twenties whom I had never seen before came in. Before I had time to ask her please to bring me a cup of coffee or anything hot, and kindly to close the door when leaving, she shouted at me, "Whatsa matta, boy?"

I was nonplussed by the rudeness of her tone and her vocabulary, but I managed to lodge my double request. "Breakfast at eight-thirty," she snapped, and went out immediately—without closing the door.

She went out so fast that I had no time to formulate an appropriate reply. The word "boy" had stung me more than the nurse's tone and manner. I did remember that before my American father-in-law died, my mother-in-law used to explain his occasional absence from their cottage in Florida by saying "He must be out bowling with the boys"—by which she meant a group of gentlemen who were in their seventies. But I also could not forget my personal knowledge that the French in their colonies use the word "boy" to mean "servant." They even call a female servant a "boyesse." Suddenly angry, I wanted to ring for the nurse again and explain all this to her, but then I remembered my conversation with the internes and decided to live up to their high opinion of the stoicism of Orientals.

Around eight-thirty, several nurses invaded my room, all shockingly healthy and cheerful, and chattering like parakeets. I heard a jumble of overlapping greetings and questions, such as "Hi, boy!" "How do you feel this morning, sweetie?" "He looks wonderful!" "Where did you get this beautiful silk robe?" "Here's your breakfast." "Don't you like coffee? You prefer Chinese tea?" and "Soft-boiled eggs—no chop suey here!" I was confused, and I couldn't sort out the questions fast enough to answer any of them. Then a couple of male attendants walked into the crowded room, one of them shouting at me in Chinese, "*Ni hau ma? Ni hau pu hau?*" When I did not answer, he added, "You Chinese? What dialect you speak? . . . No Chinese? Jap?" The other attendant turned on the television, which responded with a blurred image and a blare of sound.

Suddenly my surgeon came in and the nurses and attendants became silent at once and filed out of the room. Gently he examined me. When he was through, he asked, "How do you feel?"

"Physically, as good as possible," I answered. "Mentally, not so good."

"Why?"

I explained to him that I had the impression of being a rare animal in a zoo. In fact, I added, this was worse than a zoo, because in a zoo the public is not supposed to excite the animals. The surgeon tried to cheer me up, telling me that there was a lack of privacy and social amenities in almost all hospitals. He went as far as to explain the psychology of nurses and hospital workers, who tend to become insensitive because they, fully clothed and ablebodied, habitually deal with more or less helpless patients who are stripped of their business suits and their vertical dignity.

This reasoning cheered me slightly, and I pondered over it later, when a nurse came to wash me. Her method was without consideration or kindness but efficient and thorough. No wonder nurses have a superiority complex, I reasoned as she rubbed by back, and no wonder I feel inferior, being babied like this. I quoted Spinoza to myself. "An emotion which is a passion ceases to be a passion as soon as we form a clear and distinct idea thereof."

But matters did not improve in the succeeding days. I was a "boy," I was a dumb Oriental. I was addressed in what sounded like pidgin English. I heard allusions to what the hospital staff thought of as Oriental ways and Oriental foods. Even my American wife was not spared rudeness, vexation, and humiliation. Although she had an M. A. in Greek before many of the nurses were born, these young ladies took it for granted that the wife of such a strange man could not amount to much. Several times I nearly exploded, but my wife, who can always guess my mood with accuracy, succeeded in calming me. I tried to remember my Maternal Uncle Number Three's teaching about the Superior Man. It was not my job, I told myself, to enlighten the hospital staff about world tolerance or the sensitiveness of one normal Oriental. My job was to restrain my animal, emotional soul and allow my physical, vegetative soul the best possible chance to heal my two incisions.

The moment of drama came unexpectedly. Its protagonist—the external, visible, and immediate cause—was a nurse, but as I think back on it, I realize she was no protagonist at all but only the last straw. Try as I may, I cannot even recall exactly what I said to her, or why I said it. I only remember her reply. "*I* am the supervisor," she said. "*I* am the head nurse here. *I* know my work and I know people like you!"

Jumping hastily and unnecessarily out of bed and fumbling with the telephone, I shouted to the operator, "I want my surgeon! I want him immediately!" Then I raved confusedly, incoherently, childishly, ridiculously. I don't remember most of what I said; I remember only that the hand grasping the telephone shook and that my legs would barely hold me up. The nurse herself did not seem to trust her eyes; it must have been a scene she was not used to. I shouted at her, "I am a patient! I'm not a nurse! I'm not under your supervision!"

The surgeon came, and I poured out to him all my bitterness as a patient in general and as an Oriental patient in particular. In a loud, shrill tone I told him that a hospital should take care not only of the physical welfare of its patients but of their mental welfare as well, and that nurses should treat their patients as human beings, whatever their race, sex, religion, and state of health. In the middle of my ravings, I again saw the nurse staring at me, her eyes wide open, her mouth slightly ajar, and her arms hanging foolishly down. "If you have nothing to do, get out of here!" I shouted at her. "Get out of here!"

Abruptly, my excitation and exhilaration subsided, and I felt ashamed of myself. I was also angry—angry with myself, with all the nurses on my floor, with the whole hospital, with the entire United States of America, and with all the human stupidity in the world. The surgeon had listened to me in silence. When I had calmed down, he quietly asked me, "Would you like to change floors?"

His gentle suggestion made my anger flare up again, and I cried out, louder than necessary, that I would not retreat. Suddenly finding myself in command of the English language, I said that I wanted to stand my ground and fight it out, to shout back at those who shouted at me, to be sarcastic when I met sarcasm, and to make myself either respected or hated as a patient and as an Oriental.

Gently the doctor eased himself out, and my wife came in. She told me that I had been wrong. I knew she was right, but I shouted at her, too, angrier than ever. She left. I was alone for a long, long time. A feeling of shame overcame me—only shame, nothing more.

Someone knocked at my door—a thing I wasn't used to any more—and I managed a "Come in." A young nurse with red hair appeared with a tray. "Your dinner, sir," she said without any emphasis. It was the natural thing for her to say, but I felt embarrassed, as if I were being shown a special treatment that I did not deserve. Guardedly I smiled at her and thanked her. I readied myself for dinner, cooperating eagerly as she set up the collapsible table. I pointed out to her a box of liqueur chocolates from Holland and invited her to help herself. She did so with grace. I asked her if she spoke French, and—miracle!—she did. She spoke it with a Canadian accent, but it was French all the same. I felt like kissing her then and there, just as I had felt like kissing the first girl I saw in the Free Zone of France after I left Frontstalag 152 in the Occupied Zone, in 1941. In both cases, however, I did not feel that I had won a battle.

From that day on, all the nurses I encountered treated me decently, finishing all their sentences with "sir"—even their supervisor, who reappeared discreetly the next day. I knew that I had behaved badly, that I had not been even faintly civilized, and that I had reacted in sheer animal passion. But I did not know how to apologize to the head nurse without embarrassing her. To make up for my inability to formulate an adequate apology, I cooperated with all the nurses and attendants beyond the call of a patient's duty. I took my own temperature. I took my own bath, sitting on the edge of the tub in my bathroom. I ate all my breakfast, although the eggs were never the way I liked them and the coffee was too American and too weak. I shared my gifts of candy and cookies with all the nurses. My guilt, nevertheless, lingered on, and I wondered if the head nurse now tolerated me as a spoiled and incurably ill-bred boy beyond redemption, whether she hated me or possibly even admired me for my outburst, whether future patients in this hospital would profit or suffer from my wild explosion, and whether Orientals would be received here from now on with special attentions or would not be admitted at all. These were some of the questions I was left with as a result of my first experience in a hospital, and I am afraid that I will not find satisfactory answers to them even after my scars fade and are forgotten.

How the Sick View Their World

HENRY D. LEDERER

The experience of illness is a complex psychological situation. To clarify the responses of the sick to this experience it is necessary to consider three main time periods, each of which has a characteristic orientation[1] These stages of the experience of illness are: (1) the transition period from health to illness, (2) the period of "accepted" illness and, (3) convalescence.

THE ORIENTATIONS OF THE SICK IN THE TRANSITION PERIOD FROM HEALTH TO ILLNESS

Upon falling ill most persons become aware of undesirable, unpleasant, and painful sensations; of a disturbing reduction in strength and stamina; of a diminution in ability to perform habitual acts. For example, at the onset of virus pneumonia, the patient experiences headaches, vague chest pains, tightness of the skin. He fatigues easily, desires more than usual rest,

Reprinted with permission from the *Journal of Social Issues*, Vol. 8, 1952, pp. 4-15.

and "plays out" quickly on prolonged tasks. In addition, he finds the performance of his daily routine of work and play tiring and aggravating to his discomforts.

One finds certain definite patterns of response to these initial events. Some degree of apprehension or anxiety is felt as in any situation in which a painful, unpleasant, and threatening circumstance is encountered.[2] Consequently the pattern of response to the initial symptoms is often the characteristic mode of reaction to anxiety whenever it arises. Many persons attempt to ignore this threat and through such a denial of the frightening experience to allay their anxieties. This denial may be reinforced by a "plunge into health" through engaging in more than routine activity. In this manner the patient seems to be reassuring himself by saying, "If I can manage to be so very active there is nothing to fear—the whole affair is an illusion." Another form of denial is to minimize the importance of the symptoms by identifying them with symptoms of benign or trivial indispositions. Thus the "coronary vascular accident" symptoms are identified with "an upset stomach" and the chest pains of lobar pneumonia with a "touch of pleurisy."

Still further, one observes other patients who meet anxiety aggressively and such persons in the initial stages of illness are irascible, querulous, and ill-humored. Conversely, others allay anxiety by passivity and behave in a compliant, obsequious, and pitiable manner.

The ordinary day-to-day life routines of most persons constitute a source of satisfaction of various needs and defenses against anxiety. Since illness renders painful and tiring participation in such gratifying and reassuring activities, anxiety is compounded and frustration of many needs is felt.[3] Thomas Mann has written humorously and understandingly of this experience in "*The Magic Mountain.*" His hero, Hans Castorp, in the early febrile stage of an activated tuberculosis tries to preserve his daily rituals which have formerly proven gratifying and soothing. One of these practices is the smoking of the after dinner cigar, a luxury of great importance to Castorp; but now he finds an evil taste and light-headedness in the place of a delightful aroma and general feeling of well-being.[4]

Certain men become especially anxious when they find themselves having to restrict their activities and to admit the existence of their discomforts.[5] To these persons, manliness depends on being active and never yielding to a physical discomfort; to them, passivity and any intolerance of pain are equated with femininity. Consequently, becoming ill is viewed as an emasculating process and, thereby, highly provocative of anxiety. There may be a dangerous denial of symptoms in such a person through his abortive attempts to reassert his masculinity in sports, late hours, heavy work, etc.

For many persons, parts of their bodies or certain bodily functions have been invested with intense emotion. The skin, the facial structures, the head, the genitals, the breasts are examples of bodily parts often intensely loved by the patient. Obviously great apprehension is experienced when symptoms seem to indicate dysfunction of these treasured parts.

There is a continuing folk tradition in some areas that suggests that illness is the just desert of the sinner. Persons holding to this misconception feel guilty when developing an illness and may even be impelled to malinger health rather than appear with the stigma of immorality.

Specific illnesses exhibiting a familial occurrence are particularly alarming since most persons do not want to discredit the purity of their families. This attitude has been one of the impedances to early diagnosis of such illnesses as carcinomata and tuberculosis. Often the afflicted person has great anxiety because of the unconscious fantasy of rejection and wrath by other members of the family. Most physicians have had contact with patients who are deeply shamed by symptoms which they interpret as a possible disgrace to their family lines.

Many persons, who because of emotional immaturity and stressful living have been reduced to a psychoneurotic level of functioning, may react paradoxically to the advent of physical illness. Often there is an amelioration of the neurotic symptoms and the patient seems to welcome the concrete threat of physical illness which can divert his attention from his neurosis. With some neurotic persons, physical illness may actually bring emotional relief through its symbolic meaning as a penalty for unconscious guilt feelings. Moreover, the anticipated care and consideration as well as release from social responsibilities can be highly appealing to a neurotic patient. His feelings of guilt and shame for his withdrawing, dependent, and infantile wishes are relieved by the occurrence of physical sickness which "legitimizes" these claims. "The individual with a relatively weak ego may find an escape from his (neurotic) anxieties in the less demanding situation that illness provides."[6]

An example of this type of response to physical illness was observed in a young, single woman who was undergoing psychotherapy for severe phobias. Her neurosis developed in reaction to the stress of her approaching marriage for which her previous psychosocial growth had not prepared her. In the midst of this emotional distress, she developed visual and gait disturbances which were definitely diagnosed as symptoms of multiple sclerosis. At the onset of these grave symptoms and her entrance into the hospital, she announce with elation that her phobic obsessions had departed and that she was entirely rid of anxiety.

To recapitulate, in the initial symptom phase of many illnesses, one may encounter evidence of anxiety, guilt, and shame as well as the many personality defenses against these disagreeable affects. Moreover, in certain neurotic patients there may be a paradoxically positive acceptance of illness.

The continuing pressure, and often the increase, of symptoms forces the patient into another psychologically difficult set of experiences—those of diagnosis and the beginning of therapy. At this time the former habitual patterns of health still exert a powerful attraction on the patient whereas his submission to diagnostic and therapeutic procedures involves entering an unknown area. But in order to be rid of his discomforts and dysfunctions he must face this unknown situation.

(It is important to note that at this point another crucial factor is met which influences the orientation of the patient—this factor is the behavior of the medical personnel who are responsible for his diagnosis and therapy.)

Whenever one enters an unknown or partially understood situation, he exhibits fairly typical responses. Once again anxiety is aroused because of fantasied dangers and because of unfamiliarity with what one may expect. Under these circumstances there is much indecision reflected in vacillating behavior. For example, urgent requests for diagnostic examinations are rapidly alternated with failure to appear for examination. Physicians must learn to expect such vacillating and indecisive behavior and not to be angered or disgusted by it. The firm, patient, and understanding attitude of the physician will help in allaying the patient's anxiety.

The highly scientific nature of medical diagnosis places these affairs beyond the full understanding of the average layman. The physical paraphernalia of many diagnostic processes are awesome to many persons. In addition, the technical language of medicine is an unknown tongue to the layman who can only hope that what he overhears is an optimistic statement rather than a pronouncement of doom or further pain for him. When these mystifying matters are coupled to the impersonality of diagnostic activity in many modern hospital and clinics, it is easy to empathize with the mounting anxiety of the patient and his problem of cooperating in diagnosis.

Much attention in recent years has been centered upon ways of cushioning the effects of these experiences by the attitude of the physician. The awe and fear of the cold, aseptic, impersonal atmosphere of the clinic can be considerably diminished by attitudes of personal interest in, and exhibitions of respect for, the patient in his contacts with medical personnel.[7] A concise but specific and clear-cut explanation of diagnostic procedures can undercut most of the mystery of diagnosis. Excluding all but the necessary equipment from the examination room is still another aid in this direction. Many clinics are now furnishing waiting rooms in styles which lessen their resemblance to operating rooms or laboratories and consequently are reassuring.

Unnecessary repetitions of diagnostic examinations and tests should be avoided because any signs of indecision or insecurity shown by the physician augment the patient's apprehension. When the doctor demonstrates his skill by his determination and decisiveness, the patient is usually grateful for such real reassurance; then he is sure he is in capable, trustworthy hands. There is much wisdom in the old medical dictum that "in any contact between doctor and patient there is room only for one anxious person—the patient."

The future course of the patient's behavior often depends upon the manner in which his diagnosis is presented to him. If the doctor speaks simply and forthrightly, in most instances anxiety is relieved. Clouding the issue in technical jargon or discussing equivocal findings usually increase the patient's emotionality. For example, nothing is gained and much may be lost by announcing "borderline" findings to a patient. It is easy to imagine the confusion aroused by informing a person: "I don't think you have much to worry about. Your heart seems O.K. but we want to watch your electrocardiogram because it was a little abnormal." After this report the patient is in a dilemma about understanding himself, his physical limits, and what, if any, dangers confront him.

Experienced physicians expect a possible distortion of facts when interviewing patients about their symptoms and the histories of their illnesses. These distortions stem from the patient's anxiety and his defenses and should be taken with a benevolent skepticism. Some of the art of interviewing rests on the doctor's recognition of these unconscious distortions. If the doctor behaves like a detective in pursuing facts, the patient is made even more tense.[8]

Most persons view with conflicting, mixed feelings the start of therapy. Actually, some therapeutic maneuvers do cause discomfort and pain so that the patient has to accept a paradox—that is, to be relieved of discomfort, he must at times submit to a transitory increase in it. Usually a sick person anticipates far more discomfort than is involved in most treatments. This gloomy expectation is a reflection of his apprehensive state and calls for an equivocal frankness from the doctor for correction. Again, a concise, unambiguous description of the therapy and the rationale for it alleviates anxiety and goes far toward gaining the patient's cooperation.[9] Vagueness about details of therapy must be avoided in order to reduce the opportunities for the patient to imagine the worst. Whenever possible, impersonal contact between the patient and his therapist should be reduced. For example, a visit by the anesthetist before an operation neutralizes some of the fear that most patients entertain about general anesthesia.

When treatment requires a hospital setting, the doctor and his aides have the responsibility for explaining hospital procedures to the patient. The patient is able to cooperate more easily when he knows about such routine matters as the duty hours of the floor nurses, when meals are served, visiting rules, the names of his internes, etc. Often antagonistic, belligerent behavior can be charged to negligence in clarifying the hospital situation when the patient was admitted—it is his way of aggressively resolving his anxiety. The rate of "sign-out against medical advice" is inversely related to the success of the medical personnel in their handling of these problems.

THE STAGE OF "ACCEPTED" ILLNESS

When the patient has accepted diagnostic and initial therapeutic procedures, he enters another distinct time period in his experience of illness. Now, he views himself as ill and abandons pretenses of health. In our society, accepting illness includes accepting help from physicians and their aides. He temporarily withdraws from his adult responsible activities and, cooperating with his doctor, dedicates himself to the problem of getting well; he substitutes preoccupation with his symptoms and illness for the many concerns of mature life. Whereas in health he has made his own decisions, he now transfers this right to his physician, nurse and other attendants. These changes in orientation are reinforced by the doctor's prescription that he not pursue his work, his usual recreations, nor his responsibilities. Society as a whole also frees him for the duration of his illness from the discharge of ordinary duties and obligations.

All of these changes determine the structure of the patient's world which can be described as a simpler, more childish, constricted life. His illness has led him into a social setting which is similar to his childhood.[10] Therefore, one can refer to this arrangement as being very regressed and infantile.

To such a regressed social situation the patient now reacts with behavior used earlier during his childhood. His actions, thoughts, and feelings are regressive in response to the childlike world of illness. The main features of this behavior are: (1) egocentricity, (2) constriction of interests, (3) emotional dependency, (4) hypochondriasis.[11]

Charles Lamb, in his essay, "The Convalescent," accurately described the egocentricity of the sick when he wrote, "How sickness enlarges the dimensions of a man's self to himself! he is his own exclusive object. Supreme selfishness is inculcated upon him as his only duty."[12] Like a child the patient is concerned with the selfish matters of satisfying simple needs for rest, food, absence of pain, physical comfort, and relief of bodily tensions such as the urge to urinate, defecate, pass flatus, or to belch. Satisfaction of these needs assumes precedence over more social ones. The patient presumes that his attendants share in these preoccupations and he feels resentful or hurt if the doctor or nurse is distracted by other concerns.

His egocentricity renders him provincial and highly subjective, like a child, in his judging the events occurring around him. If the nurse frowns for a moment, he is worried that she has taken a dislike to him; if she does not respond to his ring, she is damned as lazy and uninterested in his welfare.

Often the patient becomes a sick-room tyrant, dominating others and intolerant or often unaware of their rights and needs. "If there be a regal solitude, it is a sick bed. How the patient lords it there"—"He keeps his sympathy, like some curious vintage, under trusty lock and key, for his own use only." This egocentric despotism frequently disturbs the friends and relatives of the patient who are accustomed to his former consideration and objectivity.

Dynamically related to his egocentricity is the constriction of interests of the sick person. The narrowing follows partially from the reduced scope of the patient's world and partly from his regressed narcissism. The ill person shows an often amazing disinterest or even apathy toward the impersonal events of the day. He has abandoned his concern for politics, business, social events and will not persist in discussion of these matters.

Lamb outlines this constriction of interest as follows: "A little while ago he was greatly concerned in the event of a lawsuit, which was to be the making or the marring of his dearest friend. He was to be seen trudging about upon this man's errand to fifty quarters of the town at once. The cause was to come on yesterday. He is absolutely as indifferent to the decision as if it were a question to be tried at Pekin . . . he picks up enough to make him understand that things went cross-grained in the court yesterday, and his friend is ruined. But the word 'friend' and the word 'ruin' disturb him no more than so much jargon. He is not to think of anything but how to get better."

The protection and devotion accorded the patient by his medical attendants relieve him of adapting himself to interests other than his own and thereby increase his provincialism. There is often little or no check to his regressive, constricted, and narcissistic behavior so that apathy appears.

Dependence on others is imposed by the physical helplessness stemming from illness and by the psychological inadequacy secondary to egocentricity and constricted interests. The patient's physical weakness, like that of the child, requires the strength of other persons to meet his needs. His regression into a self-centered, subjective world demands that healthier persons apply their more mature and objective judgment to his affairs—again paralleling the experience of the child whose parents assume responsibility for most important matters. With this dependency, one observes much ambivalence toward the benefactors. Like a child the patient often exhibits an uncritical "love" and admiration for his benefactors, but at the same time resentment toward them because of his weak and inferior relation to them. All persons working with the sick should anticipate and learn to recognize this ambivalent dependency and neither be flattered, nor offended, by it.

The unpleasant sensations of illness, in combination with the reduced regressive world and perceptions of the patient, lead to a great concern with the functioning of the body. There is usually much hypochondriacal worry over medical matters such as pulse rate, temperature, bowel movements, weight changes, etc., all of which may dominate the patient's thoughts and conversations. This hypochondriasis resembles in some ways the curiosity and exploration of the body and its functions undertaken normally by all children.

The attitudes and behavior of the medical personnel can limit or extend the emotional regression of the patient. The appearance of apathy as a response to over-protection has already been cited.[13] In recent years, many warnings have been sounded against unnecessary restriction of patient's activities.

The indiscriminate prescription of prolonged bed-rest has been demonstrated as a cause of invalidism out of proportion to actual physical incapacity. The current practice of encouraging patients to get on their feet as early as possible following operations has proven both physically and emotionally beneficial; it has prevented lengthy convalescence. It seems that the best course for the physician is to encourage the minimum amount of regression necessitated by the physical limitations of the patient and to avoid any unnecessary infantilizing.

This regression, during illness, is adaptive and often significant for survival. It is conceivable that through social and emotional regression the sick person re-distributes his energies to facilitate the healing process or possibly that the regressive integration is in itself an essential factor in the healing process. The biological task of the sick is to get well and this work is furthered by the focussing of personality energies on the self and withdrawing them from other uses and purposes.[14] Recognition of this utility in the regression of the sick should make medical attendants welcome it rather than deplore it.

In persons, whose general character development has led to elaborate behavior defenses against regression and the expression of dependency, there is little or no phase of "accepted illness." Denial of physical limits and symptoms continues to some extent; the advice and ministrations of medical personnel are challenged and not followed; hospital care may be refused. All in all the neurotic defenses of such a patient militate against the healing benefits of regression and the course of his illness may be worsened or fatal. His behavioral adjustment to his neurosis takes precedence over adaptive regression during physical illness.

To illustrate: A physician, in middle age, sustained an acute coronary heart attack. His professional colleagues, who diagnosed his illness, advised immediate and absolute bed rest, quiet, and heavy sedation, all of which the patient stoutly refused on the grounds of his heavy schedule of work with his own patients. He persisted in his medical work and died suddenly in his office twenty hours later. This patient's personality was structured largely to deny any dependent emotional trends. He was a "self-made" man who had labored hard to graduate from medical school. He steadfastly pursued his career, never permitting himself a vacation. In his personal life he lavished gifts on his family, but was Spartan in any self-indulgence. It can be conjectured that his neurotic character was a considerable factor in his early death.

Under those conditions, the total medical management must include measures to aid the patient in accepting regression and dependency. At times a psychiatrist or psychiatric social worker must be included in the therapeutic team to contribute their skills in meeting this neurotic complication of a physical illness.

The period of "accepted illness" gradually ends after optimal regression and medical therapy have reversed or arrested the pathogenic process. The patient then enters the convalescent period of his experience of illness.

THE STAGE OF CONVALESCENCE

Convalescence is the time period of transition from illness back into a state of health. This recovery of health involves a return of physical strength and a re-integration of the personality of the patient who has been living, feeling, and thinking in a regressed, more or less infantile way.

The return of physical strength and health is usually an automatic process but it is not necessarily paralleled by a restoration of "healthy," adult behavior; getting well physically must be associated with the patient's relinquishing his dependent, egocentric and provincial reactions.[15]

Many students of convalescence have recognized its structural and dynamic similarities to adolescence. This analogy is instructive in understanding the problems of the convalescent and suggests many techniques for helping the convalescent "grow up" again into adult health.[16]

The convalescent, like the adolescent, has to leave a protected world in which responsibilities were minimal and the satisfaction of his self-centered needs the major concern of himself and those attending him. These pleasant aspects of illness attract the convalescent so that he wants to remain in his "regal home" of regression. It is hard for one to give up the attentions, protection, and kindnesses of doctors and nurses and to fend once more for oneself. "Farewell with him all that made sickness prompous—the spell that hushed the household—the mute attendance—the inquiry by looks—the still softer delicacies of self-attention—what a speck is he dwindled into (by his physical recuperation)."[17]

If the patient has suppressed his resentful hostility toward his medical attendants during the preceding phase, he frequently remains regressed because of a guilty over-dependence upon them. Recent studies on poliomyelitis patients who require respirators have shown that the patients who are slowly weaned from the "artificial lung" are those who have been unable to express openly any negative feelings toward their doctors and nurses.[18]

Convalescence is often prolonged in persons whose previous state of health did not provide them with sufficient gratifications and relief from anxiety. Examples of this situation are seen in military service where full recovery from illness means re-entering a hazardous and depriving existence.

Fortunately, for most convalescents, the broader scope of their "healthy" worlds is more attractive then the regressive pleasures of illness. In such persons the stronger motive is toward health but may be impeded by continuing feelings of inadequacy. Like adolescents who yearn for adult life but feel unsure of themselves, these convalescents wistfully long for health but are afraid to try it. These fears may be related to neurotic self-depreciation which was part of the original behavior pattern in childhood, reactivated during the period of regression.

Certain convalescents repeat their adolescent method of "growing up" by rebelliously wrenching themselves loose from dependency. These persons are in a tremendous hurry to get well, often prematurely dismiss their physicians, and over-step their physical strengths.

Again one realizes that the participation of the physician and his aides can profoundly affect the course of convalescence. Under these conditions the medical personnel occupy roles similar to those of the parents and counselors of adolescents; the successful medical management of convalescence is the analogue of proper parenthood during adolescence.

To illustrate: The parent who gradually and progressively relaxes his protection and instead offers guidance and advice is encouraging the adolescent toward adulthood. He quietly retires to the side-lines ready to reassure but willing to let his child experiment with new strengths, Only stepping in when gross errors of judgment may arise. The adolescent senses the confidence of the parent and is reassured by it, especially when immediately perfect or ideal results are not demanded. Moreover, the helpful parent is not threatened by his child's interest in other persons or new activities.

Convalescence can be promoted and enhanced by similar attitudes on the part of the doctor. Physicians must have the courage to recommend more activity and to lift the restrictions on the patient's behavior. Some physicians, like parents, are unconsciously gratified by the dependency of others upon them; this narcissistic pleasure must be abandoned by no longer encouraging regressive dependency through protection. The physician sometimes is loath to risk his reputation through the possibility of a relapse and thereby continues to treat the convalescent with great caution; this is frequently the event when the patient is a person of some prominence in the community so that his illness has been under a public scrutiny which makes the physician uneasy.

The rehabilitation of the convalescent has become a matter of growing medical concern, research, and progress. During the war the military medical services were alert to these problems and contributed many important findings to this aspect of medical management.[19] Since the war some of the medical colleges have established departments of rehabilitation as integral basic training units.

Offering the convalescent stimulation for re-integration is stressed. Increasing visiting privileges, permitting the wearing of ordinary rather than hospital clothes, providing radio and television, permitting trial leaves overnight from the hospital are examples of opportunities which may stimulate the patient toward a state of health. Transferring the convalescent to a special rehabilitation center or ward has been recommended as an aid in helping him relinquish the regressive patterns of life followed on ordinary hospital wards.

The modern physician is urged to lead a team of therapists in the guidance and support of the convalescent just as the wise parent welcomes the contributions of the teacher, youth leader, student counselor, etc. who promote the growth of the adolescent. Social workers, occupational therapists, vocational counselors, recreational therapists, etc. can broaden the scope of the convalescent's world, encourage him and help reestablish his self-confidence and self-sufficiency.

While the patient is still in the state of "accepted illness," the caseworker may have discovered sources of tension and dissatisfaction in his family, home, work situations and can initiate changes which will make the return to health more attractive. In addition the cooperation of the family in the management of convalescence is often won by a skillful caseworker.

Much attention has been given to occupational therapy through which the patient is gently led into a more self-assertive, creative life. Moreover, he is given the opportunity to re-exercise rusty talents and techniques in an experimental setting. Here he can regain self-confidence through a series of progressive "successes."

Well-planned recreational therapies provide practice in socializing and in engaging in gradual competition. Here again the success in group living encourages the patient to re-enter the large arena of adult "healthy" society.

The expanding use of vocational counseling is an indication of its value to the convalescent. Many patients cling to regressed behavior because they cannot engage further in past occupations. For example, convalescent tuber-culous patients frequently must find less strenuous jobs to protect them from relapses. In such a situation, hopeful and realistic planning can be con-structed through consultations with a competent vocational counselor. The convalescent, like the adolescent, is less afraid of his future when his voca-tional potentialities are clear to him.

In addition to the special services each member of the therapeutic team has to offer, there is the over-all benefit of providing the patient contact with many mature, healthy persons with whom he can emotionally identify. This process is similar to the identification of the adolescent with key adult per-sons in his environment. Both the convalescent and adolescent find such identification a most positive aid in accepting an adult status. Conversely, emotionally immature persons serving on therapeutic teams can seriously retard the convalescent's recovery by not providing the bridge of a healthy identification.

All of these various services and stimuli can be offered to a patient but it is necessary to realize, no one can force him to use them constructively. For the majority of persons "health" is preferred to regression. With the few patients who cannot respond positively to planned convalescence, one usu-ally finds that an earlier neurosis has been revived by the trauma of illness; these persons should be offered psychotherapy to resolve the neurotic dif-ficulties prolonging their full recovery.

To summarize: the state of convalescence is structurally and dynamically similar to adolescence. The behavior of the convalescent is analogous to that of the adolescent. The success of helping the patient is dependent on the recognition of his "adolescent" emotional status which then should call forth from his medical attendants attitudes similar to those of the parent who encourages and aids the growth of his adolescent child. Opportunities must be provided for re-establishing self-confidence through graded "suc-cesses" in groups and in the exercise of one's returning physical strengths. The convalescent phase of illness terminates with the parallel recovery from physical limitations and psychological regression.

FOOTNOTES

1. Barker, R. G., *et al.,* "Social psychology of acute illness," in *Adjustment to Physical Handicap and Illness* (rev. ed.). New York: Social Science Re-search Council, 1953.
2. Binger, C., *The Doctor's Job.* New York: Norton, 1945.
3. Upham, Frances, *A Dynamic Approach to Illness.* New York: Family Service Association of America, 1949.
4. Mann, Thomas, *The Magic Mountain.* New York: Knopf, 1945.
5. Barker, *et al., op. cit.*
6. Upham, *op. cit.*

7. Barker, *et al., op. cit.*
8. Levine, M., *Psychotherapy in Medical Practice.* New York: Macmillan, 1942.
9. *Ibid.*
10. Conference on Convalescent Care, New York Academy of Medicine, 1940.
11. Barker, *et al., op. cit.*
12. Lamb, Charles, *Essays.* New York: Viking, 1949.
13. Barracough, W., "Mental reactions of normal children to physical illness," *American Journal of Psychiatry,* 1937, 93.
14. Ferenezi, S., "Disease or Pathoneurosis," in *Further Contributions to the Theory and Technique of Psychoanalysis.* London: Hogarth, 1926.
15. Romano, J., "Emotional components of illness," *Connecticut State Medical Journal,* 1943, 7.
16. Barker, *et al., op. cit.*
17. Lamb, *op. cit.*
18. Unpublished data from studies in progress, Department of Psychiatry, College of Medicine, University of Cincinnati.
19. Watson-Jones, R., "Rehabilitation in the Royal Air Force," *British Medical Journal,* 1942, 1, 403-407; Wilson, E. H., "Rehabilitation in war-time Britain," *Archives of Surgery,* 1943, 46; and Thorndike, A., "Convalescent reconditioning," *American Medical Association Journal,* 1944, 126.

"Should the Patient Be Told the Truth?"

PAUL H. BRAUER

▰ Scientific progress has made it possible to delay the outcome of much terminal illness and to alleviate many of the accompanying physical discomforts. Yet paradoxically, because of this very scientific advance, man rarely dies with dignity, in the comfort of his own home, surrounded by his family and friends gathered to pay their last respects. Rather, he is "comforted" by oxygen tanks, tubes in every natural and surgically made orifice, and busy hospital personnel intent on carrying out the physician's orders. Gone too, is the comforting archaic custom of being accompanied to the sepulcher by all his prized possessions, including, in some cultures, his wife.

Reprinted with permission from *Nursing Outlook,* Vol. 8, No. 12, 1960, pp. 672-676.

In our present culture, we need to focus our efforts on achieving psychological support for the patient with a diagnosis of terminal illness, and to do this requires considerable depth of understanding of what the patient is experiencing.

When a person becomes ill with anything more serious than a mild cold, there is an immediate and revolutionary reorientation of all his drives and interests. Nothing concerns him more than the re-establishment of his healthy state. The only thing that matters to him is getting well. If this fact is kept in mind as we work with patients, we will better understand their feelings, actions, and reactions. The single exception is the severely depressed patient with active suicidal thoughts who might hope for the disease to take over for him.

Now, whereas members of the "normal" family want a return to health almost as much as the patient, this focus is neither so sharp nor so exclusive for them. Moreover, one or more of the relatives may have a slightly different, or a very different hope: severe illness can stimulate and encourage the wish for the patient's demise. Since we are usually treating both the patient and his family, it is vital to keep clearly in mind that the protagonists may be operating and focusing on different horizons. Consequently, whereas we may take for granted that the patient's goals are straight, clear, and unadulterated, it behooves us to observe and evaluate with more discrimination just what and how much contamination there is in the various family members' goals.

When a relative asks, "How long will he last?" The question may derive from a sense of impending, grievous loss, or from a fainter or brighter hope that it will be pretty soon—"because I never liked him anyway; the illness costs a lot in time, energy, and money, and I can use his insurance money."

Even when there is a good, loving relationship, there comes a time near termination when the survivor-to-be feels the patient might be better off really dead: "I think I want death at last to free you—and me."

Some physicians and nurses who are unaware of the frequency and intensity of negative attitudes in the relatives become reproachful, even denunciatory if the key family member shows a lack of responsibility. This denunciation can then produce any one of three types of response: one, the effect may be good, and the family member rises to the occasion for shorter or longer periods; too, he may be able to give more of himself, and if he has the complementary super-ego, he may suffer from guilt which may produce depression and limit his usefulness; or three, his denunciation can backfire altogether, producing the perverse reaction of "I won't do anything at all." Nor will we take such a statement literally. It may mean, "I must be difficult and stingy or you'll expect too much from me."

THE PATIENT'S REACTIONS

To return to our regressed, frightened, self-centered patient, who is saying at each moment: "I can't give and take now. I'm interested only in getting well and what you, my doctors, nurses, and family can do for me." This is the basic, primitive pattern, but of course the manifestations of it go through the transformer housing all his mechanisms of defense and his total personality. For example, if he has always been immature and narcissistic, he will become more so, and exasperate the personnel, and more likely, the relatives. This in turn may or may not get him more attention, depending upon the resiliency and training of those around him. Some times in his regression he calls for his mother, rather than his wife who should be the key figure.

In another type of patient characterized either by reaction formation, or excessive denial, or stoicism, there can be such understatement of his needs that the medical staff and family overlook his real feelings and requirements. A little restaurateur, in the truly terminal phase of bronchogenic carcinoma, was the most popular patient on the ward because he never asked for anything from the doctors or nurses. He always met them with a smile, and with lavish expression of eternal gratitude for their devotion and assiduous care, promising them free meals whenever they would come to his café after he got well. Only one person on the ward, the newest intern, intuitively sensed that his behavior was a mask, beneath which as my later consultation revealed, was a pathetic sense of hopelessness, depression, and loneliness which he gallantly kept secret lest the ward personnel avoid him. In others, the same background can produce at one extreme, elation; at the other, severe, even psychotic, depression.

Other victims regard their disease as something shameful, to be hidden. They feel defective. They, too, conceal or underplay, and may be passed up by the staff, because they are too ashamed to ask for help.

At the other pole is the paranoidal reaction in which the patient blames the world and the people in it for his lot. He seeks a scapegoat, and in effect, accuses the doctors, nurses, social workers, and family for being responsible for his illness in the first place, and for its course. No one does anything right, and he reproaches each one for lack of responsibility, gross stupidity, and complete inefficiency.

Professional people, doctors and nurses, are not immune to the above reactions. In fact, the impulse for us to underplay, to feel a sense of shame, is perhaps even more frequent than in the nonprofessional person, so we must be more acute in our observation of our colleagues. A social worker, living in a hotel with many fellow workers, waited before asking help in meeting a problem until it had reached a crisis she could no longer conceal.

With our help, she regained her equilibrium, but the moment she did, she dropped us precipitously, and cleanly, and apparently forever. Her sense of humiliation was too much for her.

Since all patients regress, with limitations of their capacities and abilities, we must help the patient and family achieve that delicate balance between overindulgence and neglect, which not only facilitates his further regression but also tends to suggest that he must be in a more desperate condition than he thought. On the other side of the scale is the danger of expecting too much from the patient who then feels unloved and cruelly misunderstood as a weakling or even malingerer. The better we know the personalities of patient and family, the more effective will our guidance be. Sometimes consultation with a psychiatrist is indicated to help assess the interplay of the newly remodeled emotions and reactions the disease elicits in a patient.

THE FAMILY'S REACTIONS

We must also observe how the family reacts to certain symptoms and manifestations of the disease. How much has the relative regressed? How great is his anxiety? How does he understand illness? Does he fear it is contagious (very common in bronchogenic cancer because endless coughing is equated with tuberculosis)? What is his reaction to secretions, bleeding, unpleasant odors? Does he hover too much about the patient, perhaps at the expense of other family members? Does he understand that he need not be doing something every moment, that his mere presence is often sufficient to reassure and help? Is he able to administer drugs without too much anxiety? Is he properly sympathizing or does he convey grief? Is he mourning? What is the meaning of the relative who insists that only he be told the diagnosis, and conversely, the patient who insists that no one in his family be told? Can we take literally, and how do we handle the patient who tells us, "don't hedge with me, I can take it . . . and besides I have a right to know." I refer you especially to *Death of a Man* by Lael Wertenbaker.[1]

THE MEANING OF TERMS

As a first step toward a constructive approach to terminal illness, we must examine the term itself. In its general application, I observed it refers not only to the true terminal or moribund state, but includes any severe progressive disease as soon as the diagnosis is made (at which time the patient may be functioning at close to his full normal capacity). I would substitute such terms as "advancing," "progressive," or "severe" illness, and reserve "terminal" for that period when the patient is more or less moribund. These terms leave out the element of *Time* and emphasize the *Quality* and *Process* involved. The objection to the word "terminal" does not stem from the naive hope that a euphemism can effectively alter the frame of mind of the patient and family, but from the fact that the word "terminal" quite accurately reflects the current fundamental psychic orientation—the prejudices, conscious or unconscious attitudes evoked by serious illness in which the outcome is considered to be eventually and surely fatal. The implication of the word "terminal" is not that the patient will die some time in the future from the disease, but rather that for all practical purposes this patient is dead.

Cancer is an example of a chronic, progressive, often fatal disease, has distinctive characteristics. The word "cancer" strikes terror in almost every adult. It conjures up a frightening destructive specter, equaled by no other disease today. Perhaps infantile paralysis was a rival until the Salk vaccine significantly neutralized the terror. Leprosy might be considered an eligible rival were it not considered to be so rare by the layman that he regards it essentially as a legendary disease. The word "cancer" evokes an image not only of a fatal disease, but one that consumes, devours, envelopes from all directions, creeping like a monstrous crab (which is what the word means), sometimes slowly and insidiously, often rapidly, but always relentlessly, impregnable to the feeble emanation of an x-ray machine or a cobalt capsule of the primitive carvings of a surgeon's scalpel. Even the physician may retain, to some degree at least, this concept of cancer in his unconscious. And with this image, the next step is inevitable: the victim is immediately struck from the records of the living. This reaction is independent of the degree of devotion the relative or physician has toward the patient.

An articulate nursing student on one of her first cancer cases once commented to me, "I was shocked to observe that the family was exasperated because I regarded the patient as still living." A mother whose love for her 30-year-old daughter left nothing to be desired, once said to me some five months after the daughter had undergone a bilateral mastectomy, "I look at her as she goes about her tasks and I see her flat chest beneath her padded blouse, and beneath that, I see nothing. It's horrible! She acts as though she is well, and that makes it only worse. I know she is really . . . no more. I can't bear it!" Today, after six years, her daughter is very much alive, functioning essentially on the same level as before she had cancer. It is only recently that the mother has been able to accept the good prognosis of the surgeon and can feel that her daughter is living.

These cases also illustrate another frequently observed finding—that the patient is less likely to write himself off than would his family and friends. And if he does, he re-enters himself on the records of the living more quickly than does his family. So, if we can influence the family's attitude, we can help the patient whose capacity to adapt to his illness may be inadequate. Attitudes and emotional states are contagious, especially in states of anxiety and regression, both of which occur in any illness. The excessive fear of using the word "cancer" when talking to the patient who knows his diagnosis reflects, to a large degree, a projection of the fears and anxieties of the user. Avoiding reference to the diagnosis, or even to death, when these terms present themselves in the normal course of daily activity, only confirms and reinforces the universal fear of death and the specific fear of cancer as something too horrible to mention.

ATTITUDES TOWARD DEATH

It is a fact that we are less prepared for death than any other of life's manifestations, and I think part of the explanation for this is that we avoid thinking and talking about it frankly. Consequently, we do not handle it effectively. It is, unlike even sex, still taboo.

The patient's formulation is: "If you are frightened, shocked, and horrified, it must be for good reason, so I am, too. But if you are calm and feel in control of the situation and act as though I still belong here, then I can too." The closer and more important the person is to the patient, the greater is the "contagion" or susceptibility to the other's state of mind. Consequently, it is especially important for the physician and nurse to avoid acting in a way which implies or suggests fear, horror, helplessness, or grief.

This explains, in part, the intense attachment and security which the patient and family develop with unscrupulous agents who promise a cure. We call them charlatans, and, to various degrees, they are. But if we do not dismiss these para-practitioners as beneath our notice, we can learn something important from them, for they, perhaps more than anyone else currently, treat and regard the patient as having a disease which is really not very different from other serious diseases. This is the critical and constructive difference in point of view. Whereas the charlatan peddles false hopes and may, and often does, deprive the patient of treatment which could prolong his life, we can act more scientifically, more wisely, more efficiently.

The charlatan's attitude teaches us that if we minimize the imminence of death and still provide the best treatment available, the patient may regain his equilibrium and perspective. Instead, far too many patients are subjected to a procession of professional people who more or less unconsciously communicate their own unhealthy reactions and frightening fantasies about cancer and other chronic illnesses—their own hostility, impatience, threated omnipotence—and so, reject the patient. It is translated to the patient as: "You have a fatal disease. The prognosis is bad, hopeless. Since there is nothing I can do don't bother me. I don't like to deal with unresponsive cases. You threaten my sense of omnipotence. You make me feel inadequate, and I don't like to be reminded of it. So please go away. You are really dead, anyway. Besides, if I don't tell you the diagnosis, some other doctor may, and then you will think I am incompetent, and I have to think of my reputation." Fortunately, this denunciation is never delivered so starkly, nor in its entirety. But it does illustrate what can be conveyed to the cancer patient.

This takes us to the controversial question: "Should the patient and family be told the truth?" We tend to think of truth as something circumscribed, immutably bound, mathematically accurate—an absolute as precise as a digit. Thus, 10 is obviously not 9 or 11, or even 9 and 9/10, but exactly and only 10 in any country, in any culture. But we are talking about a disease which is as inconsistent as the weather, and with people whose concepts of "disease," "prognosis," "pain," "disability," and "metastasis" are as individually and personally defined as "God," "devil," "good," "bad," "work," "leisure." Dr. Bernard Meyer, of Mt. Sinai Hospital in New York, suggested that when the question, "Should the patient be told the truth?" is raised, we ask, "Pray, which patient, and what truth?"

WHAT IS THE TRUTH?

All words have different meanings for different people. Unless we know what the patient's fantasies are, his distortions, his associations with words which at best, are not precise, and at worst, highly emotionally charged, how can we talk about telling the truth? Thus, to tell a physician with a nodule on his cheek, "You have basal cell carcinoma" is the truth. And if you tell the same thing to a frightened, medically illiterate housewife with the same nodule, you are also presumably telling the same truth. But actually, you have said quite different things to each, although you used exactly the same words and uttered them in exactly the same matter-of-fact way. What the physician heard was, "This nodule is the most benign of cancers. It is only locally malignant. It never metastasizes. Although new nodules will appear over the years, each one tends to be very slow-growing and is quite easily removed, leaving little or no scar. You are more likely to die of a coronary thrombosis 25 years hence than from your cancer, which is a type that is rarely fatal."

The same words to the little housewife may mean something entirely different. To her, cancer is cancer with all that term evokes. And even if her physician carefully describes the characteristics and prognosis for the type of cancer she has, she suspects that the doctor is merely trying to comfort her—to give her false hope. How can she evaluate that this time when the doctor says the prognosis is excellent, he means it.

Now granted for a moment that we could give a very accurate prognosis in terms of time for more malignant cancer than a basal cell (we really can't, but suppose we could), the fact is that the time-span concept of, for example, one year is very much more or very much less than one year, depending on the given individual's age, personality, cultural background, experience, and his whole life experience and status. To a 20-year-old youth, a one-year prognosis is much less than one year; and to a 75-year-old man, who has been in pain and semi-invalid from arthritis and high blood pressure for the preceding 15 years, the concept of one year is very much more than one year. Furthermore, the appreciation of time varies within the same individual, depending on what is involved.

The truth is that for a given case, no one knows the prognosis in time, even in the absolute or mathematical sense. When the textbook says that the prognosis for adenocarcinoma of the breast in a woman under 30 is six months to two years, the doctor is giving a statistical average, and he has seen extremes of three months to more than five years. How can he tell this particular patient or her family how long she will live? Now is it significantly better if he decides to give an optimistic estimate of five years or more, for there are documented cases of spontaneous remission of an even advanced cancer.

Dr. T. C. Everson of New Haven studied one thousand cases of spontaneous regression of cancer collected from the world literature.[2] To date he has irrefutable proof of remission on only 90, but it is sufficient to validate my essential point: that for the specific case we are treating we do not know what the prognosis is.

CAN WE TELL THE TRUTH?

There are medical theories and speculation, including emotional factors to explain this rare, but nevertheless occasional, factual, spontaneous resolution of even advanced carcinoma, but sure it must further give us pause when we talk about "telling the truth." The truth is we do not know how long the specific patient will live, not what his course will be.

We must be guided by these facts in talking with the patients and families, and in thinking about the specific case. It is not evasive to say "I don't know. We will observe and follow this case. Everyone is different. I will not confuse you by quoting statistics which cannot apply to this patient. I just don't know. No one can know, but we will do whatever is necessary as we observe what happens." Rather, I think it is presumptuous and destructive, to give any more specific a prognosis than that for the time or course of the illness. We must be firm and not succumb to pleading for a "little more information" when the latter is not information, but distortion. We must resist seduction by statistics and control our impatience with the questions which challenge our sense of omnipotence and omniscience and may prompt us to quote a valid statistical number which stops the questions, but which is almost certainly inaccurate for this patient.

To really "tell the truth" means first to assess carefully the patient's and the family's understanding of disease, their understanding of certain words, and their intellectual and emotional patterns—and then scientifically, artistically, and wisely present a picture of what is involved, judiciously ignoring or even denying the statistical probability of an early fatal outcome.

The doctor and his aides must feel the validity of the fact that he does not know what will happen to this patient. And if he feels this, he will be able to treat the patient, regard him, and talk with him and about him in ways that reflect in every word, gesture, and action that he considers the patient as being alive; that he will strive to keep him alive with the same conviction, devotion, ardor, and dedication which he has for the patients with diseases that do not evoke the prejudice and distaste that severe progressive illness does.

THE HONEST APPROACH

This is the scientific application of what the charlatan inadvertently dispenses. But the latter is a charlatan whether he actually believes or deliberately deceives his patients about the promised cure. Consequently, he does not properly treat the disease or the patient. Ethical and competent physicians and nurses need not, and should not delude themselves or the patient, but they must be on the alert for each new development which may cause a modification of the treatment plans and goals, and be ready to employ whatever new techniques science develops. Such attention and attitudes can make critical difference in helping the patient and the family establish a realistic adjustment to the patient's illness, his current status, and his future. It helps him achieve a healthy balance between the reality of a serious progressive illness and the denial of the reality that he will die. This allows for sensible planning for the future, no different from the healthy individual who considers the future even in terms of death: a will, provisions for his family, insurance, burial preferences, and the general management of business and domestic affairs.

We can observe whether this honest, realistic approach promotes too much denial, and be ready to handle the situation if the degree of denial interferes with proper planning for the future and the special care that the patient's physical status requires. A certain amount of denial is desirable and healthy. To some extent we are all living a "myth of invulnerability" and a "myth of eternity."

The same holds true for advanced illnesses. The illness has shattered the patient's myth of invulnerability, and it is part of our therapeutic aim to help him re-establish his equilibrium.

THE WHEN OF TIME

I cannot overemphasize that the fundamental difference between terminal illness and other illnesses is what the word terminal implies: *Time*. Any illness, including the common cold, can be fatal—terminal—so the reaction to the element of the when of time stimulates a series of characteristic predictable attitudes and emotions which vary only in degree and intensity, according to the total personality of the patient and family.

The assumption that the end is near, or even at hand, evokes quite appropriately all the patterns that characterize mourning. The patient, as well as his family, may begin to mourn. With mourning come grief and despair which tend to confirm for the patient that he is for practical purposes dead. And here again is another area for constructive approach. The tendency to grieve for the patient must be checked and replaced with sensitive, properly dosed sympathy and empathy, not necessarily verbal, but reflected in one's total manner and attitude.

A particularly severe problem arises in certain families and individuals who have a predisposition to mourn, who, in effect, literally enjoy mourning almost as a perversion, often seen in certain obsessive compulsive neurotics. These people can't wait to begin mourning and when informed of the "horrible" truth, rush to the nearest telephone to announce through tearful triumph, in effect that "the time has come for us all to assemble as soon as possible and as often as possible to grieve for the deceasing one and mourn our fate."

The fact that the corpse has returned to his office after the consultation to continue his business, and may actually outlive some of these harbingers of doom, is quite beyond their ken. But not ours. With skill and patience, we must try to convince these "angels of death" that there has been an understandable but false alarm. Neither we nor they know that the time is now.

REALITY AND DENIAL

I think this explains why the reaction of patient, physician, and family to the diagnosis of coronary thrombosis is so much more hopeful and wholesome than to cancer. In the case of coronary thrombosis, the physician reflexly and accurately gives an honest prognosis. It is easier than in cancer because its statistical course automatically makes the physician say: "I don't know. With proper care and reorientation of your activities you might not have another one for 20 or more years, and I cannot predict whether such a recurrence would be mild or severe."

I believe this is why cancer patients are more apt than others to think of suicide early in the disease. The thinking is, "If I had a coronary, I'd have a chance to live. I might not have another attack for years and years, so I could go along with it, accept it . . ." But in cancer he feels it as a relentless, hopeless process and reacts with, "I would rather determine the end myself, than leave it to this uncompromising monster that never gives anybody a chance . . ."

But the fact that there are available all the counterbalancing reconstructive forces, which we, as therapists can encourage and support, is proved by the startling statistics that few cancer patients do commit suicide. This lends further support to the impression that the average patient is susceptible to a healthy reorientation and adjustment and can balance the reality of his disease with the proper amount of denial. It is the family, more than the patient, who needs our help.

THE MECHANISM OF DEFENSE

This brings up another related point. Many workers have expressed fear that telling the patient he has cancer makes it more difficult for him to adequately "deny." It is my own experience that this is rarely so. Others, too, have observed that the patient who doesn't want to hear his diagnosis, simply doesn't. He uses effectively the mechanism of defense that he has used all of his life.

It is often startling to hear a patient who has been told that he has cancer talk during the rest of his life in a way which reflects that he has never heard us. To be sure, this is not universally so and it is true that some patients are made worse by being told the diagnosis. But by and large, I think that if the total program as outlined is mobilized it will help many more people than it will harm. No therapy is without complications and unwanted side effects. Even morphine produces increased rather than decreased discomfort in some patients.

A person who wants to deny does, regardless of the facts. A woman I have known for many years has worried about cancer every time she has had an ache. Actually during her 60 years, she has had many moderately severe illnesses, as well as a hysterectomy five years ago, and surgery for a subdural hematoma, which was almost fatal, two years ago. When she was recently hospitalized for anemia, a cancer of the cecum was found. To our surprise, she did not pursue her inquiries when told she had diverticu-litis. It is not uncommon for the patient to unconsciously sense the diagnosis, even if we judiciously deceive. She accepted at once the benign diagnosis. There were no further questions and no anxiety, whereas in the past when cancer didn't exist she had to be told many times that she did not have cancer.

I may seem to be contradicting myself because in this case we did not give the patient the diagnosis. But this is a good case to illustrate that each one must be handled individually. This woman has a large family, almost all of whom are seriously compulsive and many of whom would be striking examples of the premourners. All of them are very aggressive, almost mega-lomaniacal. Our final evaluation was that this well-meaning, devoted family could not possibly conceal their grief and their need to mourn, and that in this situation, it was best to conceal. The decision not to tell the family was based on our knowledge and careful appraisal of the total situation.

As suggested earlier, when the question arises, "Should the patient and family be told the truth?" we must forget statistics, and then we must ask ourselves: "Which patient? What truth?"

REFERENCES

1. Wertenbaker, Lael J., *Death of a Man.* New York: Random House, 1957.
2. Everson, T. C., Spontaneous regression of cancer. *Conn. Med.* 22:637-643, Sept. 1958.

A Way of Dying

ANONYMOUS

1

There is a new way of dying today. It is the slow passage via modern medicine. If you are very ill modern medicine can save you. If you are going to die it can prevent you from so doing for a very long time.

We cannot inquire from the dead what they have felt about this deterrent. As they fight for spiritual release, and are constantly dragged back by modern medicine to try again, does their agony augment? To those who stand and watch, this seems like a ghastly imposition against God's will be done. Apparently there is no mercy which the family may bestow at such a time. Only in an entirely hopeless situation may doctors desist in their effort to preserve life.

Enter the sickroom and sit with your beloved, and endure the long watch while this incredible battle between spirit and medicine takes place. It may continue for weeks, sometimes for months. But the victim is going to die. It is just a question of time. Every new formula, all the latest wonder drugs, the tricks and artificial wizardry, are now prescribed and brought to bear. The dreary dreadful days and nights proceed. "We are doing all

Reprinted with permission from the *Atlantic Monthly*, Vol. 199, January 1957, pp. 53-55. EDITOR'S NOTE: We sometimes forget that the value to be placed on health, and even life itself, is a decision which each person is free to make. Value decisions are not testable scientifically and thus are not issues that can be settled by scientific research. They are, however, culturally patterned. Persons belonging to the medical subculture probably are more inclined by law, tradition and personal convictions to place greater value on health and life than are members of other subcultures within our society. Within this group the preservation of life is the ultimate goal, overriding all else, even the "dignity of death."

This selection was written by the widow of a patient who died in a large metropolitan hospital. Note that this member of the patient's family did not value the prolongation of the life of her loved one over giving him the right to a dignified death. Note also how the hospital personnel unintentionally made the way of dying an ordeal for her by failing to perceive her definition of the situation.

A discussion of this article occurs on page 30 of the March 1957 *Atlantic Monthly*.

we can," say the doctors. The patient, however, is too far from us already to tell us in what way he is doing all he can.

He came out of surgery alive. He had not succumbed to this first ordeal. Could I let my tears fall now and then rush in to hug him? Could I tell him there would never be an end to us? Could I tell him he had won this fight against all odds, that he was brave and fine? I went to his room and found that he was just barely there. The intensity of quiet held me spellbound. Thus they return from contesting the inevitable. How desperately he must have tried to gain his reprieve. Softly I let the waves of my love pass over him, believing their spiritual balm might somehow help him. And then I left, as they told me to do, and went home.

On the surface one soon becomes accustomed to the rhythm of hospital routine. The early morning telephone call, then the visit, away for the lunch hour, back to the hospital in the afternoon. Sometimes a return there at night, but in any event a final telephone call. This becomes a regular schedule. At home one goes through a kindred round of activity. Any activity in order not to remove the armor. One laughs too much mirthless laughter and drinks with the realization that this is the hour of strain, when respect for the stricken demands that one carry on, achieve it how one may.

The intravenous feeding globes showed yellow and white, while the patient's arms were red and purple from so many hours of this treatment. He lay pitifully upon his pillows watching the liquid drain. I sat in the chair by the window endlessly, but he did not care. He did not want to waste his strength in talk. He must have known it was too late for that. Sometimes, very rarely, he would ask a question, wondering what had brought him there. Then I would tell him about the emergency operation, and he would thank me, saying he was so glad to get it straightened out in his mind.

No one thought he could survive a necessary second operation. This I could sense, but the formula called for hope and a language communicating merely that "the patient is holding his own." What does that mean exactly? Is it like lying back on your oars and taking a last look at some beautiful aspect of color or scenery that you wish to inscribe permanently upon your mind? Does it compare to enjoying the swell of the ocean as it rocks one gently before assuming its surf form and careening up the beach? Or can it be that a very horrible interlude occurs, a space of time and place where one is lost, a no man's land where one creeps and crawls about in twilight, calling and searching for some clue that is recognizable. An agony of trying to reach shores unseen because the fog is thick and mystifying and the bodily pain so terrible that all one is really crying for is death. "Where is my end?" must be the constant chant.

One afternoon I arrived at the hospital to make my usual visit and found his room empty. Surprised, I asked the reason at the corridor desk.

"Your patient is up in surgery. There was need for some repair" was the answer. I was afraid, and I was proved right to be so, as the wound was raveling. But not until the assistant surgeon came into that sad little waiting room and talked with me could I have guessed the dreadful ordeal which had just occurred. It had been necessary to perform this operation without anesthesia. I am not brave about physical pain and I began to feel the nausea of fear creeping over me at this news. "There is no use going in to see him," said the doctor; "he will not know you, and now that it is over we are going to give him some sedative." I knew that I must see him. There would never be any aspect of him that I would not want to know. And now, if we were nearing the end of our time together, I must memorize every detail of this scene. Perhaps I would need to draw on it for courage some day when I should be riddled with pain and bereft. He was sitting bolt upright in his bed. They had put the metal bedsides up so that he would not fall out. His eyes and face were wild and he was declaiming, though one could not understand him. The long thin arms were still all bruised, red and blue. I choked with anguish and horror, and the spectacle was written into me with a raw indelibility. My heart swam in a stream of pity, and the thought that I could do nothing to help him nearly maddened me.

Then came a morning when his delirium passed. There had been three savage days when he would call for me and cry out to have the sights removed which were disturbing him. He was being tortured and torn by imagery that was not present in the room. He could not be left alone a moment. He would try to arise. And once I had to throw myself across his chest, his poor sick desperate body, until the ringing of the bell brought help to me. But on this morning there was a change. He was quiet and absolutely conscious. His face was flushed and he was not enunciating too well. He told me he had something important to tell the doctor.

When the assistant surgeon came I rose as usual and stood behind the screen at the doorsill. I heard him clearly, every word, and it wrung my heart and sent my soul spinning. "I can stand anything you have to tell me, Doctor," he said, "and I realize how badly off I am, but you must give me help, real help. I can't pull myself up by my bootstraps any longer."

He lay back. I waited. The doctor told him they would do for him what they could, and left. I re-entered.

"There you are," he said, "they just don't care."

I took his hand. "I promise you, my darling, that I will stand in that hall until your surgeon comes by, and insist that he give you what you want."

Later in the day the sedatives had their effect. He appeared drowsy and relaxed. When the nurse went to supper I fed him his ice cream. God . . .

I thought; ice cream when one is kneeling at the threshold! I kissed him good night but he was not really there.

2

I had been asleep only a short time when suddenly I was awakened by the rasp and ring of the telephone. A step at my door. "The hospital is on the wire," the voice said. At the telephone I heard: "Your husband went into a coma at eleven o'clock. We are doing all we can. We do not know the reason for the coma." I said Amen as I dragged on my clothes.

The glaring, merciless rays from a powerful ceiling light displayed what was a human form, now portrayed in ghastly hue, in hunched position, with two tubes one in each nostril, eyes half open, breathing a noise of horror, while the oxygen tank at one side bubbled, bubbled merrily, and the nurse stood counting the heartbeat, taking the pulse. I saw, I reeled, I froze to my depths. I managed somehow then to leave. We sat in that same little waiting room hour after hour after hour. We stayed there sixteen hours.

Many times I tiptoed down the hall and looked again into that dreadful room. It was always exactly the same. They brought us coffee in the night. We talked and sometimes we dozed. At 8 A.M. the place began to come alive. I stirred. I went out into the morning, I walked about the garden, I stood beneath his window and I shook my fist at God. "They can't do this to you any longer. I must put a stop to it," I cried. I wanted to sob but I did not dare. When the first doctor came on duty I accosted him and begged that they cease this torture. He explained that except under the most unusual circumstances they had to maintain life while they could. Very well, I thought, if it has to be so, so be it.

We had breakfast and time dragged on. I went down the hall to the room again. I called on all my courage and I went in to stay. The day nurse whispered to me that his pulse was very poor, that he could not last much longer. I stood at the side of the bed with my hands clenched together, a little behind him so that I could look down upon his still beautiful head. And when I wanted I could look out the window at the clear blue morning sky. I stood and watched with my beloved while he attempted to cross the great divide. The oxygen bubbled merrily, it sang of its false gift of life. "I am a fake," it hissed and sang and purred. My own heart was pounding at such a pace I thought it might burst. It almost shook me. I have never been here before, I thought, and I am very much afraid. How difficult it is for him to gain the flood tide, and how can I assist in this perilous crossing? I was growing faint. I knelt down and put my arms and head on the side of a chair. I prayed a constant and continuous chant of "Please, God! Please, God!" I tried my utmost to help him. I was utterly lost in a paralysis of effort when—bang—the door burst open and with noisy footsteps a nurse had intruded on the scene. I sprang to my feet and faced her, and my distress was real. I wanted to kick her tray of medication and knock her from the room. She was here to snare him back just as he might have reached the other shore. I asked her why. "Doctor's orders," she replied. "I am to give him a hypo." I staggered out the door; there was nothing else to do.

For a long while I walked about the garden with my son. I picked up an oak leaf already turned red and put it in my handbag. It will always be somewhere in my room, saying, "On such a day you lost your love." It will solace me to see it because on such a day I was still doing for him what I could. It was hard not to weep, not to submit to anguish. The fine young man who walked at my side doubtless helped me retain my poise. What good being old if incapable of setting an example? We went back inside to the waiting room. It was Sunday, and the room was noisy and crowded with visitors. A woman in a wrapper came to me and said, "I'm glad your husband is better. He was quiet last night. I know because I am opposite his room." I could only nod and hope that the armor would not fail me. The afternoon nurse came on duty. By now I was seated in the hall and my son sat on the floor at my side. So much fuss and noise on Sunday, I thought; how dreary it is in a hospital. Finally the medical doctor appeared and addressed me. "Well," he said, "he's rallied." I remember feeling almost no emotion when I replied, "How horrible." So, after sixteen hours, we went home to sleep.

I was sleeping hard when I felt a cold draft, and I got out of bed and shut my window. I was just climbing back when the ring of the telephone caught me. I knew. He was too quick for them. He had come to me directly and placed his lover's hand on my shoulder. He had said good-by to me in his own way and reassured me that his spirit would always be at my side. "My darling" was all I could say. Of course we went directly to the hospital, driving without panic or unnecessary tears. I was calm knowing that he deserved to be released. I asked my son to step to the door of his room for a moment and render homage; then I went in and stood beside him. How unbelievable that you are gone! I kissed his forehead, which was still warm; I laid my hand on his; I let the scene permeate my being so that it would leave its indelible mark. That was all. Quite quietly I tiptoed out. We gave our instructions and went home.

I say "Hello, darling" to the night sky, the moon, the stars; to the daylight creating a vivid brilliance; and to the sunset so various in beauty stirring in me the wish to touch that distance and fathom it. When I say hello at these times I have a desperate desire to weep, feeling so poignantly my loss, but knowing also that such weeping would be to no avail. One must live out one's life. That is all there is to do. That is all there has ever been since the day that one was born. Struggle to fulfill oneself by living to the utmost. Efface ego and be at peace.

I am the emblem of a love affair that was important because it saw, and felt, and held great beauty. Through sickness and health, for richer for poorer, there remained always a magic bond until death did us part.

A Case of a "Psychotic" Navaho Indian Male

DONALD P. JEWELL

INTRODUCTION

☙ Increased psychological and ethnological rapprochement has resulted in a greater understanding of American subgroups and the processes of acculturation. Examples of this integrated approach are to be seen in Barnouw's study of Chippewa Indian acculturation[1] and, on the individual level, Devereux's psychotherapy of an alcoholic Sioux.[2]

Sometimes identified as the "culture-personality" orientation, this approach has reached a degree of clarification which justifies consistent designation. It is suggested here that it be defined as ethnopsychological. It is an approach which, as Kluckhohn has shown, has about a century of development.[3] Ethnopsychology has generally concerned itself with the definition

---

[1] Barnouw, V., "Acculturation and Personality Among the Wisconsin Chippewa," *American Anthropologist,* Memoir Number 72, Vol. 52, 1950.

[2] Devereux, G., *Reality and Dream,* International Universities Press, Inc., 1950.

[3] Kluckhohn, C., "The Influence of Psychiatry on Anthropology in America During the Past One Hundred Years," eds. J. K. Hall, C. Zilboorg, and E. A. Bunker, *One Hundred Years of American Psychiatry,* Columbia University Press, 1947, pp. 589-617.

Reprinted with permission from *Human Organization,* Vol. 11, No. 1, Spring, 1952, pp. 32-36.

This study was undertaken during the writer's internship in Clinical Psychology at Patton State Hospital, Patton, California. The writer wishes to gratefully acknowledge the supervision of this study by Mr. William Walcott, Clinical Psychologist and Supervisor of Interns. This study was made possible by the interest and cooperation of Dr. Otto L. Gericke, Superintendent of the hospital.

of general normal personality characteristics of other cultures, only occasionally with the neurotic individual, and rarely with the psychotic.

PURPOSE OF THIS STUDY

The writer had the opportunity recently to make a rather extensive observation of a Navaho Indian institutionalized as a psychotic in a California state mental hospital. By drawing from the literature of Navaho ethnopsychology and the writer's own experience among the Navaho people, it was hoped that the dynamics of the patient's maladjustment would be revealed. It was also anticipated that some sort of psychotherapy would evolve.

This report is a summary of those endeavors to understand and assist the Navaho patient. Cultural and linguistic obstacles prohibited an ideal approach, but enough was accomplished to permit considerable insight into the patient's behavior. There were features about the patient's personality which would not fit harmoniously with concepts of psychiatric symptomatology derived from European culture, those concepts dealing particularly with the dynamics of the patient's diagnosis of catatonic schizophrenia. The unique characteristics of this individual's personality leads, in fact, to the question as to what extent he should be considered psychotic, and whether that consideration should be viewed from Navaho or Anglo perspective.

During his many interviews with the patient, some of them with the aid of a Navaho interpreter, the writer developed an increasing awareness that to call the patient psychotic was an arbitrary matter. When this Navaho is referred to as psychotic, then, it is merely because he carried such a diagnosis during his 18 months of hospitalization as a mental patient.

ORIENTATION

Considerable literary attention has been given to the general psychological characteristics of Navaho Indians.[4] These have related psychological findings to ethnological contexts, and so offer a background against which the atypical Navaho individual may be examined.

On the behavioral level, the Navahos are in many ways unique, not only with respect to white people, but other Indian tribes as well. One of their most characteristic traits may be seen in crisis situations. Kluckhohn and Leighton describe it as a passive resistance, the individual masking his

---

[4] Henry, W., "The Thematic Apperception Technique in the Study of Culture-Personality Relations," *Genetic Psychology Monographs,* Vol. 35, 1947, pp. 3-135; Kluckhohn, C., and Leighton, D., *Children of the People,* Harvard University Press, 1948.

fear by quiet unmovingness, an appearance of stoicism. If forced into action, the response is a mechanical, apparently uncomprehending behavior.[5]

Another form of withdrawal is often expressed in periods of depression, apparently a morbid preoccupation with health.[6]

These being salient aspects of the typical Navaho personality, the question now arises as to how those traits would be characterized on the psychotic level. Under prolonged psychological stress, what would develop from the stoicism and moods of morbid preoccupation?

In an endeavor to answer this question a survey was made of those mental hospitals which would most likely be caring for Navaho patients. The Bureau of Indian Affairs' policy is not to concentrate Indian patients, but to subsidize their care in whatever hospital they may have been committed. It is thus possible that a few Navahos may be hospitalized some distance from their reservation area of New Mexico, Utah, and Arizona, and have not been located in this survey. It is felt, however, that a survey of those mental hospitals in the Southwest only would be adequate to show general trends. The findings are summarized in the following table.

DIAGNOSIS	NUMBER	SEX AND AGE
Psychosis with syphilis of the C.N.C.	2	1f: 47; 1m: 31
Psychosis with cerebral arteriosclerosis	1	1f: 62
Psychosis due to trauma (organic)	1	1m: 47
Epilepsy	8	6m: 20, 24, 29, 33, 37, 39; 2f: 20, 32
Schizophrenia, simple type	1	1m: 25
Schizophrenia, mixed type	1	1f: 26
Schizophrenia, hebephrenic type	1	1f: 30
Schizophrenia, catatonic type	7	4m: 26, 28, 28, 36; 3f: 20, 30, 38
Depressed state	1	1f: 37
Manic depressive psychosis, manic type	1	1m: 42

Legend: f: female; m: male

Summary of survey of Navaho Indian mental patients hospitalized in southwestern United States, excluding mental defectives. (Acknowledgment of the hospitals cooperating in this survey must be regretfully omitted due to the need to protect the identity of the patients.)

Elimination of the organic psychoses leaves one manic, one depressive, and 10 schizophrenics. Of the schizophrenics, seven are catatonic. This is an unusually high incidence of catatonic schizophrenia, and seems to indicate that Navahos are predisposed toward that particular psychosis. This

[5] Kluckhohn and Leighton, *ibid.,* p. 108.
[6] *Ibid.,* p. 110.

immediately suggests that the above described stoicism has been carried to pathological extremes, and possibly that the stoicism is actually a transient form of catatonia. It was with this problem in mind that the Navaho patient discussed in this report was studied.

THE PATIENT

The patient was a 26-year-old Navaho male. For purposes of anonymity he will be referred to as Bill. He came to the writer's attention through a survey of Indian patients at the hospital. He was the only Navaho of 13 Indian patients scattered throughout the various wards and cottages, and of the 4,000 general patient population.

The outlook for examination and therapy seemed at first quite discouraging. The patient was in a cottage ordinarily reserved for the most regressed patients. Unlike most of the others in this cottage, however, he was not there because of repeated failure of such routine therapies as shock treatment, occupational therapy, etc. It was unusual for a patient in his condition, who had been at the hospital for eight months, not to have received at least electric shock treatment.

A preliminary period was spent at the cottage, observing Bill's behavior. He was very withdrawn. Most of his day was spent in inactive sitting or sleeping. He would rouse himself only for eating or attending to other personal needs. He would assist with floor waxing, dish washing, or other activities the attendants might require of him, but in a perfunctory and apathetic manner. His behavior was not patently catatonic, but certainly suggestive of it.

Most of the attendants reported never having heard Bill speak. A few, however, indicated that Bill would occasionally approach them and, in almost unintelligible English, ask if he could go home.

Shortly thereafter Bill was brought to the writer's office where he was greeted in Navaho. Bill responded in that language, glancing briefly at the writer before returning his gaze to the floor.

This closer inspection of Bill revealed occipital flattening, resulting from the cradle board as a child, and the pierced ear lobes of a conservative Navaho. During this first interview he complained about the close hair cuts he received at the hospital, further evidence that he belonged to the old fashioned, "long hair" conservatives of the reservation.

The interview proceeded very slowly, but gradually a system of communication began to evolve. By utilizing mutually understood Navaho and English words, by means of pantomime, and with the aid of penciled sketches, the system became increasingly refined during the following interviews.

Bill was seen three hours a week for three months. The writer then took an eight months leave of absence from the hospital, during which time he spent several months in Bill's home area near Shiprock, New Mexico.

While in the Shiprock area, the writer endeavored to locate Bill's family to advise them of the patient's circumstances. Bill had previously drawn a map indicating the approximate location of his family's *hogans* (dwellings), but it proved impossible to find them. The *hogans* were located about five miles from the nearest road, and even if a horse and interpreter had been available the chances of locating the specific *hogans* were slight. The situation was complicated by the fact that the family did not have American names and the writer did not know their Navaho names. Missionaries and Bureau of Indian Affairs personnel were consequently given the problem of finding the family but several months elapsed before they were equipped with sufficient information to do so.

Although he could not communicate with Bill's family, the writer succeeded in talking with several Navahos who had known Bill, and in obtaining ecological and further case history material.

Shortly after the writer's return to the hospital a Navaho interpreter was brought in from the Sherman Institute, a large Indian school not far from the hospital. Interviews with the patient through the interpreter corroborated the case history material obtained, and further satisfied the writer in his clinical evaluation of the patient. Both of these areas are separately discussed in the following text.

CASE HISTORY

The gathering of Bill's history extended over a period of 11 months, and was obtained piecemeal from a variety of sources. In summarizing, however, this material will be integrated for greater coherency.

Bill was born in a part of the reservation noted for being both very conservative and poverty-stricken. Only 50 miles away is the markedly contrasting community of Shiprock, considered to be one of the most acculturated Navaho communities. It is also prospering from recently developed uranium operations in the region.

During his early years Bill saw very little of Shiprock, and was reared in the traditional Navaho way. He was born during an eclipse (it is not known whether of the sun or moon), and was thus destined to take part in a periodic ceremony identified to the writer as the "Breath of Life" sing. The first of this series of ceremonies was held while he was still an infant, the second about six years ago. During the ceremony he inhales the breath of a great deity, and is thus assured of continued good health in the respiratory and vocal organs.

Bill lived with his immediate family until he was six years of age. He had only one younger sister at that time, although the family was later to include seven living siblings. He did not become well acquainted with his family, however, as he was given to his grandfather when he was six years old. The grandfather, a widower, lived several miles deeper into the reservation and required Bill's assistance as a sheep herder.

Bill worked for his grandfather as a sheep herder until he was 17, except for one interruption when, at the age of 15, he spent 50 days in the Shiprock hospital with a back ailment. Bill reports that the old man never talked to him.

At his grandfather's death Bill went to work for the railroad in Colorado. This was cut short by an illness which confined him to the Navaho Medical Center in Fort Defiance, Arizona. The illness was diagnosed as tuberculosis, pulmonary, moderately advanced. He was in the hospital for eight months and was discharged in the summer of 1944.

Bill returned to railroad employment, and worked in Utah, Oregon, and Nebraska. He was always part of Navaho crews and thus never exposed to acculturative influences. His father and a younger brother were also part of these crews.

Bill returned home for a brief visit in 1949, accompanied by his brother and father. He had saved $1,022. Subsequently, he went to Phoenix, Arizona to pick cotton, a job that had been found for him by the employment agency at Shiprock. This was his first trip from home without a family member.

The employment at Phoenix did not last long and in December, 1949, on the advice of an Indian friend he went to Barstow, California seeking railroad employment. At the section camp there his attempt to find work was unsuccessful, and after three days he started by bus back to Phoenix.

On this return trip he stopped for dinner at Colton. A white man he met there promised to obtain railroad employment for him. The stranger said that he required funds for this effort and in some way relieved Bill of his savings which had now dwindled to $725.

Bill returned home penniless, pawned some jewelry, borrowed some money, and returned to Colton to try to find the man who had taken his savings. He also looked for Navahos who might have information about employment. The many hours of waiting around the bus station searching for his man apparently caused suspicion, for he was arrested for vagrancy.

In jail he met some Navahos with whom he went to Barstow after his release. But in Barstow he was still unable to find employment and after six days he was completely out of funds. He started walking toward Phoenix, and was picked up by a man driving a truck. This man gave Bill one day's employment which allowed funds for a return to Barstow and another attempt to find work.

He managed to raise a little money doing odd jobs about the section camp near Barstow, and then returned to San Bernardino on the first lap of his return to Phoenix and home. It occurred to him that if he could get to a hospital, the officials there would send him to a reservation hospital, from whence he would be sent home. This was logical thinking: on the reservations, the hospitals, schools, and trading posts are the major source of assistance in all sorts of troubles.

As this idea occurred to Bill, he noticed a woman dressed in white whom he took to be a nurse. He approached her and endeavored to explain that he was sick, but his endeavors were misinterpreted and he was taken to jail.

At the county jail Bill was apparently mistaken for a Mexican since a Mexican interpreter had tried to interview him. When the interview failed he was transferred to the psychopathic ward. Interviewed by the medical examiner there, he reportedly demonstrated an anguished appearance and repeated, "Me sick." He was diagnosed as Schizophrenia, Catatonic Type, and delivered to the state mental hospital.

Upon admission to the hospital, Bill was first taken to be a Filipino. The psychiatric admission note indicated that he was, ". . . confused, dull, and preoccupied. He has a look of anguish and appears to be hallucinating. . . . He repeats, 'I don't know.' " He was diagnosed as Dementia Praecox, which was later specified as Hebephrenic Type.

Several months later the psychiatrist on Bill's cottage tested him for *cerea flexibilitas* (waxy flexibility) and, finding it to be present, altered the diagnosis to Catatonic Type.

Eight months after his admittance he was discovered by the writer.

PSYCHOLOGICAL ASPECTS

Concomitant with gathering the case history material presented above, endeavors were made to evaluate the patient's intelligence and personality. The lack of culturally-biased examining techniques made this extremely difficult.

Bill's performance on the various tests that were administered led to a conclusion that his probable I.Q. was in the vicinity of 80. This had to take into consideration the patient's slowness. At best, a Navaho refuses to be put under pressure of time, and to what extent Bill's slowness was cultural rather than psychotically pathological was a question of primary concern.

Bill's apathetic and withdrawn behavior has already been described.

For diagnostic purposes, however, this syndrome is confused by cultural factors. It is common for Navahos, with their morbid fear of hospitals, to demonstrate just such a withdrawal patterning.[7] It is not known whether or not this would reach a stage of *cerea flexibilitas* or how long this behavior will persist. Accordingly it was concluded that Bill's apparent catatonia should not be accepted as a symptom of schizophrenia until underlying signs of schizophrenic processes could be detected.

During the first interview Bill was given the Draw A Person Test. The figure he drew was indistinct and without facial features and clearly reflected his withdrawal.

On the seventh interview the test was again given. Compared with the earlier attempt, the second drawing clearly reflected an improvement. It probably indicated the therapeutic benefits derived from the extensive individual treatment the patient was receiving.

The second drawing filled the paper, the facial features were portrayed, the arms were extended, and the drawing generally implied those signs which are held to indicate good contact with reality.

Although Bill's second drawing seems to infer considerable personality change, no changes could be observed in his behavior. He continued to appear apathetic and withdrawn. On several occasions he indicated his reluctance to talk because, "me no good this place," pointing to his chest. This suggested the characteristic organ cathexes of schizophrenia. However, the patient's thinking behind this statement was made clear during the later interviews through an interpreter.

Bill was concerned about the fact that he had not completed the second series of the "Breath of Life" ceremony. This matter had gone too long unattended, and he assumed that he must conserve his vocal energies until they could be supplemented by the breath of the deity. He expressed a great need to return home to pursue the ceremony.

In continued endeavor to detect schizophrenic underlay of his apparent catatonia, Bill was given a series of tests, none of which revealed responses normally associated with schizophrenia.

During the early course of the interviews with Bill, although not satisfied that the patient was not psychotic, the writer recommended that the best therapeutic environment for him would be his own home. This recommendation was not acted upon, partly because no one knew where his home was, or how he could be supervised there, but chiefly because he continued to appear catatonic.

Later, as the writer became convinced that the catatonia—if such it could be termed—was not symptomatic of underlying schizophrenia, efforts

---

[7] *Ibid.*, pp. 108-109.

were renewed to release the patient. The outcome of these endeavors are summarized in the following section.

OUTCOME

As mentioned earlier, the final interviews with Bill were carried on with the aid of a Navaho interpreter. Bill conversed quite freely with the other Navahos and expressed gratitude at being able to talk to someone in his own language. The conversations did not add much to the history and understanding previously gained, but did offer an opportunity to inquire for the presence of hallucinations, delusions, and more subtle clues of schizophrenic thinking. Unless Bill's anxiety regarding the uncompleted "Breath of Life" ceremony could be considered bizarre, nothing of significance was elicited.

The interpreter's reaction to the interviews represented their most significant outcome. He was a professional interpreter, with vast experience in interviewing Navaho youths in strange environments. He expressed a strong conviction that Bill's behavior and attitudes were not unusual under the circumstances.

The interpreter communicated his feelings to the superintendent of the Sherman Institute who took an immediate and active interest in the case. After several interviews with Bill, satisfied that he could observe nothing about Bill's behavior which could be considered atypical under the circumstances, the superintendent offered to accept him into the flexible program of the Sherman Institute.

Bill was accordingly released under custody of the superintendent and careful plans were made to assure his adjustment at the school. At first, he was quartered in the school hospital, but allowed to participate in the school's social and recreational activities. He was employed with the animal husbandry and gardening program.

The writer's last visit to the Sherman Institute disclosed that Bill's adjustment had been quite rapid. He had put on weight and after about two weeks announced that he "felt right a home, now."

It had been difficult at first, because in spite of all precautions the students had learned something of Bill's past hospitalization. To the Navahos the hospital symbolizes death, and death is particularly abhorrent to them as they have no clearly structured concepts of an after-life. The students consequently shied away from Bill a little when he arrived, but he has since found acceptance.

He will go back to the reservation in the spring, at the close of the school year, and attend to the unfinished business of the "Breath of Life" ceremony.

CONCLUDING DISCUSSION

In the course of this Navaho commitment and 18 months of hospitalization, he was routinely examined by several psychiatrists, all of whom concurred with the diagnosis of schizophrenia. Without verbal communication with the patient, diagnosis was necessarily derived from observation of his overt behavior. Diagnosis was apparently confident as the patient was not referred to staff clinic or for psychological testing, the normal procedure with questionable cases.

Most of the psychiatrists' diagnostic observations were based on information received from the attendants of Bill's cottage, who reported the patient's withdrawn and apathetic behavior. Upon closer examination the patient would demonstrate *cerea flexibilitas*. Because of these factors the patient was assumed to be catatonic and hence schizophrenic.

Actually, many of the classic symptoms of catatonia were not present in this patient. He was not markedly stuporous or mute; he was clean in his personal habits and would eat willingly; he tended to doze as he sat rather than stare fixedly into space as does the typical catatonic. The writer, too, examined Bill for *cerea flexibilitas*, but learned later that the patient held grotesque positions because he thought it was expected of him.

With the assumption, however, that the patient's overt behavior could be interpreted as symptomatic of catatonic schizophrenia, it remains to be explained why testing and closer observation did not reveal the underlying ego disintegration which should be expected.

General personality traits of the Navaho people, as briefly reviewed earlier in this paper, could possibly infer a potential for schizophrenic disintegration. Navahos do not have the imaginative activity and the inner control which is so important to adjustment in the Anglo world. The scales are balanced, however, by a defense of rigidity and constriction. In a threatening situation they strive to maintain ego structure by psychic withdrawal.

The few tests that were applicable in examining Bill did not permit a very intensive examination of the dynamics of his withdrawal, but all indications were that he continued to maintain ego strength. He could account for his acts rationally, he performed very well with conceptualization, he maintained orientation for time and place, and could hold in mind simultaneously various aspects of situations or problems. His visuo-motor performance exhibited no signs of distorted perspective. Many of his expressions could be considered naive, but hardly bizarre.

The apparent incongruity between the patient's overt behavior and underlying personality dynamics, although not fully understood psychologically, should not be considered as psychotic manifestations. Culturally derived, it can probably be explained as a defense mechanism characterized by an extreme and sustained withdrawal.

To what extent Bill's case may be typical of other Navaho patients diagnosed as catatonic schizophrenia cannot, of course, be proposed. It would be necessary to know if those patients were similarly diagnosed on the basis of overt behavior alone.

It is also unknown to what degree Bill may personify on-reservation Navaho youth. Superficially at least, his history appears quite typical. His lack of school, his years as a sheep herder for his grandfather, his attack of tuberculosis, and his railroad employment, are circumstances and events common to many Navahos. His grandfather's apparent lack of affection implies an almost feral existence for the growing boy, but even this situation is not unusual. It is, in fact, difficult to discern some way in which this patient could be atypical as evaluated against his cultural background. Except for his possible low intelligence, he appears to represent a typical Navaho youth, a fact heavy with implication when his 18 months of hospitalization as a mental patient is considered.

The previously cited survey of hospitalized Navaho mental patients shows an amazingly small percentage of the total Navaho population (which is about 65,000). This is probably because few Navahos are currently coming in very close contact with Anglo structure.

Of the catatonic schizophrenics, it would be of value to know more about the details of their admission. If they were referred from the reservation it probably meant that they were considered psychotic within the Navaho milieu; if, on the other hand, they were referred by agencies off the reservation (as was Bill), it would imply an evaluation derived from Anglo perspective. This will become a more poignant problem with increasing off-reservation movement of the Navaho people.

In addition to what this study may infer with respect to the Navaho Indians, it is hoped also that it may illustrate the need to consider the influence of cultural environment in any study of individual personality. The psychiatric approach usually concerns itself with the abnormal personality, and evaluates the individual according to concepts of what constitutes the normal personality. Too often these concepts are preconceived and stereotyped, giving very little consideration to the individual's cultural frame of reference. This factor naturally varies in proportion to the degree of the individual's acculturation.

The cultural factor seems to be particularly important in reconciling overt behavior with covert personality dynamics. This is often a difficult reconciliation even with patients of the general American cultural patterning, and becomes increasingly more difficult the farther removed the individual is from acculturation.

The need to consider emotional maladjustment with respect to cultural factors has long been recognized. It has, however, been somewhat of an academic acknowledgment which demands greater practical application on the clinical level.

Anthropological Perspectives on Medicine and Public Health

BENJAMIN D. PAUL

✍ Because man is not only a social but also a cultural animal, it scarcely surprises us to be told that cultural as well as social factors often play a significant role in man's susceptibility and response to illness. Broadly speaking, culture is a group's design for living, a shared set of socially transmitted assumptions about the nature of the physical and social world, the goals of life, and the appropriate means of achieving them. These things we know; we also know that cultures vary considerably from group to group within and between nations. But, without special effort, we cannot readily know just how given cultures differ from others and how these differences influence behavior in regard to specific illnesses and to specific programs of medical care. Anthropologists have not been the only behavioral scientists to study variations of this kind, but, as students of comparative cultures, anthropologists attracted to the field of medicine have naturally tended to fix their attention on the cultural contexts in which health, illness, and therapy are framed.

In publishing their ethnographic reports on Eskimo, Navaho, Poly-nesian, or other communities, anthropologists have usually included a siz-able section on sickness and curing, but these reports, mainly written for the benefit of academic insiders, have had little impact on members of the medical and public-health professions. During the last decade, however, a number of anthropologists have begun to collaborate with medical teams and organizations and to select research problems pertinent to research

Reprinted with permission from the author and *The Annals of the American Academy of Political and Social Science*, Vol. 346, March 1963, pp. 34-43.

physicians and other health workers. These might be called "medical anthropologists," for their activities are linked to those of the health professions, although the term is not in common usage—as is the term "medical sociologists"—and its members are not a group in any organizational sense.

Medical anthropologists generally are of two kinds, those who investigate cultural components in the etiology and incidence of illness and those who analyze popular reactions to programs of health maintenance and health improvement. Investigators in the first category study how cultural patterns mediate between conditions of climate, economy, sanitation, diet, child rearing, daily routines, and social contact, on the one hand, and death, disability, and disease, on the other.

Although mortality and morbidity rates tend to be inversely related to economic and nutritional status, the effect is often modified by cultural practices. A good example is *kwashiorkor*—a children's disease due to nutritional, particularly protein, deficiency—prevalent in many technologically underdeveloped areas. Two populations living in the same general environment with equally limited food resources may differ in their weaning practices and culturally conditioned assumptions about the kinds and quantities of nutriments suitable during the postweaning period. In consequence, the extent of *kwashiorkor* among children one to five years of age may vary appreciably as between the two populations. It is an open question whether psychological factors such as parental solicitude or indifference are also involved, but, if they are, these dispositions, too, are partly a product of cultural conditioning.

Rates of venereal disease, tuberculosis, and other communicable illnesses are affected by conditions of crowding and social contact. These conditions are influenced in turn by cultural standards, which differ from one group to another. Psychological components subsumed under the catch-all concept of "stress" are often thought to play a part in the origin and persistence of noncontagious chronic diseases and the so-called psychosomatic ailments. The presence and degree of stress, a subjective experience, are notoriously governed by varying cultural expectations and definitions.[1]

The second and larger category of medical anthropologists have been concerned not with the determinants of disease and its prevalence but with the behavior of people in the face of sickness and in the presence of medical and other community resources for maintaining health and coping with

---

[1] The literature on the role of sociocultural factors in the etiology of disease has been critically reviewed recently by an anthropologist working with a physician: see Norman A. Scotch and H. Jack Geiger, "The Epidemiology of Rheumatoid Arthritis," *Journal of Chronic Diseases,* Vol. 15 (1962), pp. 1037-1067. Also see "The Epidemiology of Essential Hypertension" by the same authors, as well as "Sociocultural Factors in the Epidemiology of Schizophrenia" by Elliot G. Mishler and Norman A. Scotch, both mimeographed, Harvard School of Public Health, 1962.

illness. While sociologists have taken the lead in studying social class as a variable in medical behavior, some of the anthropologists working with segments of our own society have selected ethnicity as a variable. Comparative studies designed to disclose subcultural variations do indeed reveal characteristic group differences among "Old Yankees," Irish, Italians, Jews, Spanish Americans, and others with respect to a variety of circumstances, for example, responses to pain and to programs of physical rehabilitation, drinking behavior and alcoholism, deciding to seek medical care, tolerance of mentally retarded children in the home, reaction to mental illness.

Perhaps the kind of health-related research for which cultural anthropologists are most uniquely qualified by temperament and training is the study of popular reactions to programs of public health carried out in foreign cultural settings. Personnel of action programs generally strive to measure the success of their efforts in such terms as number of mothers attending clinics, quantity of latrines installed, or extent of altered dietary practice. But usually they are not in a good position to ascertain the reasons why parts of the message are lost or transformed, why certain parts of the program work and others not, or why certain segments of the target population accept the assistance offered while others do not. Without this knowledge of the dynamics that intervene between action and outcome, it is difficult to profit from experience, avoiding past mistakes and repeating past successes.

It is here that the anthropologist can help. For he is accustomed to work in alien settings, patiently establishing his role as an interested but detached observer, developing relationships with reliable informants, slowly building up a picture of the local culture by watching, listening, making inquiries, and collecting incidents, cases, and statistics.

> In most general terms the [anthropological] field worker aims to gather and relate two sets of data, a description of the situation as he sees it, looking from the outside in, and a description of the situation as the native sees it, looking from the inside out. The first comprises the visible world of objects and actions: the people in their material and environmental setting, their groupings and interactions, their techniques and activities. This objective frame of reference the ethnographer shares with the human geographer, the economist, and the natural historian. The subjective frame of reference embraces the world view of the people, the pattern of assumptions that guides their perceptions, the network of meanings that binds their precepts into the semblance of a system, the hierarchy of values animating their actions. The student of culture cannot ignore the objective situation, but it is the subjective view that constitutes his distinctive concern. He needs to know the what and the how, but he also wants to know the cultural wherefore.[2]

---

[2] Benjamin D. Paul, "Interview Techniques and Field Relationships," *Anthropology Today*, ed. A. L. Kroeber (Chicago: University of Chicago Press, 1953), p. 442.

By this method, anthropologists in recent years have produced a fair number of instructive case studies of interaction between health teams and local populations. A pioneer report of this kind was an analysis of the operation of bilateral health projects in several Latin-American countries by George M. Foster and his anthropological colleagues.[3] Additional detailed case studies based on programs in Africa, Asia, the Pacific, Latin America, and North America have since been assembled in a volume prepared primarily to assist teaching in schools of public health.[4] In a very useful essay, Foster has summarized some of the recurrent problems and processes encountered in intercultural health programs.[5] Another anthropologist, Steven Polgar, has published an organized and comprehensive review of the literature on health and human behavior generally.[6]

INTERCULTURAL HEALTH PROGRAMS

The profession of public health prides itself on being in the forefront of the campaign to increase the productivity of peoples and nations and to elevate their standard of living. Sick and undernourished people cannot work efficiently; improved health is often a precondition for economic improvement. Of all forms of technical aid, health programs, if soundly conceived, are most likely to be welcomed and least likely to be feared as forms of political or economic interference. Of course, programs of health improvement can proceed only so far without parallel development in agriculture, transportation, education, public administration, and general economic development. Moreover, mortality reduction, if not accompanied by per capita economic growth, will only increase pressure on the food supply.

Despite the generally uncontroversial nature of public-health aid, it should be recognized that new modes of behavior, whether they concern health or anything else, are seldom accepted simply on their intrinsic merits. The success or failure of a health program is largely governed by the way in which it fits the modes of thought and action of the recipient population. Thus, public-health workers, like other agents of social change, need to

---

[3] George M. Foster and Others, "A Crosscultural Anthropological Analysis of a Technical Aid Program" (mimeographed; Washington, D. C.: Smithsonian Institution, 1951).

[4] Benjamin D. Paul and Walter B. Miller (eds.), *Health, Culture, and Community: Case Studies of Public Reactions to Health Programs* (New York City: Russell Sage Foundation, 1955).

[5] George M. Foster, *Problems in Intercultural Health Practice,* Social Science Research Council, Pamphlet No. 12, 1958.

[6] Steven Polgar, "Health and Human Behavior: Areas of Interest Common to the Social and Medical Sciences," *Current Anthropology,* Vol. 3, No. 2 (April 1962), pp. 159-205.

understand the nature of sociocultural patterns, what purposes they serve, why they persist, and how they change. In their planning and in their approach, health experts need to be particularly aware of four gaps which often impede realization of program aims: the cultural gap, the status gap, the urban-adjustment gap, and the research gap.

THE CULTURAL GAP

There frequently exists a considerable gap or difference between the culture of the beneficiary population and that of the action team. What seems obvious, feasible, and desirable to health personnel, looking at the world with their own culturally tinted glasses, may seem quite otherwise to the people they serve.

Cultural gaps complicate the problem of elementary communication. Caudill provides an amusing example from Japan. He writes:[7]

> If one wants to refer rather roughly and familiarly to one's own mother, one may use the word *ofukuro*. This word, without the prefix "o" which is honorific, means "bag" or "sack." If a Japanese patient working with an English-speaking [psychoanalyst] were to refer to his mother as an "honorable bag" I expect the pattern of the analyst's emotional associations with this would go off in directions other than those of the patient's. The term has invidious connotations in English that it does not have in Japanese.

The cultural gap can also impede the acceptance of new health services. People of other societies often find the new modes incompatible with their own notions of illness and curing, and it is therefore practical, not to say considerate, to understand their beliefs and practices before trying to change them. Anthropological field work on folk medicine yields several generalizations. One is that local disease taxonomies, though seldom explicit and varying greatly from culture to culture, are often as orderly and systematic as they are complex. This has been well documented, for example, by Adams for a rural community in Guatemala[8] and by Frake for a pagan group in the southern Philippines.[9]

Another generalization about folk medicine is that the local population tends to divide afflictions into two great classes: those that respond to folk methods of treatment and those amenable to scientific medication, although

[7] William Caudill, "Some Problems in Transcultural Communication (Japan-U.S.)," *Application of Psychiatric Insights to Cross-Cultural Communication* (New York: Group for the Advancement of Psychiatry, 1961), p. 420.

[8] Richard N. Adams, *An Analysis of Medical Beliefs and Practices in a Guatemalan Indian Town* (Guatemala City: Pan American Sanitary Bureau, 1953).

[9] Charles O. Frake, "The Diagnosis of Disease Among the Subanun of Mindanao," *American Anthropologist*, Vol. 63 (1961), pp. 113-132.

the dividing line may shift from one culture to another. Drawing on field material from northern India, Gould asserts that the inhabitants view village medicine as applying mainly to chronic nonincapacitating ailments such as arthritis, while modern medicine is seen as applying to critical incapacitating dysfunctions such as acute appendicitis.[10] Of course, people who repeatedly fail to find relief under one type of medicine will often try the other type as a desperate last resort.

Still another proposition is that local concepts of etiology and curing serve more purposes than the technical one of maintaining physical health. Within the context of their culture, they may also serve psychological as well as expressive and symbolic needs, although these functions are seldom made explicit.[11] But perhaps the most important of the latent purposes is that of social control, namely, providing sanction or support for the moral and social system. Rubel describes "evil eye" and several other folk illnesses which remain firmly embedded in the sociocultural matrix of a Mexican-American border community, despite the introduction of an alternative system of belief and ways of healing, because they function "to sustain some of the dominant values of the Mexican-American culture, those which prescribe the maintenance of the solidarity of the small, bilateral family unit, and others which prescribe the appropriate role behavior of males and females, of older and younger individuals."[12] Here, as elsewhere, diseases interpreted as punishment of violation of social norms are usually held to fall outside the ken or competence of the technically trained physician. However, health workers who have taken the trouble to master the rationale of the native system of medical concepts have usually gained greater acceptance of their own.

Cultures are layered. What we call customs rest on top and are most apparent. Deepest and least apparent are the cultural values that give meaning and direction to life. Values influence people's perceptions of needs and their choice between perceived alternative courses of action. Although sound health is everywhere appreciated, a deliberate quest for good health as such does not rank equally high in the hierarchy of every society's value system. Concern for health may be masked by a quest for merit, virtue, or staying in harmony with the moral and cosmic order.

Cleanliness for its own sake, apart from its role in reducing infection, occupies a high place in the scale of values implicit in the culture of the American middle class, but this is not always the case in other cultures.

---

[10] Harold A. Gould, "The Implications of Technological Change for Folk and Scientific Medicine," *American Anthropologist,* Vol. 59 (1957), pp. 507-516.

[11] Benjamin D. Paul, "The Cultural Context of Health Education," *Symposium Proceedings, School of Social Work* (University of Pittsburgh, 1953), pp. 31-38.

[12] Arthur J. Rubel, "Concepts of Disease in Mexican-American Culture," *American Anthropologist,* Vol. 62 (1960), pp. 795-814.

Although the Japanese likewise place high value on cleanliness, they are less dedicated to the cluster of values which Americans, invoking democratic ideals, often try to export via health promotion and other improvement programs. With America as a model, health workers have tried to stimulate group discussion as a method of achieving health education in rural areas of Japan, but group discussion does not come easily where respect for authority is a built-in value and where the concepts of voluntarism, self-help, and citizen participation are still alien to the basic value system.

Appeals to pride or invitations to gain prestige or excitation of other strong motives outside the sphere of health can sometimes stimulate people to implement new health measures. To start a program of rural sanitation in a demonstration village in Thailand, Textor appealed to the head priest to enlist the aid of lay citizens in building latrines at the Buddhist temple for the use of temple priests, citizens coming to sleep at the temple on holy days, and children attending school on temple grounds. The latrine-construction project was completed in two days not because the volunteer laborers valued improved sanitation but because they were willing to earn religious merit by performing good works for the temple, an important value in their culture.[13] Whether or not this kind of approach yields favorable long-run results is a matter for empirical investigation; whether or not it is warranted is a question of policy and a legitimate subject for debate.

The public-health approach rightly stresses the prevention of illness and the promotion of good health habits, not just the cure of illness. Some positive measures can be carried out—such as malaria control—without enlisting the active involvement of the beneficiary population; others require their participation. The latter kind, which depends for its successful implementation on engaging and sustaining human motivation, obviously demands much effort, patience, and ingenuity.

But even the former type of program, which asks only for passive acceptance, can arouse unexpected resistance, as many supervisors of DDT campaigns can ruefully attest, because the people affected may bring to the situation culturally conditioned expectations and interpretations at variance with those held by public-health specialists. In North Borneo, delegations from the countryside petitioned the government to stop antimalarial teams from spraying their houses, complaining that they disliked having strangers enter their homes, that their religion forbade them to allow any toxic substance in their houses, that their farm animals and even children were being killed by the poison, and that they were prepared to go to jail rather than submit to the spraying. In Peru, antitriatoma spraying brought Chagas' disease under control according to plan, but the

---

[13] Robert B. Textor and Others, *Manual for the Community Health Worker in Thailand* (Thailand: Ministry of Public Health, 1958).

citizens mistakenly assumed that the aim was to eliminate bothersome flies. Judging the campaign a fly-control fiasco, they drew up a resolution, submitted it to the national congress in Lima, and forced the health officer responsible for the project to answer charges of malfeasance.

Although programs of prevention are justifiable from the standpoint of long-run efficiency, they are frequently difficult to implement for several interrelated reasons. One is the relatively low salience of health as a value among some groups, as already indicated; able-bodied people are often disposed to leave well enough alone rather than worry continuously about keeping fit. A second reason is the difficulty of perceiving the connection between a given action and its beneficial effect. Thus, people in tropical areas may readily accept antibiotic treatment of yaws because the effect is rapid and visible but hesitate to use latrines designed to break the invisible cycle of infection from feces to water to mouth.

A third reason is the limited future-time orientation of people in most technologically underdeveloped areas. Accustomed mainly to short-term planning, they find long-run goals unrealistic and uncompelling. A fourth reason is the existence in the local culture of competing "preventive" measures, namely, the dos and don'ts of proper behavior which are supposed to forestall sickness and other types of misfortune.

This array of possible impediments does not mean that preventive medicine programs are doomed to failure. It means that they should be shaped to fit the cultural profile, as well as the health profile, of the population involved. It also implies that long-range goals stand a better chance of being implemented if they are combined with measures to meet immediate needs. For medical programs this usually means offering curative along with preventive services. A mother who receives attention for a sick child by that token will be a little more disposed to heed advice about how to prevent the illness of a healthy child. Folk medicine and folk practitioners may be trusted, but they do not always provide relief, and at least some of the disappointed sufferers will be impelled to seek help elsewhere, especially if the new services are not too inconsistent with existing conditions and expectations.

THE STATUS GAP

In any social system, there are likely to be gradations of classes and social statuses. In many technologically underdeveloped areas, the status gap between the educated elite and the bulk of the population is apt to be particularly marked. The difference between the "felt needs" of these divergent social strata has important implications for health programing and other forms of technical co-operation. The people-to-people approach is laudable enough, but usually it is neither prudent nor possible to bypass the ruling elite, whose vested interests may discourage reforms essential to improving the lot of the common man. However, this is not always the case, especially where leadership is based on education rather than land ownership.

Let us assume that the elite are genuinely eager to assist the masses, a condition that exists in some newly emerging states such as India. The problem here is the divergence of outlook and aspiration between the peasantry and the city-bred elite, coupled with the inability or unwillingness of the elite to acknowledge this gap. While the peasants are reluctant to abandon time-tested ways, the elite of technologically underdeveloped countries are eager to bring their nations, overnight if possible, up to the level of the well-developed nations.

Ruling elites understandably lay claim to knowing the people of their own country. But, as Freedman points out on the basis of his experience as a health consultant in Asia:[14]

> I am impressed by three kinds of error which spring from [this unwarranted claim]. The first of these is the error of supposing that within a given political territory all local communities conform to a standard pattern of social organization. The second error is to confuse the legislated pattern of rural life with the actual pattern. The third error is to entertain a view of rural life which I can only call romantic; in this view—and it is a common one—the inhabitants of rural communities are credited with powers of spontaneous cooperation and harmonious co-existence to the extent that they resemble no human community which has ever been studied.

There is often status gap enough in the United States between physicians and other health personnel, as well as between physicians and patients. But the status gaps are greater in Latin-American and other countries where physicians usually come from the upper class (rather than middle class, as in the United States), nurses from less privileged strata, and patients in public clinics from the lowest level. In these circumstances, as Simmons[15] and others have shown, the health "team" may in fact be a hierarchy of command, mistrust may mark the relations between the team and clientele, and teams made up of American and local physicians may operate under strain due to conflicting social postures vis-à-vis the public.

---

[14] Maurice Freedman, "Health Education and Self-Education," *Health Education Journal*, Vol. 15 (May 1957), p. 79.

[15] Ozzie G. Simmons, *Social Status and Public Health*, Social Science Research Council, Pamphlet No. 13, 1958.

THE URBAN-ADJUSTMENT GAP

In many places, the population surge from rural and tribal areas into the cities creates unhealthful conditions of overcrowding, poor sanitation, and malnutrition. Uprooted from familiar surroundings and not yet assimilated into city life, the migrants often face difficult problems of adjustment. How traumatic this experience actually proves to be depends on the particular combination of material, social, and psychological factors, as anthropological studies of slum conditions in different countries are beginning to show.

In an effort to assess the role of social factors in the etiology of hypertension, Scotch compared African Zulus situated at different points on the rural-urban continuum. Blocked by a policy of apartheid, destitute Zulus from rural reservations who live in squatter settlements near Durban suffer degradation and other forms of frustration which seem to exact a heavy toll in antisocial behavior and psychosomatic illness, particularly among the young men, who bear the brunt of the strain. With few opportunities to express their resentments directly against the whites, African men apparently seek displaced targets, venting their hostility on wives (higher rate of broken homes), other Africans (increased rates of bewitchment and accusations of sorcery), and against themselves (alcoholism and markedly increased essential hypertension).[16]

On the other hand, Mangin found little evidence of psychological stress or social disorganization among low-status mountain people who migrated to Lima, Peru. They, too, move into squatter settlements which are often crowded, with flimsy houses, poor sewage disposal, and no water supply. The new residents feel themselves under attack, and they experience a sense of separateness from the city. Nevertheless, for most migrants, the new environment represents progress in terms of housing and income, and urban residence spells improvement over the semifeudal life of the Indian or lower-class mestizo in the Andean hinterland.[17] Thus, the precise effect of the urban-adjustment gap often depends on more factors than meet the eye on first inspection.

THE RESEARCH GAP

As detached observers of interaction between representatives of different cultures (the health team and the beneficiary population), anthropologists

---

[16] Norman Scotch, "A Preliminary Report on the Relation of Sociocultural Factors to Hypertension among the Zulu," *Annals of the New York Academy of Science,* Vol. 84 (1960), pp. 1000-1009.

[17] William Mangin, "Mental Health and Migration to Cities: A Peruvian Case," *Annals of the New York Academy of Science,* Vol. 84 (1960), pp. 911-917.

can add insight into social processes activated by intercultural health programs. But, so far, they have been able to provide only a modest amount of assistance to program administrators. Too few anthropologists have yet had an opportunity to become familiar with the field of health and the subculture of its practitioners, and too few public-health administrators know enough about the way anthropologists work. These deficiencies are diminishing as case studies of health and culture accumulate and as anthropologists are added to the faculties of medical and public-health schools. These are encouraging signs, but they are not enough.

Compared to the sums of money spent on basic medical research to generate new technical knowledge and on program operations in the field, the amount of money available for studying the human aspects of community development, including health improvement, is disappointingly small. In their report to the International Cooperation Administration (ICA) on community development programs in India, Pakistan, and the Philippines, submitted in 1955, Adams, Foster, and Taylor found:[18]

> Recognition of the potential usefulness of scientific research in the broad fields of social and economic development generally is conspicuous by its absence. . . . The United States supports research in agronomy, animal husbandry, medicine and education in many countries as parts of development programs, but contributes very little to the research that will promote more effective utilization of the fruits of these technical investigations. . . . There is almost no exploitation of the rich research possibilities inherent in community development programs. . . . We believe that, until such time as social science research techniques and knowledge are utilized much more fully in planning and operations, community development programs will not realize their full potential.

The research gap that impressed Adams, Foster, and Taylor in 1955 is no longer so wide and so disheartening. There is growing awareness of the problem, and steps are being taken to do something about it. Narrowing the research gap would help bridge the other gaps—the cultural, status, and urban-adjustment gaps already reviewed.

Social scientists should not aim merely to facilitate the implementation of predetermined plans and policies. Questions of *how* to induce response to a program should be set in the larger frame of *whether* to promote a given program at all. Although not directing his remarks specifically at work in the health field, Ralph Beals expresses this concern when he criticizes "the view that the basic problem is how someone can do something to other people tacitly understood as inferior or subordinate. . . . It is time some

---

[18] Harold Adams, George Foster, and Paul S. Taylor, *Report on Community Development Programs in India, Pakistan and the Philippines* (Washington, D.C.: International Cooperation Administration, 1955), pp. 41-42.

emphasis of applied anthropology should be on determining what people want and aiding them to get it rather than how they can best be persuaded to do what people in another culture think is best for them. The latter too often is a rationalization really concealing what is thought best for the dominant culture."[19]

Diversities in Conceptions of Health and Physical Fitness

BARBARA BAUMANN

THE PROBLEM

In recent years, sociologists as well as physicians have devoted an increased amount of attention to the study of attitudes toward health and illness. Koos, for example, discusses the relationship of socioeconomic status to attitudes toward health and illness, and reports that an attitude of indifference to symptoms is expressed more frequently as one descends the socioeconomic scale.[1] Di Cicco and Apple, in a study of persons over sixty-five of low socioeconomic status, report that, for their sample, "health was important only as it became poor health and interfered with daily activity and maintenance of independence."[2] Weeks, Davis, and Freeman suggest that apathy toward medical care is related to the economic value

[19] Sol Tax and Others (eds.), *An Appraisal of Anthropology Today* (Chicago: University of Chicago Press, 1952), p. 189.

[1] Earl L. Koos, *The Health of Regionville* (New York: Columbia University Press, 1954).

[2] Lena Di Cicco and Dorrian Apple, "Health Needs and Opinions of Older Adults," in Dorrian Apple (ed.), *Sociological Studies of Health and Sickness* (New York: McGraw-Hill Book Co., 1960), pp. 26-40.

Reprinted with permission from the author and the *Journal of Health and Human Behavior*, Vol. 2, 1961, pp. 39-46.

This research is part of a study supported by the Commonwealth Fund and conducted under the auspices of the Comprehensive Care & Teaching Program, George G. Reader, M.D., Director.

The author gratefully acknowledges the suggestions of Dr. Reader, Mary E. W. Goss, Ph.D., Gene Kassebaum, Ph.D., and Margaret Olencki, M.A., in the preparation of this report.

placed on health in comparison with other expenditures.[3] Either explicit or implicit in these studies is the concept that different attitudes toward health may reflect different meanings that are attached to the term. For some individuals, ability to carry on usual activities is central to their conception of good health. For others, good health is identified with "physical fitness," conceived as an absolute state attainable by following certain rules, and which may be assessed in terms of performance on various tests of gymnastic proficiency.[4]

It is therefore clear that, before any meaningful comparison of attitudes can be made, it must first be established that the objects of the attitudes are indeed comparable. The above citations indicate that, in the case of terms like "health" and "physical fitness," such an assumption may sometimes be unwarranted. Before evaluating an individual's attitude toward health, one must ascertain the conception he holds of the term. Conceivably, persons may fail to respond to measures designed to improve their health because they fail to perceive the measures as related to their conception of health. When such a difference in conception goes undetected in the interaction between physician and patient, each party may find the other's attitudes incomprehensible, and, in consequence, an unnecessary strain may be imposed on the doctor-patient relationship.

The study reported here examines conceptions of health and physical fitness held by two groups of respondents who have reason to be concerned with such matters from different perspectives of the doctor-patient relationship; one is a group of patients, the other, a group of medical students. The relationship of conceptions of health to other characteristics of the respondents is also explored.

METHOD

The group of patients consisted of 201 persons with one or more chronic illnesses as primary diagnoses, who attended the General Medical Out-Patient Clinic of The New York Hospital during a three-month period in 1958. The diagnoses represented are the three most prevalent among the clinic population: arteriosclerotic heart disease (57 patients), diabetes (46 patients), and psychoneurosis (47 patients). The remaining 51 patients had more than one of these primary diagnoses, and are referred to as pa-

---

[3] H. Ashley Weeks, Marjorie Davis, and Howard Freeman, "Apathy of Families Toward Medical Care," in E. Gartly Jaco (ed.), *Patients, Physicians and Illness* (Glencoe: The Free Press, 1958), pp. 159-165.

[4] W. Kenneth Lane, M.D., "The Role of the Pediatrician in the Physical Fitness of Youth," *Journal of the American Medical Association*, 169 (1959), 421-427. Also, "Fort Ritchie Conference on Youth Fitness," *Journal of the American Medical Association*, 169 (1959), 46-47—an editorial.

tients with "multiple diagnoses." The group of students consisted of 262 persons in the first three years of medical school at an eastern university.

The two groups were widely divergent in age, educational background, and socioeconomic status. Almost without exception, the medical students were in their early twenties, and had, of course, attended college. In contrast, although age and education in the patient group ranged widely (from fourteen to ninety years, and from no formal schooling to college degrees) the average age of the patients was 56, and the average educational level attained was eighth grade. Since a limitation on income is one criterion for eligibility as a clinic patient, all of the patients have incomes of $5200 or less. Unintelligible responses and failures to respond reduced the number of cases to 182 from the patient group and 252 from the student group.

The following question was posed to the two groups of respondents, in an interview in the case of the clinic patients, and in a self-administered questionnaire in the case of the medical students:

> We are trying to find out more about what people regard as "health," or as being "physically fit." What do you think most people mean when they say they are in very good physical condition?

The question was phrased in this manner in order to permit maximum freedom in replying. By asking what "most people" mean, it was hoped that replies would reflect the respondent's own conceptions, but would avoid the self-conscious, artificial answers that a direct request for a definition often elicits. Also, in the case of the medical students, the investigators wished to reduce the likelihood of receiving highly technical responses which the students would not be apt to make to laymen. In this respect, the question must be considered to have achieved its purpose, since there were no replies in terms of blood-pressure readings, red blood cell counts, or the like.

A content analysis of the responses was carried out[5] and recurrent themes emerged which appeared to reflect three general orientations to health, physical fitness, and good physical condition. The terms appeared to be perceived by the respondents as interchangeable, since in only one case did a respondent (a medical student) discriminate among them.

RESULTS

The first type of response refers to *a general feeling of well being*, and has been called a "feeling-state orientation." The second type identifies

[5] Bernard Berelson, *Content Analysis in Communications Research* (Glencoe: The Free Press, 1952).

health with *the absence of general or specific symptoms of illness*, and has
been called "symptom-orientation." The third type consists of responses
phrased in terms of *what a person who is in good physical condition should
be able to do*, and has been called "performance orientation."

Typical of the responses classified as expressing a feeling-state orientation received from both the medical students and the clinic patients are
the following:

> They mean they are alert, satisfied, energetic, and good-
> humored. (Medical student.)

> They just feel perfect—I can't explain it. Nothing bothers them.
> They're always in good spirits, never irritable or cranky, and have
> a good outlook on life. (Office worker with diabetes and arterio-
> sclerotic heart disease, hereafter designated by ASHD.)

Clinic patients whose responses were symptom-oriented often described
the symptoms of their own diseases, and indicated that a healthy or
physically fit person would be one who did *not* have these symptoms. Responses of symptom-oriented medical students typically lacked a personal
referent, and tended to describe a general symptom-free state, as comparison of the following typical responses will illustrate:

> She or he doesn't get dizzy spells, or pain in the arms like I do.
> Such people wouldn't get other things I've had—the pressure in
> my chest, for instance. (Housewife with ASHD.)

> Most people consider they are in good health when they are
> unaware of any disease process being present. I would define it as
> the absence of any predisposition to disease, no pain, fatigue, or
> loss of appetite; a total absence of somatic complaints. (Medical
> student.)

Among the performance-oriented, only, nine persons, all from the group
of medical students, emphasized physical fitness primarily in terms of
athletic prowess. In both groups of respondents, the great majority of
people who talked about what a physically fit person should be able to
do mentioned everyday activities connected with the discharging of usual
role obligations: shopping, working, social activities, and the like. In fact,
were it not for differences in vocabulary between the two groups, it would
be difficult to tell, on the basis of content alone, which responses came
from clinic patients and which from medical students. These are typical
replies:

> Most people mean they are able to carry on their normal life—
> business, social, and recreational obligations—without restriction.
> (Medical student.)

> Doing the subway and bus crowds without difficulty. Being able to put in a 40-hour week and still have enough strength for social life. (Salesman with psychoneurosis.)

> They're able to work, do household chores, shopping, washing and ironing, whatever would be expected of them. (Housewife with ASHD and diabetes.)

Of the nine responses which referred to the ability to perform in situations other than the normal routine of everyday life, the following is a typical example:

> They mean they are in the top fraction of their age group in physical strength and stamina. Such persons could play a brisk game of tennis without becoming exhausted or muscularly ruined the next day. (Medical student.)

The extremely small number of responses which mentioned ability to pass tests of physical agility or endurance, or even to engage in strenuous athletic recreation, suggests that physical fitness is not perceived in these terms, even among a majority of young men in their twenties. Since it is the more youthful segment of the population at which exhortations to achieve fitness *via* calisthenics are usually directed, it is possible that such campaigns may be ineffective if their immediate goals are not perceived as relevant to the fulfillment of social roles. On the other hand, it must be considered that were the same question posed to a group of marine recruits, for example, one would expect considerably more emphasis on these aspects.

While the foregoing illustrations have represented typical examples of each single orientation, such "single-minded" conceptions of health were actually in the minority. In the majority of cases, two or three orientations could be distinguished in the responses of a single individual.[6] For example, the first of the following responses is clearly both feeling-state and symptom-oriented, the second is symptom-oriented and performance-oriented, and the last partakes of all three orientations.

> When one feels they're operating on 16 cylinders instead of two. A condition that doesn't require any medical attention. No bad dreams, not being overly or unnaturally fatigued. To just have a "glow," an incandescence. (Writer with psychoneurosis.)

> Most people mean they can adequately carry on the physical activities dictated by their occupation and environment, and that they have no prominent signs or symptoms of physical illness. (Medical student.)

> They don't have heart trouble or kidney trouble. They just feel wonderful. Do anything they want to within reason—go out

---

6 Responses were coded by two coders with intercoder reliability of 92 per cent.

every day, be on the go, have lots of company. (Housewife with ASHD.)

As Table 1 indicates, for more than half of each group of respondents, health is not a unidimensional concept. Although the two groups mention varying numbers of orientations in similar proportions, they differ somewhat as to the particular orientations that predominate, as Table 2 shows.

Since, with the previously noted exception of nine medical students, similar conceptions of health appear in both groups, it is interesting to compare the frequency with which each orientation is found in each group. As sole orientation to health, feeling-state appears more often among patients than among students, although in each group it is the least found of the three conceptions. Of the one-dimensional responses, performance-oriented replies occur most frequently among the patients, while symptom-oriented replies are most prevalent among the medical students. The same tendencies may be seen in the two-dimensional responses; patients tend

TABLE 1. NUMBER OF ORIENTATIONS MENTIONED BY CLINIC PATIENTS AND MEDICAL STUDENTS

NUMBER OF ORIENTATIONS	PER CENT MENTIONING	
	CLINIC PATIENTS	MEDICAL STUDENTS
One	43	40
Two	45	49
Three	12	11
	100	100
Total number	(182)	(252)

TABLE 2. DISTRIBUTION OF RESPONSES OF CLINIC PATIENTS AND MEDICAL STUDENTS

TYPE OF RESPONSE	PER CENT MAKING RESPONSE	
	CLINIC PATIENTS	MEDICAL STUDENTS
(1) Feeling-state oriented only	10	4
(2) Symptom-oriented only	14	22
(3) Performance-oriented only	19	14
(4) Feeling-state and symptom	11	11
(5) Symptom and performance	15	30
(6) Feeling-state and performance	19	8
(7) Feeling-state, symptom, and performance	12	11
	100	100
Total number	(182)	(252)

TABLE 3. PREVALENCE OF EACH ORIENTATION AMONG CLINIC PATIENTS AND MEDICAL STUDENTS

| | PER CENT OF MENTIONS | | PER CENT OF RESPONDENTS MENTIONING | |
| | CLINIC PATIENTS N: 307* | MEDICAL STUDENTS N: 427* | CLINIC PATIENTS N: 182 | MEDICAL STUDENTS N: 252 |
TYPE OF RESPONSE				
Feeling-state oriented	31	20	53	34
Symptom-oriented	31	43	52	74
Performance-oriented	38	37	64	59
Total percentages†	100	100	169†	167†

* Total number of times mentioned.

† Totals are greater than 100 because some respondents have more than one orientation.

least often to use category 4, which does not include performance, while the least popular combination among medical students is category 6, where symptoms are absent.

Differences between the two groups in the relative emphasis they place on each orientation are more clearly indicated by combining the figures in Tables 1 and 2 to show how often each orientation is mentioned, whether alone or in combination with one or more of the others. This has been done in Table 3.

Given the obvious differences between the two groups of respondents in age, education, and socioeconomic status, the tendency of clinic patients to emphasize performance more than the medical students, while the latter tend more often to emphasize symptoms is consistent with the findings of other investigators. Di Cicco and Apple found among their respondents a "conviction that aches and pains and physical limitations are a part of old age, and a general skepticism that anything can be done about them."[7] That is, unless the symptoms experienced produced some disability, their presence tended to be tolerated as an inevitable concomitant of the aging process. Koos found that indifference to symptoms, which may be considered as the opposite of a symptom-orientation to health, increased as one descended the social scale. He also observes that, among other influences, "perception (of health) results from the communication given by formal education" and that "the fact that social class membership affects the degree of education a person gets means that those who are the least educated are also likely to be least conversant with current ideas of what constitutes good health."[8]

[7] Di Cicco and Apple, op. cit., p. 28.

[8] Koos, op. cit., p. 140.

It is, however, interesting to note that fully half of the patients include freedom from symptoms in their conception of good health, while 59 per cent of the medical students mention performance.

Since each clinic patient has at least one primary diagnosis of chronic illness (and there is no reason to suppose that many of them are symptom-free) it is to be expected that, as a group, they would be more symptom-oriented than a non-patient group of similar socioeconomic status. Nevertheless, since similar non-patient groups are not necessarily symptom-free[9] it is likely that the high proportion of clinic patients who mention symptoms do so not only because they have the illnesses they have, but because those illnesses have been diagnosed. Symptoms to which one has previously been indifferent may become a matter of concern once a diagnosis has been made and the individual has been defined as a patient. There is also reason to believe that many patients presented themselves for medical treatment precisely because their symptoms, previously tolerable, had finally resulted in some degree of disability.

If a symptom-orientation to health is more typical of persons with more education and upper socioeconomic status, as Koos' findings would indicate, then the prevalence of this orientation among medical students, who possess both of these characteristics, is readily understood. The large proportion of performance-oriented responses given by this group, however, suggests that this orientation is sufficiently widespread in our society to cover more than only persons of low socioeconomic status.

Just as it is likely that tendency to be symptom-oriented is enhanced in the patient group by virtue of the respondents being defined as patients, it is possible that the prevalence of symptom-oriented responses among medical students is enhanced by factors other than their relatively high socioeconomic status and general level of education. One such factor is the medical curriculum, which emphasizes identification of symptoms. Another is their relative youth, compared with the clinic patients. As a group, they are young enough not to expect to tolerate symptoms as part of the aging process at this time, and thus perhaps personal experience of symptoms is viewed by them with especial concern. In order to examine the effect of age, education, and socioeconomic status on conceptions of health, cross-tabulations were run within the clinic patient group.

Within the group of clinic patients, a symptom-oriented conception of health is found less frequently at successive age levels (Table 4). Among the youngest group of patients, its frequency is virtually the same as among the medical students. Age does not appear to have any consistent effect on the other two orientations.

---

[9] See Koos, *op. cit.*, and Di Cicco and Apple, *op. cit.*

TABLE 4. HEALTH ORIENTATIONS OF 182 PATIENTS OF DIFFERENT AGES

| | YEARS OF AGE: PERCENTAGES | | | | |
| | UNDER 40 | 40-49 | 50-59 | 60-69 | 70 AND OVER |
ORIENTATION	N : 21	N : 32	N : 48	N : 46	N : 35
Feeling state	71	41	56	57	43
Symptom	76	56	48	48	43
Performance	57	72	56	67	69
Total percentages*	204	169	160	172	155

* Greater than 100 because some respondents have more than one orientation.

Among both groups of respondents, people with more education include freedom from symptoms in their conceptions of health more often than less educated people do. It may therefore be concluded that education in general, not only medical education, increases the tendency to be symptom-oriented. Since there is no reason to believe that first, second, and third year students differ significantly in their social class affiliations, it would also appear that amount of education affects orientation to health within a social class.

Table 5 also shows that while the proportion of symptom-oriented responses increases with education, the proportion of feeling-state oriented responses decreases. This suggests that a symptom-orientation to health tends to replace a feeling-state orientation as more education is acquired.

Occupation, employment status, and clinic payment rate (which is based on reported income) were used as indicators of socioeconomic status. None of these discriminated among orientations to health in this group of patients. This is perhaps due to two limitations which, it is believed, tend

TABLE 5. HEALTH ORIENTATIONS EXPRESSED AT DIFFERENT EDUCATIONAL LEVELS

	PER CENT WITH EACH ORIENTATION				
	CLINIC PATIENTS		MEDICAL STUDENTS		
	8TH GRADE OR LESS	BEYOND 8TH GRADE	1ST YEAR	2ND YEAR	3RD YEAR
ORIENTATION	N: 97	N: 85	N: 87	N: 77	N: 88
Feeling state	58	46	45	29	27
Symptom	44	60	66	77	78
Performance	66	63	63	56	67
Total percentages*	168	169	174	162	172

* Totals are greater than 100 because some persons have more than one orientation.

to make this group socioeconomically relatively homogeneous despite occupational and economic differences. First, the range of income represented is very small, due to the eligibility requirements of the clinic. Second, a similar limitation applies to the range of occupations represented. Due to advanced age or to disability, many patients have either retired or adapted their occupations to conform to reduced physical capacities. It is most likely, however, that in a more heterogeneous population, differences between occupational groups (particularly between the more and the less physically demanding occupations) would be found to be associated with differences in orientations to health.

While some investigators have addressed themselves to the problem of social class influences on attitudes toward health and illness, others have been concerned with the influence of cultural values and ethnic group membership. Parsons has observed that "somatic health is, sociologically defined, the state of optimum capacity for the effective performance of valued tasks."[10] Because the American value system and social structure place particular emphasis on achievement, which is most obviously demonstrated by economic productivity, and this in turn involves fulfillment of role obligations, "it is in the first instance as an essential condition of valued achievement, that the health of the individual is itself valued."[11] Thus, what has here been called a performance-orientation to health would appear to be consistent with the American value system as described by Parsons. This may help to account for its prevalence among medical students.

Zborowski[12] has found that attitudes toward pain differ among patients of different ethnic background. Since pain is itself a symptom, this suggests that differences in attitudes toward pain might reflect differences in underlying orientations to health and illness. He observes that, for patients of Italian origin, the chief significance of pain lies in the undesirable feeling-state it incurs, while for Jewish patients, the significance of pain is perceived in terms of its ultimate relationship to future capacities for role performance. The "Old American" patient is described by Zborowski as experiencing some future-oriented anxiety in response to pain, but the emphasis is on the stoical behavior displayed by this type of patient. A rough comparison with these findings is made possible by dividing the clinic patients according to religious affiliation.

If one may compare Catholic patients with the Italian patients studied by Zborowski the response distribution in this group appears to be quite consistent with Zborowski's findings. Table 6 shows that Catholics, more

---

[10] Talcott Parsons, "Definitions of Health and Illness in the Light of American Values and Social Structure," in E. Gartly Jaco, *op. cit.*, pp. 165-187.

[11] *Ibid.*, p. 179.

[12] Mark Zborowski, "Cultural Components in Response to Pain," in Apple, *op. cit.*, pp. 118-133.

TABLE 6. HEALTH ORIENTATIONS OF PATIENTS OF DIFFERENT RELIGIONS:
PER CENT WITH EACH ORIENTATION

ORIENTATION	RELIGIOUS AFFILIATION		
	Catholic N : 93	Protestant N : 54	Jewish N : 35
Feeling-state	60	50	37
Symptom	52	54	49
Performance	56	70	77
Total percentages*	168	174	163

* Totals are greater than 100 because some patients have more than one orientation.

often than Protestants or Jews, hold a feeling-state orientation to health, and presumably this is reflected in their attitudes toward pain. Differences among religious groups in proportion of symptom-oriented responses are quite small.

Table 6 also shows that Jews and Protestants are considerably more performance-oriented than Catholics, a finding which appears to corroborate the observations of both investigators cited. The similarity of responses of these two groups of patients suggests that different behavior may be displayed by different kinds of patients who nevertheless hold the same underlying orientations.

Among the ways in which the individuals in this group differ from or resemble each other is the fact that they are different illnesses. It is, therefore, pertinent to ask whether these different diagnoses are associated with different emphases placed on one or another conception of health.

Table 7 shows that, while three of the diagnostic categories have ap-

TABLE 7. HEALTH ORIENTATIONS EXPRESSED BY PATIENTS WITH
DIFFERENT DIAGNOSES

ORIENTATION	PER CENT WITH EACH ORIENTATION BY DIAGNOSES			
	ASHD N : 47	DIABETES N : 45	PSYCHO-NEUROSIS N : 44	MULTIPLE DIAGNOSES N : 46
Feeling state	49	60	52	50
Symptom	40	62	59	46
Performance	64	51	70	72
Total percentages*	153	173	181	168

* Totals are greater than 100 because some respondents have more than one orientation.

proximately the same proportion of feeling-state oriented responses, diabetics appear to emphasize this conception of health more than other patients. Also, diabetics and psychoneurotics appear more symptom-oriented than ASHD patients or patients with multiple diagnoses. It must be noted, however, that diabetics and psychoneurotics, whose mean age is 48, are more than ten years younger, on the average, than patients in the two other diagnostic categories. Thus, while they appear to be more symptom-oriented than patients in the older groups, it is not unlikely that age differences are reflected in the distribution of symptom-oriented responses. Recalling the tendency of patients to respond in terms of personal experience, it is also likely that the slightly greater proportion of symptom-oriented responses offered by patients with multiple diagnoses, compared with ASHD patients reflects a greater variety of symptoms felt by the former group.

It will be noted that diabetics also give a considerably lower proportion of performance-oriented responses than other patients. Again, in terms of the personal experience of these patients, this may indicate that their illness is less disabling to them in activities of daily living than is the case with patients in the other diagnostic categories. Perhaps because they do not find their performance capacities hindered, they are less concerned with ability to perform than are other patients. The relatively nonrestrictive regimen for management of diabetes which is the practice in the General Medical Clinic tends to support this interpretation.

IMPLICATIONS

Although the findings reported here are based on small numbers of cases, nevertheless, they appear to have certain implications which warrant further study. First, the responses made by both groups clearly indicate that health is, for many people, a multidimensional concept. The relative emphasis an individual places on a particular dimension of health or physical fitness appears to be affected by various factors: age, education, social class, and religious affiliation, as well as by his current physical condition. Thus, perhaps the most interesting finding to emerge from these data is not that two groups of people, who differ as greatly in demographic characteristics as do the medical students and the clinic patients, emphasize different orientations to health and physical fitness, but rather that the same three orientations appear, albeit with different frequency, in each group. A tendency to conceive of health in terms of ability to perform social roles was characteristic not only of persons of low socioeconomic status, but was nearly as prevalent among medical students as among clinic patients. There is reason to believe that this orientation reflects the prevailing value system in our society. Formal education appears to be associated with a symptom-oriented conception of health, and lack of education with a feeling-state orientation. Because of the relationship between social class and education in our society, it is suggested that, if there is a particular orientation to health characteristic of persons of low socioeconomic status, it is not a performance-orientation, but a feeling-state orientation. It is also suggested, although further investigation would be required to confirm, that a symptom-oriented conception of health replaces the feeling-state orientation as more education is acquired.

It is not to be assumed that the three orientations identified among two such limited groups of respondents represent an exhaustive classification. Doubtless, other orientations could be distinguished among other groups. Nevertheless, the identification of these three is sufficient to call attention to the desirability of further exploration in this area. Apparent incongruities in attitudes toward medical care may be explained by identifying the conceptions of health underlying the attitudes. For persons interested in planning public health programs, or physical fitness campaigns, these findings suggest that it may be necessary to interpret the objectives of such programs differently to target groups with different characteristics, in order that the objectives be perceived as relevant to the concerns of the individuals involved. For the individual physician, an awareness of differences in conceptions of health can provide another tool for the management of his patient, enabling him to interpret a medical regimen in the focus most meaningful to the patient's frame of reference and, thus, providing an additional incentive to cooperation in achieving their common goal.

SUMMARY

Studies made by other investigators of attitudes toward health have suggested the possibility that differences in attitudes may reflect differences in conceptions of health which underlie the attitudes expressed. In the present study, conception of health, physical fitness and good physical condition, as expressed in responses to an open-end question, were analyzed for two groups of respondents: clinic patients with one or more chronic diseases, and students in the first three years of medical school. Three major orientations were identified: an orientation in terms of feeling-state, an orientation in terms of freedom from symptoms, and an orientation in terms of performance of activities of daily living. No general tendency was found to identify physical fitness with gymnastic proficiency. Cross-tabulation of responses with various attributes of the respondents suggests that orientation to health is related to age, education, and group membership, as well as to current physical condition. Further investigation is indicated, both in order to control effects of the variables used here, and to explore other conceptions which may be identified in other groups of respondents.

The Nurse From the Patient's Point of View

Daisy L. Tagliacozzo

🔖 In recent years a number of important changes have taken place in the organizational role of the professional nurse, most notable among which has been the trend toward forcing the nurse to become more of a bureaucrat and an administrator and less concerned with bedside care.[1] Despite this trend, evidence to be reported in this paper suggests that hospitalized patients persist in evaluating the "good" nurse in terms of those attributes that are associated with her traditional role. From the point of view of the patient, the nurse's purposes—the care and cure of the sick—are unchanged. Data from this research show quite clearly that hospitalized patients react with great sensitivity to the personality and the attitudes which they infer from the behavior of nurses.

The data of this report are culled from interviews with male and female hospitalized patients at one large urban hospital. The patients were all between the ages of 40 and 60 and were suffering from either cardiovascular or gastrointestinal diseases. All patients were Caucasion and had had previous hospital experience.[2]

DISCUSSION OF DATA OBTAINED

When patients were asked what they "ideally expected from a nurse," they mentioned specifically a "kind and friendly personality," a "cheerful (smiling) personality," "knowledge of the patient," "dedication," "spontaneous services" and a "fast response" to their calls for a nurse. Patients also emphasized that nurses "ideally" should give the sick "some encouragement," should have "patience and tolerance" for more difficult patients

This paper is based on an address made by the author to a Regional Conference of the Department of Hospital Nursing, National League for Nursing in St. Louis, Missouri, December 5, 1962.

and "enough time" for those patients whose illness demands more attention from a nurse.

When these expectations were combined into more general categories, it was found that 81 per cent of the respondents stressed the importance of personalized care; 81 per cent also emphasized personality attributes; and 45 per cent expected prompt and efficient services. Fewer patients (29 per cent) mentioned specifically that they expected knowledge and technical skills. For most of the patients interviewed, evidence of knowledge and skillful nursing care was inferred from their perception of appropriate sentiments and motivations.

The emphasis on the foregoing qualities remained essentially the same when patients were asked how they identified a good nurse and when they were asked to describe who should become a nurse. In answer to the last question, "dedication" and "interest in the patient" were mentioned most frequently as desirable attributes.

Ideal expectations represented more than idealized descriptions of nurses or nursing care; they were based on personal experience. Over half of the patients remembered vividly those nurses who responded to them with interest and kindness, and over half of them also recalled experiences that illustrated the absence of such desirable care. The same standards were applied to the evaluation of current hospitalization. Patients praised any evidence of personalized care, any sign of kindness, and promptness and efficiency. They criticized a slow response most frequently but also reacted negatively to any behavior that seemed to be lacking in friendliness or interest.

Many patients expressed their awareness of the changing responsibilities of the professional nurse. This was most often reflected in the intensely grateful reactions to nurses who met their expectations. From the point of view of these patients, good nursing care was accomplished only with difficulty, because nurses were obviously harassed and "burdened with a lot of paper work."

The expectations of patients are demonstrated in their efforts to find in the hospital environment evidence that denies their fears, confirms the presence of reliable practitioners, and encourages free expression with a minimum of risk in disturbing relationships with nurses and physicians.

It was apparent during the interviews that some patients were disturbed profoundly. Some of them cried when they were given an opportunity to talk about their concerns; others relieved their tensions in aggressive criticism of care and cure procedures. The often intense demand of these patients for "kind nurses," for "interest and some sympathy" appeared symptomatic of their impaired capacity to cope with a threatening experience alone. Many of these patients had been or still were severely ill.

However, the majority of patients in the sample were not severely ill at the time of the interview. Most of them did not give evidence of emotional disturbance or intense concern with the nature or consequence of their illness. By and large, they were satisfied with the care they received. Yet, while they were not "problem patients," their adjustment to hospitalization was disturbed occasionally. The strains that many of these patients seemed to experience periodically appeared to be the consequence of overstrenuous efforts to submit to the assumed expectations of nurses and physicians, to accommodate demands to the assumed problems of nurses, physicians, and other patients, and to express themselves in terms of what they considered proper behavior, with an eye to the consequences of improper demands.

Some of the impressions that these patients had of the modern hospital developed long before their hospitalization. They had learned about the high cost of hospitalization, the shortage of skilled nursing personnel, and widely publicized errors in care and cure procedures. Some of their friends had exposed them to stories about their more traumatic experiences during hospitalization. Thus, many of these patients came to the hospital with some doubts and apprehensions.

The more apprehensive patients found their preconceptions confirmed in many direct and indirect ways. Long waiting periods and casual comments by those who took care of them confirmed their suspicion of a shortage of skilled personnel. Over 90 per cent of the patients in the sample observed that nurses and physicians are overworked and rushed, causing patients to be reluctant to take up their time "for anything but the most urgent matters." The same observation also intensified the patient's gratitude and sense of obligation to hospital personnel who showed an interest in them.

Concern With Possible Mistakes

Patients' admiration for the overworked functionaries of the hospital did not eliminate widespread concern with possible medical or nursing errors. This fear of what was considered an inescapable risk was intensified in those patients who were sensitive about the relatively impersonal nature of care, the constant change of personnel and the infrequent presence of the head nurse. Some patients also reacted apprehensively to the abundance of less skilled personnel.

A concern with the possibility of mistakes was expressed in many ways during the interviews. It found expression in the recollection of significant episodes during past hospitalization, in discussions of the needs of patients, and in the intense preoccupation with apparent irregularities in care procedures. Thus, a patient was upset because, from his point of view, the specimen ordered by his doctor should have been picked up sooner; another patient was worried because the color of his medication had changed without apparent reason. One patient was upset because an aide had not washed her hands after manipulating a bedpan, and another was concerned because his medication was administered somewhat later than the time ordered by his physicians.

Patients were most outspoken when they discussed the needs of other patients. Here the demand for safety, i.e., for efficient and prompt care procedures, stood second in importance only to that for interest and attention. Without being specifically questioned, 45 per cent of the respondents stated that other patients needed to feel that they were protected from "negligence" and "confusion."

Fears and Dissatisfactions

Many patients admitted that they were reluctant to reveal to nurses or physicians their apprehensions or dissatisfactions. For example, some patients refused to discuss with anyone their fears of cancer or other serious illnesses. Others were not ready to express to nurses their desires for certain services; for instance, a back rub. One patient was upset because he had heard the word "tumor" when listening to a discussion between physicians, but he was unwilling to ask any questions. A female patient admitted to the interviewer that she was upset because she did not like the expression on her physician's face. Another was convinced that her condition must have deteriorated, because more than one physician came to examine her. Several patients were irritated by "the manners" of individual members of the nursing staff. None of these patients had attempted to seek support or clarification, or to express a negative reaction.

Sixty-eight per cent of the patients in the sample mentioned that they had refrained from expressing their desires, fears, or criticisms. When explaining this reluctance, the majority stressed the obligation of a patient over and above the privileges of a paying consumer and over and above the prerogatives of a sick person. The emphasis of these patients was on self-control, on a minimum of dependency, on being "cooperative," "undemanding" and "considerate." Patients were eager to cite instances confirming their adherence to these standards. When they were asked to describe themselves on an attributes scale they were guided by the desire to appear to others as "good" patients. They saw themselves as grateful, confident, trusting, cooperative, considerate and undemanding.

Patients were not only eager to present themselves as "good" patients, they also were convinced that nurses expected such behavior from them. Thus, when asked what nurses expected of patients, 66 per cent of the respondents felt that they were expected to cooperate, 38 per cent believed that nurses expected them to be moderate in their demands, 33 per cent felt that they were expected to show respect, and 26 per cent thought that they were expected to be considerate. In spontaneous discussions of their obligations, 52 per cent of these patients stressed the obligation to be cooperative, and 30 per cent spoke of the obligation to be considerate.

The willingness of patients to be "good" was motivated partly by gratitude and admiration for the "overworked and rushed" nurse and physician. It also was prompted by self-interest, because of the relationship between cooperation and recuperation. But these attitudes also expressed the insecurity that restrains the uninitiated lay person in his relationships to professional personnel.

Judging Quality of Service

Insecurity not only prevented many patients from assessing the quality of care and cure procedures, but also from determining which care procedures were, in their cases, really necessary rather than merely desirable. This judgment was important to most patients because they believed that legitimate claims derived from the degree of severity of their illness. In their view, being a paying client entitled them to no more than room and board; all other services depended on "how sick you really are." Patients who demanded more than their illness seemed to justify were criticized for being too demanding and inconsiderate. However, many patients were not quite sure what they could legitimately demand without going too far. The urgency and real necessity of their own demands also were thrown in doubt when they observed other, possibly sicker patients.

Dependency and Powerlessness

The "good patient" restraint was enhanced further by a realistic awareness on the patient's part of his dependency on hospital personnel and of his powerlessness in affecting the course of events during hospitalization. Adherence to the expectations of nurses was of particular importance to those patients who feared that any deviant behavior would be followed by negative sanctions. Some of these patients were convinced that good services were more readily available as long as they succeeded in making themselves acceptable to members of the nursing staff. Some patients presented such assumptions as matter-of-fact observations:

> I've been around a long time. I have learned that you can't go expressing yourself under any situation. You can't unless you hire someone who is going to listen to you and won't kick back. . . . It doesn't pay to make enemies anywhere. If they see their button light up, they could just keep you waiting. They could make the bed poorly.

Other patients observed more sympathetically that nurses were "only human" and "naturally would not like to look after you if you are demanding and complaining."

The assumed power of nurses to sanction the behavior of patients was resented by some patients. Such resentment was reflected typically in the refusal to talk to nurses because one would not want to "get all upset," because "talking to anyone around here is futile," or because the patient felt that he was "at their mercy." The following quotation is an illustration:

> I don't want to get into trouble with any of them. All they have to do is not answer your bell. I don't care how bad you are hurt. If you are crying or if you are in pain they still can refuse to answer your bell.

Fears of displeasing others were intense for patients who felt dependent on a fast response to their calls and who dreaded being alone during a sudden, unanticipated crisis. Some of these patients refused to make less urgent requests, in the hope that they could secure for themselves reliable services when the "real need" arises. They tried, as one patient expressed it, to "save that button" in the hope that any call for a nurse would be taken seriously.

Expectations for Personal Care

The attitudes and the reactions of patients which compel compliance with expected behavior, be they insecurity, gratitude, fear or strategy, also intensify the desire of patients to be approached by those who take care of them. The "good patient" is reluctant to seize initiative. His desire not to disturb the equilibrium of significant relationships results in the hope that he will obtain services without having to ask for them. Thus, patients expect that services be given "spontaneously," that the nurse "knows my case well," that she "takes a personal interest in me" and "asks me what I need:"

> I'd say what would make a good nurse is anticipating a patient's needs. Not waiting until they are needed but trying to anticipate it which you cannot do all the time. But there are certain things that one can, I imagine, anticipate.

The "nice" nurse with the "pleasant personality" also makes it easier for patients to seize initiative and to express their feelings and reactions without fear. She makes the task of being a "good" patient less difficult:

> You feel that services are rendered willingly, not grudgingly. You do not feel so much like a burden.

The conditions that have caused such profound changes in the functions of the professional nurse also contribute to an intensified demand for those approaches toward care which are increasingly more difficult to provide. Patients repeatedly deprecated the impersonal nature of hospital care. The smile meant more because of its rarity. Influenced by their culture's sharp distinction between physical and emotional needs, patients repeatedly emphasized that legitimate demands stem only from physical needs and that the hospitalized patient must "cope alone with his emotional problems." Other reactions, however, reflected the difficulties that some patients had in adhering to this principle and in accepting the consequences of purely physical care:

> They just treat you as a number in a place like this. Nothing personal left any more.

The relatively impersonal nature of care procedures also seemed to intensify the concern with mistakes and organizational confusion. This concern found expression not only in the expectation of a prompt response to the patient's call, but also in the desire for personalized care. From the point of view of many patients, mistakes are less likely to happen if nurses know their patients and if they take a personal interest in them. Many patients emphasized that their confidence increased when they could observe such attitudes. Often they appeared to be victims of first impressions, which can cause patients to relax or, conversely, to become anxious and distrusting for the rest of their stay in the hospital.

Effects of Delayed Responses to Patient's Call

A prompt response to a patient's call was considered to be, concretely, a most important and, symbolically, one of the most meaningful of the nurse's services. Patients described how a slow response intensifies physical discomfort and how it can trigger anger because the patient is made to feel helpless and dependent. Their exasperation over being kept waiting, for example, for the removal of a bedpan, found expression in spite of their attempts to take the reasonable attitude that nurses must be "busy with more important things."

In addition to these more obvious frustrations, a prompt response was also important because it communicated to many patients that the nurse was reliable, interested in them and willing to carry out even "unpleasant" tasks. A slow response, on the other hand, often became the starting point for diminished trust in the reliability of all care procedures; it kindled latent resentment; and it often constituted "proof" that the patient's demands were not taken seriously. Many patients admitted that they were not sick enough to suffer physically from the consequences of a slow response, but they also admitted that the implications were frightening:

You ask yourself: "What will happen to me if I am really sick, if I'm really in a serious condition?" You might be abandoned . . . I've seen it happen on different occasions to others.

CONCLUSION

Hospital functionaries can anticipate that most of their patients will make every effort to conform to the demands of institutional care. However, the data suggest that the "good" patient's efforts to tolerate stress may not always contribute to the therapeutic goals of patient care. The desire of patients to conform to what they perceive to be expected behavior tends to interfere with effective communication.[3] It is not easy to know a "good patient" unless he is encouraged to respond as a "sick person." Unless active steps are taken to change the patient's definition of the situation, nurses cannot take it for granted that the patient will reveal his needs or that he will seize initiative in obtaining the care which he desires or must have.

Some of the difficulties that these patients experience during hospitalization are not solely the consequences of modern modes of patient care. Patient care in large organizations may be impersonal. However, the distance between patients and those who take care of them is intensified also by attitudes that were shaped within a much broader social framework. Those who work with the hospitalized patient will also have to be sensitive to this "cultural bias."

The data suggests that the behavior of patients is, at least in part, a function of their preconceptions of and reactions to hospital reality and not solely a function of "emotional disturbances." As a result of their inability to control the professional expert, patients feel realistically dependent. They cannot easily judge the presence or the absence of efficiency, competence and reliability; and if they do they may continue to feel insecure in their judgment. They cannot observe clearly the procedures of care and cure; at best they can only absorb impressions. If they are dissatisfied, they have few means of control and they often find it difficult to place responsibility beyond doubt. If they refuse to cooperate, they threaten to harm themselves.

Their self-assertion as paying consumers is made difficult because of their moral commitment to other sick patients and to those who dedicate their life to an obviously difficult task. Thus, they try to tie their demands to the severity of their illness, an often barely understood condition. This vague means for legitimizing claims makes it more likely that patients may go too far, that they may ask for more than they are entitled to. In every social situation such violation tends to imply a risk. To those who feel that their health may depend on securing good care, efforts to avoid such deviations from acceptable behavior can appear as logical and necessary.

Generally, the easier it is to obtain from people conformity to expectations, the more such conforming behavior may come to be taken for granted. Thus nurses may feel that "good patients" have no problems. This is not true. The data suggests that the problems of "good patients" often are hidden behind a cloak of conformity. The "good patient" needs and deserves attention, even though he may not demand it. Hospital personnel must take the initiative in dealing with their patient's concern for safety in the hospital. They must consider physical arrangements, devise various ways of assuring the patient that his physician's orders will be carried out, guarantee that he can count on a prompt response during periods of crisis, and emphasize the concrete necessity of communicating their knowledge of and interest in him.

The belief that nurses are too overworked to give to the patient anything but that which is absolutely necessary may have to be corrected actively, and nurses may have to play a more active part in clarifying for the patient what he can demand without fearing the consequences. The attitudes of patients do not suggest that many would be prone to exploit such encouragement.

FOOTNOTES

1. Corwin, Ronald, "The Professional Employee: A Study of Conflict in Nursing Roles," *American Journal of Sociology,* 66, 3, 1962, pp. 103-112.
2. These data were collected as part of a research project which was conducted at Presbyterian-St. Luke's Hospital, Chicago, Illinois. The study was directed by Hans O. Mauksch, formerly Director of the Department of Patient Care Research, Presbyterian-St. Luke's Hospital. The project received financial support from the Commonwealth Fund.
3. Skipper, James K., Jr.; Tagliacozzo, Daisy; and Mauksch, Hans, "Some Possible Consequences of Limited Communication Between Patients and Hospital Functionaries," *Journal of Health and Human Behavior,* 5, 1964, pp. 34-39.

Section 4

The Structural and Cultural
Context of Patient Care

INTRODUCTION

⚡ A hospital is a type of social organization, established for the purpose of achieving explicit social functions. The functions of the hospital are carried out through its social structure, i.e., a network of role relationships in which the diverse activities of the organization are allocated and coordinated into a system. In the process of performing its functions the hospital develops its own culture, that is, its own system of shared values, beliefs and orientations. This common pattern sets standards of conduct for behavior within the organization and has its own unique effects on action not only for the staff, but also for patients. Therefore, in order to understand social interaction within the hospital, it is necessary to have at least a rudimentary knowledge of the hospital's structure, functions and culture. The selections included in this section are devoted to discussing some of these important features of the context of patient care.

The first three selections are concerned primarily with examining the structure and the functions of the general hospital—one by Wilson, "The Social Structure of a General Hospital," and two by Mauksch; "It Defies All Logic—But a Hospital Does Function," and "The Nurse: Coodinator of Patient Care." These articles point out that the primary function of the hospital, its *raison d'etre*, is the care and the cure of patients. It provides services for its clients, and its clients' welfare is presumed to be its chief concern. Hence, a hospital is a service organization. Nevertheless, even though the hospital is a social institution with a humanistic function, in order to maintain and perpetuate itself, its operations must be governed by business economics. Hospitals also have other secondary functions, foremost among which are teaching and research, and these sometimes conflict and divert the resources of the hospital from its primary function of patient care.

In addition to patient care, to teaching and to research, hospitals also provide the space, the technical equipment and a host of services that allow physicians to carry out a cure function (as distinct from care). In the strict sense, the attending physicians on the staff of the hospital are not full-fledged members of the organization. They are not employees of the hospital and are not paid by it. They are simply guests of the organization who are accorded the privilege of using the hospital facilities. Yet the hospital could not exist without their presence and therefore, medical services (as distinct from care services), are an integral part of the social structure of the hospital.

This unique relationship causes at least one major problem; conflict over control of the care function. Even though care is supposedly the responsibility of the hospital, the physician, a quasi-member of the organization, by virtue of his almost complete control of the cure function and his relative independence from the dictation of the hospital, manages to wield a great deal of control and direction over care policies. This causes difficulties for the nurse in managing the patient care unit. She faces the dilemma of two bosses and two lines of authority: the hospital administration and the physician.

The functions of the hospital are carried out through its social structure, i.e., its network of formal and informal role relationships. Its structure has many of the characteristics of bureaucratic organization. *First,* it has a clear division of labor. The many different types of activities of the hospital are distributed among the various members of the organization. Each position within the organization specializes in performing only a few of the many necessary tasks and is held responsible only for those that are fixed as its official duties. Thus, nurses nurse, cooks cook, and bookkeepers keep books. Nurses are responsible for the care of their patients, but they are not held responsible for cooking food or sending bills to patients. *Second,* the positions within the hospital structure are arranged in a hierarchy. This means that each position is under the direction, supervision and control of a higher position. Each individual holding a position in the hierarchy is held accountable to his superior for his own actions and decisions as well as those of his subordinates. In order to carry out his responsibilities, the holder of each position has the authority to make decisions, to supervise and to direct the work of his subordinates. The subordinates in turn have the duty to obey their superior. *Third,* all the activities of the hospital are guided by an explicit set of policies and regulations. This formal blueprint or plan of action attempts to stipulate, define and regulate the activities of all the members of the organization and the relationships among the members no matter what the circumstances. In other words, it attempts to set a course of action, a standard operating procedure for all possible events and situations. *Finally,* each member of the hospital organization is expected to conduct his work in a rational and efficient manner without interference from personal and emotional considerations. Thus, all hospital personnel while engaged in performing their official duties are expected to employ an attitude of impersonal detachment in their relations with other personnel, and also with patients. This impersonality is supposed to result in impartiality and efficiency in the hospital. For example, a nurse is not supposed to allow her feelings for a particular patient to influence the type of care that she gives this patient.

In many respects the combination of these four features of the social structure of the hospital (specialization; a hierarchy of authority; an explicit set of policies, rules and regulations; and an impersonal attitude in the conduct of work) result in a very efficient organization. However, the structure is not without defects. The very features that produce efficiency, in specific instances, also may create problems. For example, the effect on patients of hospital personnels' attitude of impersonality was discussed at length in several selections in Sections 2 and 3. Also, the hierarchy of authority often causes status problems among various positions in the hierarchy. Some of these problems which involve nurses are discussed in selections included in Section 5.

The fourth article in this section, "Too Many Nurses May be Worse Than Too Few," by New, Nite and Callahan, deals with problems concerning the division of labor and the rigid rules and regulations. New and his associates report on a study in which they varied staffing procedures on medical and surgical wards. Sometimes there was an excess of RN's on the ward and sometimes a shortage. One of their major findings was that when the wards were staffed with a large number of personnel, the staff nurses did not engage in activities that were not specifically specified in official rules and regulation as their duties. Even though extra time was available, the nurses did not do "aide type" of work, nor did they spend any more time with their patients. This is an example of how nurses may become so specialized, so set in their ways and so rigid in their adherence to regulations that they are unable to adapt their behavior to changing conditions.

The distinctive way of life around which behavior in the hospital is patterned may seem very strange and foreign to those who are unfamiliar with it. As Stanley King* has commented:

> The hospital is unique as a way of life, a subculture of a sort within the total society. The round of life, the customs, the relationships between people, the particular problems of everyday living are sufficiently different from those of other social organizations to warrant consideration as a unique subculture.

Through their training and experience, nurses, physicians and other hospital personnel are socialized into the culture of the hospital. They share this common orientation, but their patients do not. Personnel often forget that their values, beliefs, attitudes, ways of doing things, their very definition of the situation, may be very different from those of their patients. When this occurs, nurses and physicians are likely to become ethnocentric; that is to say, they fail to perceive cultural variation between themselves and their patients. Or perhaps even worse, they insist that their own cultural patterns and definitions are superior to those of their patients. This ethnocentric bias is a major barrier to communication between staff and patients. The article by Baziak and Dentan, "The Language of the Hospital and Its Effects on the Patient," pertains to this issue. The authors maintain that due to nurses' and physicians' cultural and linguistic preconditioning they tend to perceive only certain features of the patient's condition and fail to pay attention to his idiosyncratic problems. The following article, by Samora, Saunders and Larson, "Medical Vocabulary Knowledge Among Hospital Patients," is concerned with the cultural vocabulary of the hospital. These writers show that even some of the most common terms used in the medical and the nursing culture are incomprehensible to various classes of patients. When personnel use these terms in conversation with patients, effective communication is next to impossible.

Patients, too, if allowed to interact with each other over a period of time may develop a subculture of their own—a subculture that inci-

---

* King, Stanley, *Perceptions of Illness and Medical Practice,* New York: Russell Sage Foundation, p. 349.

dentally may or may not have a great deal in common with the hospital culture. Rose Coser in her article, "Some Social Functions of Laughter," discusses the meaning, the value and the function of humor and jocular talk in a patient subculture. She argues that the communication of humor among patients helps to relieve their tension, reassures and entertains them, and allows them to reinterpret some of their hospital experiences in a positive way.

In the final selection of this section, "The Schizophrenic No-Society," Sommer and Osmond take a broad view of the social organization of the hospital and describe how it has much in common with other large-scale organizations such as schools, nurseries and prisons. However, they imply that there are essential differences between general hospitals and mental hospitals. They discovered that schizophrenic mental patients, unlike the "normal" patients described in the Coser selection, were unable to establish a patient society or patient culture. One of the basic explanations for this situation is simply that the mentally ill patients do not have a commonly shared set of symbols and therefore are unable to communicate with each other. Once again we come upon the crucial importance of the process of communication.

The Social Structure of a General Hospital

ROBERT N. WILSON

Dr. Harvey Cushing, pioneer surgeon and philosopher of medicine, speaks in his *Consecratio Medici* of the "personality" of a hospital. He had observed that each institution seems distinguished by a style of its own, a tempo of work and an emotional atmosphere peculiar to a given hospital, its traditions, its community of staff and patients. When we turn from the

Reprinted with permission from the author and *The Annals of the American Academy of Political and Social Science*, Vol. 346, March 1963, pp. 67-76. The author is indebted to Stanley H. Udy, Jr., for thoughtful criticism of this article.

single hospital's unique organizational life toward a more general formulation, toward recurrent features of social structure, it is important to note that the flavor and tone of the individual institution are blunted. The personality which is thus left out, and must be, may be precisely the most significant element determining the shape and satisfactions of life for the persons involved as treaters or clients. But, because generalization is essential to the scientific enterprise, we shall focus on the typical environs of institutional personality; in this effort, the model of organization will be the large general hospital, urban and voluntarily supported, responsible for the three major hospital functions of care, teaching, and research.

We thus neglect many features unique to government institutions, small or rural hospitals, or the common run of hospitals which focus almost solely on patient care. The justification for selecting the major medical center as our model is that such organizations are most sharply exemplary of modern medical trends; further, although there is no more a "typical" hospital than there is a "typical" individual, most of the issues characteristic of metropolitan hospitals are largely shared by other varieties of organization.

Hospitals, like universities, often seem to place an inordinate emphasis on physical plant, on the bricks and glass which embody a viable social organization. Perhaps this is because buildings are a tangible symbol of stability and vigor for institutions which have no "product" in the usual sense; the human being who is educated or healed is not a thing but a process, and it is difficult to point to him as the concrete output of a work pattern. Perhaps, too, the vocations which minister to mind and body are reluctant or inarticulate when they come to speak of their central values. In any case, it is clear that, although architecture and human relations interpenetrate, the crucial features of an organization are manifest in social, rather than physical, structure. The social structure of a hospital consists of patterned relationships among people. It is the moving configuration of individuals joined together in the repeated performance of certain activities directed toward certain goals. For convenience and simplicity, it is probably best to think of social structure in terms of various clusters of role relationships, of those recurring nexuses of interpersonal action which center around some desired end. In the general hospital, the major role relationships are ordered to staff-staff and staff-patient activities. In contrast to the mental hospital, where lengthy sojourns generate a sense of community among patients, the relation of patient to patient is not often seen as a very important aspect of life in the general hospital.

As a social organization, the modern hospital is one of the most complicated enterprises in our civilization; partly by rational design, partly by the inheritance of historical accident, the hospital entails a multiplicity of goals, a riotous profusion of personnel, and an extremely fine-grained division of labor. Although it is intimately attached to its community setting—and the manifold relations between the institution and the surrounding society are one of the more inviting fields for social research—a general hospital is, to a considerable extent, a self-contained social universe. Because its work goes on around the clock and its life-sustaining goals demand a maximum of self-sufficiency, the hospital constitutes an internally diverse society within a society. This very complex and enveloping character of the institution is at once perhaps the first thing to know about it and a primary reason why it fascinates the social researcher. The sociologist, whether his interest is in social roles, professional organization, status and stratification, the administration of large institutions, or whatever, finds here a compelling scene for the study of behavior.

Historically, the hospital was more nearly a place of refuge than a place for medical treatment. A haven for the weary and ill on the routes of medieval crusades and pilgrimages, it has roots deep in religion and altruistic hospitality. Over the long centuries of medical ignorance, centuries in which the homeless and impoverished were many and were unsupported by schemes of social welfare, the hospital was the charitable last resort of the ill pauper. It was where one went to die, rather than to be cured; mortality rates among patients *and* staff were of a magnitude we would today think astronomical. Anybody who could afford to be cared for at home stayed there, for one's own house was a far safer place to be in the days before asepsis and sophisticated medical technique. The rise of scientific medicine in the late nineteenth and early twentieth centuries transformed the hospital from a sanctuary of simple food and warmth into a workshop of the physician and an accepted destination for the ill of diverse ailments and social standings. As recently as the 1920's, many hospitals were still construed as primarily charitable organizations for individuals who could not arrange proper treatment at home. Only in the last few decades, and especially with the burgeoning of hospitalization insurance, has the hospital come to be routinely used by the bulk of the population as the appropriate setting for surgical intervention or medical care.

The large general hospital is the prototype of the multipurpose organization; it is a hotel and a school, a laboratory and a stage for treatment. All these purposes, their attendant values and specialized personnel, must be somehow articulated into a going concern. Co-ordination of specialized activity into a whole that makes organizational sense is the huge and delicate task of the administrator, a task that is never completed to anyone's entire satisfaction. Underlying the disparate goals of patient care, teaching, and research is that first necessary aim of any institution: self-maintenance, or corporate survival, with its human and economic imperatives. If it is not quite all things to all men, the hospital is very many things to very many different kinds of people. Occupational specialization, the compounding of professional groups, the demands of patients, physicians, trustees, or whomever, all imply that the organization is likely to be marked by conflict and confusion. Yet there is a vital focusing element which serves to pull together individuals and techniques: the presence of the patient and his need. In a real sense, the patient is the implicit director of activity, his need for care setting the direction and pace of work. And the goal of treatment unifies separate parts of the hospital, centering them on the prepotent value of health. Indeed, patient care is a master value even for those whose work seldom brings them into direct contact with ill people. The administrator has, then, this ally, this overriding appeal to counter the extraordinary difficulties of medical organization.

In a curious fashion, the two most significant actors in the hospital plot —the patient and the physician—are "guests" of the organization. The patient, who has the distinction of being simultaneously the hospital's client and its product, is, hopefully, just passing through. His identity and his basic loyalties obviously lie elsewhere. The physician, with the exception of department heads, students, and the house staff of doctors-in-training, is also one who uses the organization without fundamentally belonging to it. His membership is nominal and his physical habitation transitory. Thus, these two chief figures are in the organization but not of it; without them there is no meaning in the medical process, yet with them comes a "disturbance" with which the institution must strenuously cope.

PATIENTS AND DOCTORS

The patient comes unbidden to a large organization which awes and irritates him, even as it also nurtures and cures. As he strips off his clothing, so he strips off, too, his favored costume of social roles, his favored style, his customary identity in the world. He becomes subject to a time schedule and a pattern of activity not of his own making. The patient's expectations are relatively vague; most of the initiative in social intercourse passes to the staff, which is exceedingly ready to exercise it in the service of expert knowledge and mundane convenience. Ill persons have to learn how to be patients, for being sick and performing adeptly in the role of hospital patient are not at all the same thing. Patients are passive creatures for the most part, and their passivity is linked to an understandable dependency which is inseparable from illness; pain and fear have a well-recognized tendency to reduce the mature human being toward the childlike. This very regression acts to afford the treater a necessary leverage on which he capitalizes in manipulating the patient. One of the most interesting current developments in nursing care, however, is an attempted partial reversal of the habit of staff initiative and patient receptivity; it involves a radical fixing of attention on patients' felt needs, together with an encouraging posture aimed at eliciting expression of those needs.[1]

Although the patient's expectations are vague in detail with respect to hospital procedures, he and his relatives faithfully anticipate miracles of medical care. Medical services must forever fall short of the proficiency which Americans, for a variety of reasons, increasingly tend to demand. The belief that all ailments can be diagnosed and rapidly repaired is a naive but understandable assumption rooted in the achieved excellence of scientific medicine and our traditional philosophy of environmental mastery. As patients, we cherish the notion that everything is known, or can be; we grow restive under delay in cure and unwilling to accept chronicity. The client nourishes the fallacy, intrinsic to our cultural propensity for problem-solving and for dominating the natural world, of believing "that all good things can be deliberately achieved." His impatience is exacerbated by the overwhelming importance we attach to health; physical well-being, tied to the cult of youth and the virtue of efficiency, is something of a secular religion. From the size of legislative appropriations to the medical content of the mass media, there is a good deal of evidence that health and medical research are among the few things everyone can be for, and no one against, in our national life.

An increased demandingness on the part of patients may also be stimulated by the heightened medical sophistication which now characterizes some sectors of the public and by the insured patient's feeling that, as a paying client, he is fully entitled to maximum service.

There has been surprisingly little social psychological research which holds patient care as such, or the patient's role in the hospital organization, as its central object. This neglect has been partly a matter of availability; patients in the general hospital do not usually stay very long, and their treatment clearly has priority over their subjection to the inquiring sociologist—to say nothing of the fact that they may be extremely ill. Another probable reason why the patient is the forgotten man of hospital research is that the social scientist does not ordinarily feel equipped to gauge either the quality of care or the patient's medical status. Treatment is, furthermore, at the core of the doctor's technical preserve and at the core of the hospital administrator's managerial competence. It may often be neither penetrable nor safe territory for the innocent researcher. A few current studies do focus on the patient's hospital experience—as mental hospital research has

[1] Ida J. Orlando, *The Dynamic Nurse-Patient Relationship: Function, Process and Principles* (New York: G. P. Putnam's Sons, 1961).

nearly always done—and their results promise great value to the student of the hospital as a social institution.[2]

If the patient has been *terra incognita*, the other "guest" of the hospital —the physician—has been almost too well known for the comfort of some hospital administrators. The medical staff is essentially an intrusion, albeit a profoundly necessary one, into the organized structure of authority and assigned tasks. A hospital without decisive *medical* excellence has been described as "just a hotel for sick people"; yet the administrator must run a hotel, among many other things, and doctors are traditionally the mavericks who make his life uneasy. The basic problem is the existence of two broad sets of activities, the general administrative and the technical medical, which are manned in overlapping fashion and which generate something close to two lines of authority. Moreover, although the administrator obviously heads one line, the other is captained in fragments by a changing guard of physicians who happen to be involved in a given case. Doctors are fiercely independent professionals who control expert knowledge; administrators are nascent professionals who are, in Chester Barnard's phrase, "specialists in generalities" but have not the cachet in the medical world that executives in other organizations possess.[3] Since physicians are only minimally subject to the hospital administrator's direction, it is apparent that, to some extent, the social structure of a hospital is inherently divisive. Clashes between administrative and medical desiderata are among the most disruptive of hospital conflicts; like other conflicts we shall rehearse, notably in the area of interprofessional competition, they are truly structural and thus only very partially dependent on the personal idiosyncrasies of specific doctors or administrators.[4]

THE FORMAL STRUCTURE

At the top of the hospital's social blueprint stand three dominant forces: the administrator, the trustees or board of managers, the medical staff. Well below them in formal power, but in effect the day-to-day decision-makers who fix the hospital's image, is the nursing staff. The nurse is, of course, traditionally subordinate to the physician, and she is a paid employee amenable to routine administrative strictures, yet she wields immense in-

---

[2] For instance, there is a study in progress at Grace-New Haven Hospital, New Haven, Connecticut, under the direction of Raymond Duff, M.D., and August B. Hollingshead which attempts to explore the meaning of the hospital stay to different types of patients.

[3] Harold L. Wilensky, "The Dynamics of Professionalism: The Case of Hospital Administration," *Hospital Administration*, Vol. 7, No. 2 (Spring 1962), pp. 6-24.

[4] Harvey Smith, "Two Lines of Authority Are One Too Many," *Modern Hospital*, Vol. 85 (1955), pp. 48-52.

fluence because of sheer weight of numbers and closeness to the central job of healing. It is fair to assume that the picture of a hospital held by its clients and its surrounding community is pre-eminently based on nurses' behavior; they are the persons the patient sees, the persons who express the guiding spirit of the institution in the minutiae of action. Paralleling the nurse there is a variety of professional groupings, including such specialties as social work, dietetics, pharmacology, and other vocations. These groupings possess very narrowly circumscribed authority, and they stand in a no man's land of prestige and control vis-à-vis the nurse. The "strictly administrative" staff, again such as fiscal and clerical personnel of various grades and functions, is more or less parallel to nursing, depending on just who is involved in what context of decision. With the exception of the lowest categories of hospital worker, orderlies and aides, the general principle is that prestige hinges on the extent to which an individual's work entails direct patient care; in contrast to most other types of large organization, the hospital ranks a certain kind of manual labor—the "production" job on the "assembly line"—above almost all sorts of whitecollar jobs. The surgeon, for instance, is at the peak of the prestige hierarchy, and he works with his hands.

There is no way to summarize the social structure of a general hospital in concise form; there are simply too many relationships, and the universe of action is too diffuse.[5] Two master themes, however, may help one comprehend the major contingencies of interpersonal behavior. These are, first, the diffusion of authority, and, second, the excruciating struggle for occupational prestige. Returning to the troika at the top, there is no doubt that ultimate legal authority and responsibility are vested in the trustees. But, like most trustees, these august individuals cannot exercise daily detailed supervision; they occasionally attempt to do so, capriciously, but then the administrator's essential minimum of operating autonomy is perilously undercut. The hospital administrator, the creature of his board, has directive control of the formal organization. However, because administration is a relatively new specialty in hospitals, having been conventionally performed by former doctors, nurses, or business managers, it does not have the prestige or professional stature of medicine. Indeed, one of the critical changes in the modern hospital is just the move toward professional administration, replete with master's degrees and graduate courses, and the upgrading of the administrator. The third arm of top command, the medical staff, represents the hospital's largest concentration of prestige and expert skill. It exercises absolute *medical* authority but is only tangentially in-

---

[5] A very general, primarily descriptive account is essayed in Temple Burling, Edith M. Lentz, and Robert N. Wilson, *The Give and Take in Hospitals* (New York: G. P. Putnam's Sons, 1956).

volved in administration of the total organization. Again and again, however, the medical and the "strictly administrative" interpenetrate and overlap. A typical instance might be a decision on recruitment and compensation of nursing staff, which is a clear prerogative of the administrator but obviously has potent implications for the pattern of patient care and for the close working relationship between doctor and nurse.

If authority is diffuse because of the nature of medical work and the history of hospital organization, it is also complicated by the peculiar urgency of patient need. When the patient's condition dictates action, there is no time to resolve a jurisdictional dispute or to refer the matter to higher authority. Necessary things must be done, although, in doing them, the nurse or other staff person may be confusedly vulnerable to what Jules Henry has called "multiple subordination," taking orders, sometimes opposing ones, from a plethora of sources.

The uncertain distribution of higher authority is matched as one goes down the formal hierarchy. Such pairings as nurse-dietitian or nurse-social worker are often engaged in situations of unclear power, in which resolutions can only be hammered out on an *ad hoc* basis. Granted that it is sometimes hard to tell by formal criteria who should exert what leverage in a given case, the plain fact is that the hospital's functions do get performed, for the most part with admirable dispatch. This is so because what would be a nightmare to the theorist of formal bureaucratic organization is transformed by several factors into a viable scheme of work. One of these factors is the informal organization, the network of relationships that develops over time in any human enterprise. Any hospital is characterized by innumerable groupings that spring up in the natural course of events, that cross the barriers of specialization and status in order to get jobs done and to meet the social needs of the staff. These informal ties are far from being diversions or obstacles in the pursuit of organizational goals; although they may be conceptually untidy, they are the flesh and blood of an institution as the formal blueprint is the skeleton. Another element promoting cohesion is, of course, patient need and the humane response to it. Few people in a hospital have to be convinced that their work is significant; the ill person is a magnet drawing forth unusual resources of energy and devotion and helping personnel transcend disparities of aim.

A struggle for a place in the hospital sun is unremittingly waged by most of the myriad occupational groups, especially those most closely tied to therapeutic tasks. Precisely because systems of authority are unclear, there is often a premium on flexible, not to say opportunistic, behavior. The hospital is the scene of very rapid change in the techniques of medicine and slower but still substantial change in the patterns of social organization. Because the model of occupational prestige and autonomy is the physician, other personnel strive to become similarly professionalized, with concomitant independence, corpus of technical knowledge, standards of competence, and pride in craft. Each yearns for a sphere of effort in which he and he alone can be a proficient actor. The professionalization of work has many implications, from the deleterious consequences of departmental infighting to the beneficent results of enhanced competence. Unfortunately, the patient is often the battleground of professional competition; his body, mind, and purse are scarred by the zealous attempts to do for him what each staff member's specialty dictates. The hospital, too, is a battleground, often ripped by a cross fire of professional purposes. Yet there is an increasing emphasis on the patient as a whole being, and the specialty groups are engaged in serious exploration of ways to co-ordinate their work. Further, if professionalization insures that the hospital work flow cannot be quiet or routine, it also insures the existence of a reservoir of initiative and responsibility. Professional élan, the morale-enhancing properties of "the religion of competence," lends stability and direction to a system which might otherwise resemble organized chaos.

At heart, the hospital is more like a federal system than a monolithic entity; its organization takes the form of a federation of departments, each department enjoying considerable autonomy and discretion in its management of work. The great challenge is, then, one of co-ordination, of somehow knitting these special excellences into a comprehensive framework of care. We have seen that the patient, by his very presence, is a co-ordinating force. But the needs of the ill are not enough and are today progressively supplemented by the shaping patterns of rational bureaucracy.

With its history of altruistic and undifferentiated caretaking, and under the dominion of a free-wheeling medical corps, the hospital grew in haphazard fashion. It is probably the last major institutional complex in the modern West to accede to the bureaucratic patterning of work which has long characterized government, big industry, and other large organizations. There are two persistent reasons why the hospital can perhaps never approach the degree of formal controllability, of symmetrical power and task arrangements, which distinguishes industry and government. One is the nature of the work flow, the temporal and ethical constraints imposed by intractable human material: the patient. The other is the nature of the medical profession, which resists bureaucratization and is the unchanging repository of certain fundamental decisions about the care of the ill. Despite these strictures, however, the hospital is now exhibiting many more of the faces of bureaucracy. Specifically, it is becoming rationalized and specialized to an unprecedented extent. Rationality is expressed in such features of the modern hospital as cost accounting and written personnel policies, quality control, and job descriptions; a loose benevolence is yielding to calculated, planful organization of services. Specialization, already acute in medicine itself, is now seen in administrative as well as technical guises. Task assignments and spheres of discretion are increasingly narrowed and legitimized in formal rather than accidental ways. Most hospital jobs are increasingly constricted as the assumed prerogatives of general helping roles are replaced by the deliberate mandates of announced organizational functions.

SOME ENDURING ISSUES

One key problem for the future of hospital organization is the juxtaposition of this rising tide of bureaucracy and the free professional. The physician's case is the most obvious, but many elements are common to the other hospital groups. Certainly, the doctor is bound to reshape his role in a manner more congruent with bureaucratic organization than had been true in the past; from a wise healer who often possessed charismatic qualities and enjoyed a very generalized respect, he is becoming more nearly a technical specialist who works as part of a close-knit medical team.[6] As team member, the physician sacrifices at least a certain portion of the autonomy of action and the unique prestige which have been traditionally attendant on his role. George Rosen has commented perceptively on the change:[7]

> Sociologically viewed and interpreted, the behavior of organized medicine represents the reaction of a segment of the older middle class to the process by which it is being shifted and adjusted to the modern urbanized, industrialized society characterized by a high degree of social complexity, integration, division of labor and bureaucratization. To use an analogy, one may say that the Industrial Revolution has finally caught up with medicine, and that the medical practitioner is being brought into the "factory" (the hospital and the whole bureaucratic complexity of the provision of medical care) where he is being subjected to the necessary "labor disciplines."

If "labor disciplines" are applied to the professional, the critical question becomes one of limits: how far may the professional be bureaucratized and yet retain the distinguishing talents and bear the distinguishing responsibilities of a true professional?

Akin to this issue is the conundrum of the power balance between expert and lay authority, what Sir Alfred Zimmern termed "the right relation between knowledge and power." The hospital trustees and the administrator are, in some sense, lay figures coping with a manifold of expert specialists;

---

[6] Robert N. Wilson, "The Physician's Changing Hospital Role," *Human Organization*, Vol. 18, No. 4 (1959).

[7] George Rosen, "Notes on Some Aspects of the Sociology of Medicine with Particular Reference to Prepaid Group Practice" (Unpublished manuscript), pp. 4-5.

they must take many things on faith, must render unto experts the matters that are technical, yet, at the same time, exercise the vigilance of informed citizenship. An administrator vis-à-vis doctors, nurses, social workers, and a range of technicians recapitulates the alignment of, say, the American legislator confronting Pentagon officialdom. Hospital social structure, marked as it is by a peculiar urgency of task and a highly refined division of labor, is a vivid illustration of those power accommodations which are insistently demanded by our thoroughly expert but rootedly populist society.

Many students of hospital organization have remarked on both the complexity of the internal hierarchy of task and prestige and the extent to which the heirarchy is frozen to seal off individual movement within the structure. Again, largely due to the intense specialization of medical craft, hospital jobs do not admit of very much interchangeability of personnel and do not foster many paths for smooth progression along a skill hierarchy. Thus, the hospital is a classic illustration of "blocked mobility." With the exception of a few opportunities for movement within a job category (usually at lower levels of responsibility, such as the shift from one classification of aid to another) medical advancement depends upon technical training which can only be secured through formal schooling in a setting outside the organization itself. Although varieties of in-service training schemes exist, individuals can seldom make a change of real magnitude through on-the-job education or superior performance in some parochial task: no nurse works up to surgeon; no orderly cultivates his talents in hope of becoming a hospital administrator. The relatively frozen contours of organization then create a severe problem of morale and motivation. Once more the hospital may perhaps be seen as a specific instance of a more general dilemma in the social organization of work: the provision of job satisfactions for people below the professional or managerial level. A much-simplified but germane conception of American social stratification might indeed lead one to think of the hospital as an example of our division into "two nations": the college-trained professional or executive, and all others.

It is difficult to prophesy the future of hospital social structure in clear-cut terms. Such pervasive innovations as the automation of work are not susceptible of easy analysis. Surely the automated hospital will, to some extent, lighten the problem of blocked mobility for lower-level personnel, because fewer strictly routine chores will need doing and there will, thus, be fewer employees with extremely shallow job horizons. On the other hand, automation may exacerbate the already serious problems of staff-patient relationships. The warmth and intimacy of "tender loving care," a closeness which many believe to be already greatly attenuated by professional specialization, will presumably be still less readily apparent under automation.

Other issues are equally obscure. For example, the renewed emphasis on home care of the ill, together with the unsuitability of the general hospital for sustained treatment of those chronic diseases which are an increasing part of the load of American illness, might dispose one to think that hospital use might decline—proportionately, not absolutely, of course—over the next generation. Yet there are vast sectors of the population relatively newly covered by hospitalization insurance and newly attuned to the habit of recourse to the hospital, so that hospital use seems destined to rise sharply in these sectors.

Another cloudy area is that of hospital-community relationships. Wilensky[8] predicts that these relationships will be increasingly important and that they may well become a primary sphere for the activities of the hospital administrator. Can communities be educated to more appropriate use of the hospital, especially of out-patient facilities? Will increased federal financing of hospital construction, medical research, and so on mean a decreased feeling of community identity with "its" voluntary institution? How may political debate about the role of government in medical care affect the organization and economics of the general hospital?

It seems apparent that the social structure of the general hospital is not a single inherent pattern, an unchanging pyramid of organization. Patients, staff, and the techniques of medical care are in flux. Although human relations in the hospital are subject to certain imperatives of decision-making and patterned skill, notably in surgical operations,[9] there is room for considerable maneuver and for entertaining alternative structures. The pace of change in hospital organization is far less accelerated than in medical technology itself, but there are indications that an attitude of social experiment may begin to parallel the propensity to scientific experiment. Research into social structure is undoubtedly as important to the future of medical care as is research into cell structure. Patient care is, after all, the crux, the point of application for the virtuosities of medical science.

---

[8] Harold L. Wilensky, *op. cit.*

[9] Robert N. Wilson, "Teamwork in the Operating Room," *Human Organization*, Vol. 12, No. 4 (1954).

It Defies All Logic —
But a Hospital Does Function

Hans O. Mauksch

When a car breaks down, the owner will take the car to a garage to have it repaired. A garage is organized for that purpose. The people who repair these cars, the mechanics, the order-takers, the helpers, are employees of the institution, and what they do and how they do it is part of the over-all responsibility of the garage and its administrative organization. While the car is there it will be placed in a berth where it will stand and where it will be protected from damage. When the car is fixed, the owner will call for it, and he will pay one bill which includes the cost of the repair and any other costs incidental to the storage or any other care which the car received while in the garage.

It may seem sacrilegious to compare the human being with a car, yet to the sociologist the comparisons of widely diverse, ordinary phenomena are sometimes the most effective way of gaining an understanding of his object of study. For this reason, attention is invited to the similarities and dissimilarities between these two institutions of therapy, a garage and a hospital.

The most obvious and possibly the most consequential difference between a garage and a hospital lies in the fact that the garage is organized, recognized and run as a business, while the hospital, even though the administrator is obligated to apply business economics to its administration, is conceived as an institution meeting a nonrational, humanitarian purpose, and it is so viewed by the public, by its clients, and by the people who shape its policies—the board of trustees. The manager of the garage is not likely to be visited by the wives of the garage owners with the offer of hanging expensive curtains in the paint shop "to make it look more cheerful." The manager is also not likely to be expected to buy a machine that may be needed once a year to fix a rare condition among cars.

WHAT HAPPENS WHEN THE "MASTER MECHANIC" BECOMES A PARTNER

In a hospital, however, the administrator has to cope with both of these eventualities. The charitable nature of the purpose for which the hospital was conceived justifies and supports the well meaning and genuine contributions of various groups and individuals without regard to the economic or administrative suitability of the project. An instrument, no matter how expensive, is expected to be purchased by the hospital even if used very rarely, as long as it is essential to preserve a human life. At the same time, however, the administrator must run this institution in a businesslike fashion.

Let us return to our garage. The garage we have described is but one of two basic types. This one has avowed as its purpose to fix sick cars. Should the car owner merely want his car to be stored and cared for, he will take it to the other type of garage which will not undertake any processes of car therapy but rather will confine its function to such maintenance tasks as washing, change of oil and grease, and the like.

The hospital faces the peculiar fact that the human being cannot be cured without constant concern for the care of the needs of the life processes. A car whose broken axle has been expertly fixed may be returned without having been cleaned or greased. The human being demands not only repair but continuous physical care and attention to the complex processes of his emotional needs.

This has far-reaching implications for the organization of the hospital. It suggests that the function of the hospital cannot be viewed merely as a cure of a patient's disease but also of the care of the patient himself. In order to appreciate the complexities of this organization, let us imagine that in our garage the mechanic undergoes a process of occupational mobility and organizes into a professional society. Let him become a private entrepreneur whom the car owner contacts and who in turn has a contract with the garage which will service the special skills so that he can fix the car. Not only has this imaginary change altered the position of our new master mechanic but it has profound influences on the organization and function of the garage itself. While in the present garage the cure process is in every sense a responsibility of the total organization, the responsibility for the repair of the car has now become vested in the individual knowledge, skill and judgment of the master mechanic.

While the mechanic in the garage, as we know it, is an employee within his institution, the position of the newly created master mechanic is extremely complex and different. He has, for one, a client relationship with the garage. The institution provides facilities, equipment and assistants to the master mechanic and also assumes responsibility for managing and coordinating the various problems of administration involved in curing cars. In this relationship, the master mechanic now is a fully equal partner of the garage owner as policy maker and of the garage manager as administrator.

PATIENT COMES TO BE CURED, NOT MERELY TO BE LOOKED AFTER

However, unlike many other client relationships, the institution here does not perform the service itself but merely provides the organization for it. Thus, our master mechanic leaves the policy making level, dons his overalls, and joins the lower echelon of the institution on the front lines in performing the tasks on the car himself. Our master mechanic can, therefore, not only be either client or functionary, but he is also either policy maker or worker.

One more point. The effect of this separation between the organization for "care" and the specialization of "cure" can also be observed in looking at the other members of the garage hierarchy. In most garages the cars which arrive are first seen by the order writer. He is that amazing man who can lift the hood of the car, merely sniff inside and tell the owner what is wrong with the car. Besides this diagnostic function, he also distributes the cars to their berth and to the proper mechanic. The emergence of the master mechanic leaves this person the function of space assignment but prevents him from practicing diagnosis since all aspects of cure are now the prerogative of the master mechanic.

The assistant mechanic is the person who performs under the mechanic's direction. The mechanic in the present-day garage is superordinate to this assistant both in the performance of car therapy as well as in the implementation of the policies of the institution. Should we deal with the master mechanic as an individual practitioner, the assistant mechanic is placed now at the junction of two lines of authority. He is there to perform those tasks of car cure which are directed by the master mechanic. However, at the front lines of the garage this assistant mechanic becomes now the one who is the garage employee and as such the guardian of garage policies.

The administrative channels of the assistant mechanic diverge from the therapeutic line of authority, and it may not be difficult to imagine that they sometimes clash.

This separation of lines of authority is taken for granted in the organization of medical care. It may have some historical explanation. The *hospés*, the antecedent of the modern hospital, was an institution that originated around the concept of care without essentially or necessarily involving cure. Today the textbook of hospital administration or nursing still claims as the prime function of the hospital the care of the patient. The institution as such does not claim responsibility for cure but leaves that up to the physician.

While modern thinking in psychosomatic and sociosomatic medicine would tend to break down the distinction between care and cure, the separation is still an administrative and organizational reality.

The patient, in general, comes to the hospital to be cured, not merely to be looked after. He has contacted a physician or has gone directly to the hospital to have a disease condition repaired. However, though modern-time patients may directly approach the hospital without first making contact or contract with a physician, the medical cure as such is perceived to be the prerogative, the duty, and the responsibility of the physician.

EMERGING SPECIALISTS DEVELOP NEW SYSTEM OF LOYALTIES

While we have moved our garage mechanic into the category of an independent, practicing professional, other things have happened, too. The over-all care of the car has become much more complex. The garages have become larger, and in that process, the inevitable specialization of the modern age has caused the emergence of specialists in the technic of hub cap removal, and technicians exclusively concerned with front wheel alignment.

Where once the hospital consisted of the doctor, the nurse, and the maid, the tasks of implementing the physicians' directives have become the premise of an increasing number of specialists. The original scope of the nurses' tasks has been carved up to make room for the dietitian, the laboratory technician, the oxygen therapist, the physical therapist, and many more.

Some consequences of this specialization process are obvious. The emerging specialist will organize into occupational societies, they will develop a definition of their own functions, standards and status aspirations, and, as such, will develop a system of loyalties and obligations not only to the common institution—the garage—but also to their own occupational group.

The emergence of the Society for the Maintenance of Front Wheel Alignment, the National Association of Carburetor Disassemblers and the American Society of Hub Cap Removers will have as its consequence that the continuous task of caring for the car will be performed by discontinuous groups with their own aspirations, systems of communication, definitions of work scope, and caste-like segregation from each other.

The implications of this development are not always fully faced. On the one hand the emergence of these specializations will force our large and complex garage to become organized in departments of quasi-independent groups. Our present garage manager with his single line of authority and cohesiveness of organization will become, in effect, the coordinator between department heads essentially without a front line organization of his own except in the business office. As expert in foreign relations, he becomes the mediator between the divergent interests represented by the departmental hierarchies.

Who, at this point of confusion, maintains order and continuity at the side of the car which, after all, still needs to be repaired? Let us recapitulate what has happened. The cure function itself, the determination of therapy, has become the sole prerogative of our master mechanic. Out of the vast range of tasks directed by the mechanic and originally performed by the assistant mechanic, specialized skills have been removed and organized into the aforementioned new occupations. It is in the nature of this kind of specialization that the skilled hub cap remover will move from berth to berth to practice his skills. His responsibility is the episode involving his task. The assistant mechanic, thus deprived of certain substantive skills, emerges necessarily and inevitably with a new scope of tasks. It can be said as a statement of principle that whenever there develops a multiplicity of specialists involving responsibility for episodal tasks, the role and function of the coordinator must emerge in response to the need for continuity.

Our assistant mechanic in this complex organization becomes now the one who represents the juncture of the processes of care and cure: He assumes the dissemination and coordination of those directives of therapy which are issued by the master mechanic but performed by someone other than the assistant mechanic. This assistant mechanic of necessity will be the one held responsible for the interlocking continuity of episodal specialists. Implied in the foregoing, but deserving special emphasis, is the fact that in the departmentalization of the garage and in the removal of the master mechanic from the internal structure of the garage, the assistant mechanic becomes in effect the administrative arm and representative of the garage management at the front lines of the institution.

To these changes in the nature of the garage, we need to add one more touch of magic to accomplish fully its convergence into the hospital. No matter how complex our car, it remains an inanimate work product incapable of actively interfering in the work processes of the institution. The car owner is likely to appear only when the car is ready for release.

The human being as the patient represents an interesting combination of the role of client and work product itself. The fact that the patient is human would influence the behavior and relationships of all institutional functionaries even if this patient were never to open his mouth to utter a demand.

WE NEED A NEW MEANING FOR THE CONCEPT OF THE "MEDICAL TEAM"

In this discussion, we will not delve into the fascinating and important depth of the interaction between patient and institution except for stressing that the human patient besides being the work product and client becomes also, by virtue of being human, a source of demands, of pressures, and an element in the communication processes of the institution. We will, however, briefly try to determine how a hospital functions.

We have concentrated on an analogy to bring into sharp relief certain features which may have remained blurred if direct analysis had been offered. The unique position of the physician has been outlined as one of unique power, responsibility and the right to be any place in the hospital. The administrator was described as an interdepartmental mediator with limited access to the front lines and inadequate power. The head nurse emerged via the assistant mechanic as the cordinator of the front lines, as the one who takes up the job which organizational inadequacy keeps the administrator from doing. In the triangle of patient, physician and hospital, the nurse may have to represent any of these three *vis-à-vis* the other two. This is how the hospital functions.

According to the law of physics the bumblebee cannot possibly fly; yet not having studied physics, she goes ahead and flies anyhow. According to the principles of institutional processes—according to the laws of human organization—the hospital ought not to be able to function. The sociologist, however, is not satisfied with merely asserting that the people in the hospital are not aware of this and, therefore, they function anyhow. In seeking an answer to the question as to why the hospital does function despite all the built-in dilemmas, the effectiveness of the informal organization of the hospital in maintaining its processes becomes obvious. Somehow—and many pages can be written about this alone—a communications structure, a system of informal relations, develops which overlaps and integrates the care and the cure structure.

Clearly, an objective, incisive look at the real facts is a prerequisite for intelligent action. A reexamination of the over-all function of medical care, a reevaluation of the distribution of tasks and responsibilities, an appraisal of the efficiency and efficacy of the institution which provides this care are the prerequisites for any steps ahead.

It cannot be forgotten that modern science and technology have changed functions and relationships. The notion that the hospital is merely a service organization for the physician is becoming increasingly a myth. The individual patients and society at large hold the hospital and its officers responsible for the performance of the medical processes. The nurse who must decide when to label a situation an emergency, and which sequence and priority to give to the physician's orders, practices medicine. The concept of the total patient and the recognition of the importance of the relationship between the whole of human experience and the disease condition itself, all argue for the fact that, in the last analysis, every single person who comes in contact with the patient does practice medicine. Modern insight into the nature of man has opened vistas urging a reorganization of medical care with a new and larger meaning for the concept "the medical team.

With increasing complexity of the institution, the position of the administrator must emerge as the mainspring of coordination and the center of responsibility, and as such must be vested with the prestige, power and organization to do the job.

The Nurse: Coordinator of Patient Care*

HANS O. MAUKSCH

INTRODUCTION

🔰 Probably more so than any other occupation the nursing profession today is engaged in a process of self-evaluation, and is developing a statement of policy, philosophy and function pertaining to its own role in the process of health care. Incidental to this process of self-study, much light has been shed on the complexity of the nurse's role, on the many facets of her function. The dichotomy between the nurse as a mother figure and the nurse as a healer has been described by Sam Schulman.[1] Other functional aspects of her role have been treated differently with similar results by Johnson and Martin,[2] and by Isidor Thorner.[3]

This paper will endeavor to place these apparent inconsistencies or incompatibilities of the nurse's task into the context of the hospital structure. However, rather than concentrating on the nurse in the totality of her role, the emphasis for this presentation will be on the organization of the patient care unit and the role of the nurse within it.

One assumption basic to this paper is that the expectations surrounding every position within an institution are products of processes and relationships which permeate the entire organization. The various facets of a role

---

* Specially prepared for this book.

within the institution can never be understood in isolation but must be seen as part of an interaction process involving institutional function, organization, occupational specialization and the complex of formal and informal role behavior.

THE ORGANIZATION OF PATIENT CARE

Let us start out by asking about the purpose and the function of the hospital. It is known to all who studied basic courses in nursing or hospital administration that the primary purpose of the hospital is to "care" for the sick. This does not include by tradition, organization or legal interpretation, the healing function itself—the "cure" process. While the patient and the community at large are vaguely aware of the separation of care and cure in the organization of patient care, its real penetrating separation and distinction are not clearly perceived even by some members of the health profession. Harvey Smith's classic essay[4] about two lines of authority within the hospital outlined this division with some of its consequences.

The hospital then is concerned with care. In this respect the hospital has a mutually beneficial relationship with the physician. The hospital provides the facilities, the personnel and the conditions under which the physician can perform his specialized task, and the physician in turn will bring the patient to the hospital where he may then receive the hospital services. The physician therefore is in the dual role of client and functionary and thus can deal with or within the institution. This separation of function between the generalized needs to care for the patient and the specific task of healing is therefore not exclusively within the nurse's role but finds its roots in the organization of health services. The fact that the human being continues to have the needs of ongoing life processes which must be met even while he is seriously ill gives rise to the complex organization of the care process.

A further examination of this care function is in order. The needs of patient care can be grouped into a number of logical functional subgroups. To a varying degree to most patients the hospital offers services akin to those of a hotel. They are the provisions of bed and board as such without the consideration of any incapacity on the side of the patient. On the other hand the hospital provides services which are subsidiary and supplementary to the cure process and aid in the diagnostic and therapeutic function directed by the physician. Overlapping with both of these function clusters and shifting in emphasis and definition from patient to patient is the patient's need to have certain services rendered because he is ill and, to a varying degree, physically incapacitated as well as emotionally under stress. This function of the hospital is one that is often identified in the public mind with the image of the nurse, which carries the expressive, mother-like, generally supportive theme.

As we inquire into the organization of the patient care unit we must draw two conclusions. First, the nurse who mans this unit obviously performs a considerable share of tasks falling into all of these function clusters. Secondly, the supportive, ministering function which differentiates the hospital from a hotel on the one hand and from a clinic on the other are not exclusively performed by nurses but, under certain conditions, by others within the hospital.

Institutional Self-maintenance

Before we continue with this analysis of the relationship between institutional function and organization, a principle of institutional sociology once formulated by Everett Hughes[5] has to be considered. It is generally recognized that with the institutionalization of any social function the secondary need of self-maintenance will emerge. The function of management may become competitive or even conflicting with the primary purpose of the institution as bureaucratization and specialization proceed. Thus the hospital, which is an institution, has seen the emergence of paperwork and administrative routines, and these tasks have grown as the hospital has become bigger and health care more complex. The cure structure, however, is not institutionalized but rather functions as a more or less interdependent aggregate of individual practitioners. Thus, the administrative demands of the cure process are borne by the organization which translates the individual act of therapy into an institutional process—the patient care unit.

Effects of Departmentalization on the Nursing Staff

Implementation of institutional function is accomplished through an organization of tasks and functionaries. An organization of a typical private general hospital is shown in Figure 1. It is different from the prototype of common administrative organization. We can observe the board of trustees and the administrator above the one single horizontal line in the chart. Like the teeth of a comb, the departments with their individual structures jut out from the connecting administrative line. We call this a comb-like organization which places emphasis on individual departments and decentralizes—at least formally—the forward functions of the institution. It changes the function of the administrator from being the wielder of institutional control to the role of mediator between departments, the "expert in foreign relations."

This type of organization has been favored by a historical process, important in the organization of patient care. The hospital has witnessed the emergence of specialists who, in laying claim to certain groups of tasks went through the process of departmentalization but also frequently became dis-

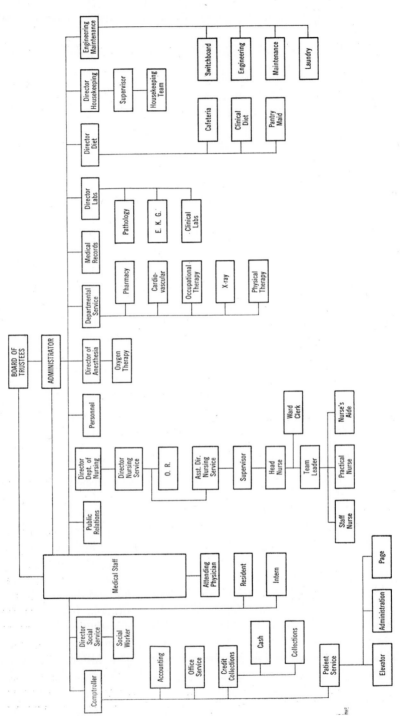

Fig. 1. Organization of a typical private general hospital.

tinct and—to a varying degree—professionalized occupations. This development has favored departmental isolation, discontinuities in patient care and conflicts between occupational and institutional loyalties.

The teeth in this comblike organization represent therefore more or less distinct suborganizations within the hospital. Since they follow a hierarchical pattern, the positions within each department are fixed and have prescribed lines of communication and contact. A lone exception is the tooth representing the medical staff. It is the only tooth that penetrates the back of the comb and reaches above the level of the administrative line. As indicated earlier, the role of the physician is a unique one in that he is an independent practitioner who has within his own confines the prerogative and the responsibility for one total function or process, namely that of cure. In view of this, he has a reciprocal relationship with the hospital, which places him on an equal level with the administrator and the board of trustees. Yet in the performance of his function he enters the hospital, he dons his white coat and he joins the workers of the front lines. Thus he not only may be within or outside the institution, but he is also in a sense privileged to move up and down across all levels. Thus the tooth representing the medical staff is unique not only by extending through the back of the comb but it is also distinguished from the other teeth in that the molecules within this tooth are free floating and may move up and down at will, while the molecules in the other teeth are hierarchically fixed and therefore limited in their relationships with the other molecules.

In order to test how this organization performs in reality, Figure 2 has been designed to include a patient; and in doing so, it includes a symbolic replication of the physical organization of the hospital. We suggest here the distinction between the regional organization of the hospital—the patient's bedside, the patient care unit, and the hospital section—and the sphere of the specialty departments. It is evident that in the modern hospital a large number of departments are organized away from the actual patient's bedside, away from the actual patient unit. According to this chart and my observation of hospital situations, three departments usually are organized in terms of the geographic division of the hospital. Primarily the department of nursing and to a varying degree the departments of diet and housekeeping follow this pattern. Looking at this chart we can suggest a very important distinction in the performance of work of any kind. Depending on a number of conditions, a worker may be responsible for the continuity of events and conditions or for the performance of a very specific episode of responsibility for a very specific task to be performed. This is a very fundamental distinction and one that distinguishes certain people within the hospital from others. Thus, the laboratory technician assumes responsibility for the particular procedure that she is to perform with the patient, but she has no responsibility,

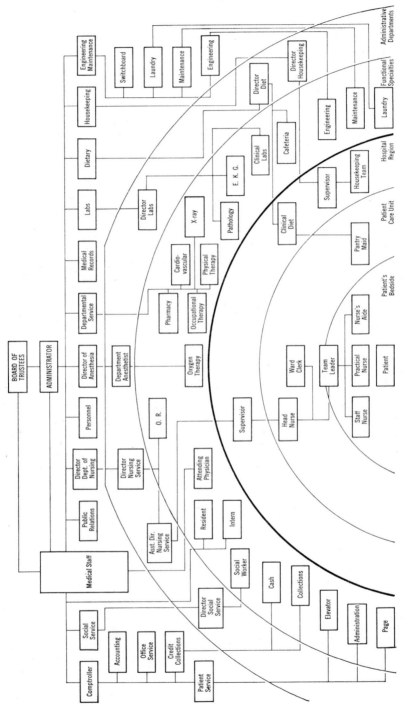

Fig. 2. The functional and territorial organization of a hospital.

explicitly or implicitly, beyond this particular episode in the patient's day. This is distinguished from the role expectation of the nurse who usually is seen as the symbol of the continuity of responsibility in patient care.

The chart shown in Figure 2 has been used to bring out two principles:

1. Tasks in the hospital are organized on the basis of either geographic responsibility or functional specialty.

2. With organization of work into functional episodes goes an implicit limitation of responsibility for the scope of the task only. This is differentiated from a more generalized expectation which attaches itself to the nurse who is identified with the patient care unit.

In order to examine the last point further, a look at the actual organization of the patient care unit is in order. Figure 3 shows the patient care unit with the patients and the nursing group. Under the leadership of the head nurse, the nursing group is the one category of workers within the hospital who comes onto the work area and stays—for an 8-hour period at least. The patient care unit is organized by this group, which consists of professional nurses, and the various recently emerged ancillary job categories. They are distinguished from all the others who come and go. The organization of the patient care unit therefore rests with those who are there permanently and on whom is placed the responsibility to maintain this unit for themselves and all the others to function in. This is a larger concept than the above-mentioned geographical basis of assignment, since it involves not only the question of territorial relationship but also the demands of time and responsibility.

Organization within an institution is affected by the location of positions and by the placement of lines of authority and communications. A look at the patient care unit as portrayed in Figure 3 makes it obvious that the lines of organization on the patient care unit focus on the head nurse, and from the head nurse to the supervisor, who connects the unit with the department of nursing. This represents organization within the care structure as discussed above. This line of communication and authority to the nursing department serves also as a channel for communication with hospital administration since, as portrayed in the chart, the hospital administrator has no echelon of his own to the front lines of the hospital. As we see it, the care structure communicates to the patient care unit via the nursing department. Directives from hospital administration do reach all departments but come to the patient's bedside via nursing.

The actual work organization of the patient care unit falls within the confines of the care structure of the hospital organization itself. However,

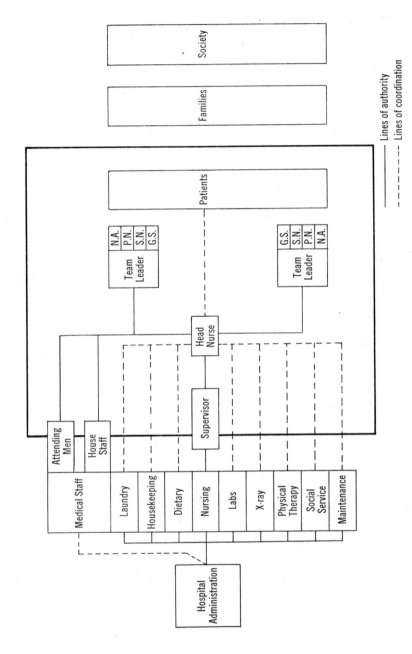

Fig. 3. Lines of authority and coordination at the patient care unit.

it is at this patient care unit that the cure processes, the healing functions of the physician, join with the processes of care. The physician in his capacity as the director of the therapeutic functions provides the second source of directives to the organization of the patient care unit represented here by the head nurse. It is at this crucial point that the two lines of authority merge and place the head nurse and her staff in the position of having to serve—in a sense—two masters.[6]

FUNCTIONS OF THE PATIENT CARE UNIT

From the point of view of this presentation, this concept does not need to be developed further at this point. We can now list those functions that the patient care unit performs by virtue of the kind of organization and functional processes which characterize patient care. This is distinct from the actual bedside function of nursing itself, and it is not implied that some of these functions need to be performed by members of the occupation called nursing. However, and this has been underscored in the previous discussion, since the nurse is the one who organizes the patient care unit, the following functions are performed by her. They can be grouped under six headings:

1. The continuity of time
2. The continuity of space
3. The continuity of function
4. Coordination within the care structure
5. Coordination within the cure structure
6. Coordination between the care and the cure structures

1. The Continuity of Time. It has already been stressed that the personnel who man the patient care unit are there for a set period of time, and that it is their responsibility and the expectation of the entire hospital community that this group will "cover" the patient care area. Even though some members of this team may occasionally leave the patient care unit, they will always be represented. This expectation has important organizational as well as work-psychological implications. The very fact that a person is expected to be present gives rise to additional frustrations. The nurse becomes heir to filling the gaps and smoothing the overlaps in the process of patient care largely because she "is around." She is never organizationally or psychologically free while she is "on duty." Those workers who have specific tasks to perform can call the minutes between the tasks their own. People whose work is organized in episodal tasks enjoy different kinds of freedoms from those who have to be continuously at a place.[7] The pressures of the institution are different when continuity of time creates accountability. It is in the nature of patient care that someone has to assume this function—that the human being who is hospitalized needs someone who assumes responsibility for being available. This does not necessarily mean that someone is at the patient's bedside but rather that someone is within reach on the basic hospital unit.

2. The Continuity of Space. It may be a shock to members of the nursing profession to hear the assertion that the concept of the patient care unit may not at all be a natural one. It may also surprise them to hear that it is a concept that is not shared by all other people who are part of hospital life.

Members of a class in school feel a certain common bond at least during the time that they share the same educational experience. They are conscious of each other and accept the fact that they represent a social unit. Patients, on the other hand, live in a more or less isolated arrangement. Their stay is not coordinated with the stay of other patients, and they frequently do not think of themselves as "the boys of Ward 17." This, to be sure, does not apply to patients in such long-term institutions as tuberculosis sanitaria and other similar situations where the ward organization of patients is a very real one. But with the decrease of large open-ward units and the shortened patient stay this point does apply to the general hospital of today. Likewise, and probably more important to the work organization of the hospital, it is not obvious that the notion of the patient care unit is a reality to physicians and other workers in the hospital as it is to nursing and to hospital administration. This administrative artifact, the spatial concept of the patient care unit, is the basis for the organization of nursing care. It is the nurse, or at least those who organize the patient care unit, who create, maintain, and administer this artifact as a means of running the hospital.

3. The Continuity of Function. There is a difference between the notion of patient care and the distinct tasks performed by the multitudinous members of the health team. There is medical care concerned with initiation and implementation of diagnosis and cure. There is nursing care, which has some dependent and some independent elements; there is dietary care; there are many other components to the care of the patient, including the various diagnostic, supportive, and therapeutic tasks. At one time in the history of medicine the nurse, the physician and possibly the maid comprised the entire division of labor in patient care. Today the complexity of medicine and of the hospital has created the emergence of specialized functionaries who converge as we have seen at the bedside of the patient. They are, as we saw, responsible for the episode of their specialized task. Warner, Meeker and Eels[8] have stated that when the division of labor in any social group becomes complex the function of coordination will inevitably emerge. Coordination, in this sense, is really responsibility for continuity of the overall function, which has been divided among specialists. Responsibility for continuity of patient care lies with those who are "around." The continuity of the total range of hospital and medical function has become the burden of those people who organize the patient unit; it has been given to the nurse.

There are, however, antecedents to this expectation that the nurse accept responsibility for the continuity of function. Many of the tasks that have emerged as independent specialties have been carved out of the original scope of the nurse's task. At one time the nurse's job included all those things performed by admissions, pharmacy, laboratory, x-ray, physiotherapy and the many other specialties in the hospital today. Like the dough that remains after the cookies have been cut out, nursing embraces the total range, scope and shape of the original pattern, even though choice bits have been removed. However, unlike the network of dough, the nurse is expected to fill in when the others are not around—at night, and on weekends. Nursing takes over many functions then—from pharmacy to occupational therapy, from administration to housekeeping.

The next three functions of the nursing group actually emerge out of this concern with continuity of function.

4. Coordination Within the Care Structure. According to the formal organization of the hospital, all departments are coordinate and relate to each other formally only on the top level. Yet in terms of what has been shown thus far, the informal expectations of maintaining continuity places on the nurse the responsibility to coordinate the various discrete tasks that are performed by the many departments within the hospital.

Within the care structure the services rendered to the patient or to the patient care unit converge into the administrative domain of the head nurse, and it is informally but forcefully expected that she assume ultimate responsibility for seeing that these things are done and that they are performed in some pattern and sequence. When a laboratory technician is late, it is the nurse's implicit task to make sure that the diet service wait a little longer so that the patient will not have food prior to the laboratory technician's arrival. This coordinating function within the care structure was dramatized many years ago by Frances Reiter[9] in an illustrated article in the *American Journal of Nursing*. It would be well worth our while to look at this coordinating function again and to question the distinction between coordination as an institutional function that must be performed by someone, and nursing in its narrower patient-centered sense, which is a ministering role.

5. Coordination Within the Cure Structure. When speaking of the physician's orders one thinks of a one-to-one relationship between the physician and the patient. Between these two, however, lies the work unit of the hospital. On a general medical-surgical unit almost as many attending men as there are patients may be writing orders for their patients. They form an aggregate of initiating forces rather than a hierarchical structure as we have seen to exist within the care organization. Not only do attending men write orders, but residents and interns do, too. The head nurse in her function as administrator of the patient care unit has the important task here to coordinate within this cure process the various individual directives—orders—which converge on her desk and which are not necessarily cognizant of each other. In this sense the nurse may be faced with orders adding up to many more man hours of work than she actually has available in terms of personnel. This coordinating function within the cure process is therefore not as it was in the care structure. The translation of individual orders into a task and work pattern creates a mediating and coordinating function that is particularly subtle, since those whose orders are translated expect unquestioning adherence to their directives.

Within the hospital the various departments may not be always on the best of footing; yet they must be aware of each other and of the interrelationships of their function. The physician, on the other hand, has no need to consider the other physicians with whom he must share the time and services of the nurse. It is within the logic of the physician's function that he demand the best and the most for his patient. In this there lies a logic of inevitable competition with other members of the medical staff, who expect the same for their patients. Thus, by virtue of these competing demands and the absence of firm organization, the nurse's coordinating function in the cure structure takes on different dimensions. This role she is expected to perform in the face of the physician's prestige and power and of the implications of a sex-linked division of positions. The physician is very much the male who expects that his superordinate role be recognized. The tradition of nursing includes some themes very much akin to the expectations imposed on the wife not so long ago that she must humor her husband and let him at least believe that he "runs" the home. The degree to which this function of the unit manager, as we might call the nurse here, has been accepted implicitly even though never formally stated can be judged by the fact that it is not uncommon for an attending man to expect the head nurse to watch over the orders that his interns write and not let "the young boys write things that I would not like." This is reminiscent of the informal function of the First Sergeant in the army vis-à-vis the new Second Lieutenants. However, in the army this tradition is more openly institutionalized and more generally supported.

6. Coordination Between the Care and the Cure Structures. The head nurse is at the point where the social organization for cure converges with the supportive and facilitating function of the hospital itself. It has been shown that within each of these two structures the nurse performs a coordinating function. It is not surprising that she is frequently in a position where she must mediate between the two structures. There are such things as hospital rules and hospital policies. There are situations in which the process of cure is superordinate to the demands of the care organization. There are times when the practitioners of healing are expected to conform to the rules of the hospital. It is important to underline that in this capacity those who manage the patient care unit do not merely represent nursing but represent in effect the hospital administrator. Since hospital policies appear via nursing on the patient care unit, and since communications within a more or less voluntary aggregate as represented by the medical staff are not always perfect, the nurse must remind the medical staff of hospital policies and occasionally enforce them. The physician who continues to remove charts from the patient care unit even though the executive committee of the medical staff has agreed with the administrator and the director of nursing that this practice should be abandoned will not take kindly to the head nurse who reminds him of this new policy and attempts to prevent him from doing so. After all, in most of the dimensions that define the relationships between the physician and the nurse it is assumed by both that the physician is superordinate. It is not easy to expect the nurse, as well as the physician, to recognize the one strand within that complex of relationships in which the nurse represents institutional authority.

Whenever there are two masters the person confronted with this situation may be caught between these two forces but may also have the opportunity to play one against the other. In mediating between the care and the cure structures the nurse is certainly in the position to use, occasionally, this situation to her own advantage. Should the head nurse desire to have a patient moved, and should the admissions office—the care structure—refuse to accede to her wishes, she can always turn to the attending physician and suggest to him that the patient be moved—for medical reasons, of course. If the physician writes such an order in the chart, the moving of the patient is transferred from the care structure to the cure structure and the nurse has won.

SUMMARY

In organizing the patient care unit, the nursing force performs duties other than direct patient care. These tasks reflect the structuring of the functions of the institution and are shaped by the organizational pattern of the hospital. The patient care unit narrows the division of labor, specialization and departmentalization which characterizes patient care. In addition to the function of providing direct nursing care, the organization of the patient care unit must perform the functions of management and coordination. It has been shown that this managerial function is one that subsumes implicitly not only the direction of the unit itself but the coordination of all those who come to the unit to perform services. By virtue of the convergence of hospital specialization on the patient care unit, this function is properly a delegation of the prerogatives and responsibilities of the hospital administrator. Yet the hospital administrator is prevented from exerting his direct influences and from assuming responsibility on any of the forward levels of the hospital, since he is confronted by departmental doors that make him a mediator rather than an administrator. It is not the purpose of this presentation actually to propose a reorganization of the hospital or the patient care unit but merely to raise the question *whether the present organization is the one that is most beneficial to the continuities in patient care and the best interest of the members of the health team.*

As an example of a different approach, the divisions of labor on the patient care unit can be evaluated by analyzing functions. As an example, Figure 4 is a diagram sketching the function of providing food to a patient. There are two dimensions to this function. One is the food itself, and the other is the process of eating. Which of the occupations should partake in these functions becomes then a secondary question. If we look at this chart we can see that we might group food under three headings: normal, supportive and therapeutic diets. This is a rough grouping, but functionally it covers all logical possibilities. Likewise we can group the eating process into three rough but reasonably clear areas. Again patients may be able to eat what we might call normally. This includes eating anything, anyplace, in the same fashion as one would at home or in a restaurant. Secondly, patients

TYPE OF FOOD

Mode of eating	Normal	Supportive Diet	Therapeutic Diet
Normal			
Bedrest			
Feeding			

Fig. 4. The function of providing food to a patient.

may be confined to bed, where, although being able to feed themselves, they may have to take their nourishment within the confines of bed rest.

Thirdly, patients may have to be fed. A fourth category, those patients who are not able to take food at all but need to be fed through other means, is not included here since it introduces a different dimension. No solutions are offered here, since no actual studies have preceded this presentation. However, it would seem that the filling in of these cells with descriptions as well as with frequencies of cases for each eventuality might suggest organizational improvement for the patient care unit, improvement for the hospital forces and, maybe, for the patient himself. If a large segment of patients can eat normal food in the normal fashion, would it not seem reasonable that in the building, staffing and organizing of the hospital, this group should be taken into account? Would this enable greater attention to the supportive and therapeutic aspects of the other cells which represent needs more demanding on the time and efforts of the hospital specialists?

Rather than providing means by which to change the organization of the patient care unit and the function of the nurse, this paper was meant to organize existing knowledge in such a fashion so that it may offer a basis of approach for objective further study and experimentation.

FOOTNOTES

1. Schulman, Sam, "Basic Functional Roles in Nursing: Mother Surrogate and Healer," *in* E. Gartly Jaco (ed.), *Patients, Physicians, and Illness,* Glencoe, Ill., Free Press, 1958.
2. Johnson, Miriam M., and Martin, Harry, "A Sociological Analysis of the Nurse Role," *American Journal of Nursing,* Vol. 58, No. 3, March 1958, pp. 373-377, and in this volume.
3. Thorner, Isidor, "Nursing: The Functional Significance of an Institutional Pattern," *American Sociological Review,* Vol. 20, October 1955.
4. Smith, Harvey L., "Two Lines of Authority Are One Too Many," *The Modern Hospital,* Vol. 84, March 1955.
5. Hughes, Everett, "Institutions in Process," *in* A. McClung Lee (ed.), *Principles of Sociology,* Barnes and Noble, New York, 1953.
6. Mauksch, Hans O., "Nursing Dilemmas in the Organization of Patient Care," *Nursing Outlook,* Vol. 5, January 1957.
7. *Cf.* Simmel, Georg, *Die Philosophie des Geldes,* Dunker & Humblot, Leipzig, 1905. In chapter IV, Simmel discusses elements of individual freedom as influenced by different kinds of commitments and obligations.
8. Warner, W. Lloyd; Meeker, Marcia; and Eels, Kenneth, *Social Class in America: A Manual of Procedure for the Measurement of Social Status,* Chicago, Science Research Associates, 1949.
9. Reiter, Frances, "Where is the Head Nurse?" *American Journal of Nursing,* Vol. 48, No. 3, March 1948, pp. 156-157.

Too Many Nurses May Be Worse Than Too Few

PETER KONG-MING NEW · GLADYS NITE ·
JOSEPHINE CALLAHAN

Recently Community Studies, Inc., completed a study that tried to determine if there is such a thing as an optimum number of hours of nursing care. The study involved shifting the number of nursing personnel on four medical and surgical wards for nine weeks, from Monday through Friday, on the morning shift (7 a.m. to 3 p.m.).

THE METHODS

For nine weeks, nine different combinations of staffing were introduced. Two variables were shifted: the total number of nursing personnel working on the units and the proportion of graduate nurses on the units. Thus, on some weeks there was a shortage of personnel with very few R.N.'s, while on other weeks there was an excess of personnel with a large number of R.N.'s.

We were interested in seeing what kinds of activities various nursing staff members engaged in when there were a great many professional nurses on the units and when there were very few R.N.'s on the floors. When we shifted the number of personnel on the units, we also changed the number of hours of care the patient received. In doing so, we were concerned with three questions: (1) Do the attitudes of the patients and the nursing personnel change with a change in the ratio of nursing hours of care? (2) Do the attitudes of the patients and the nursing personnel change with a change in the ratios of graduate nurses working on the units? (3) Is there any change in the way nursing employees use their time as these ratios vary?

When we talk about nursing activities on these hospital units, there are, of course, many complicating factors: hospital policies, the types of patients, the personality of the nursing personnel, nursing service policies, floor procedures, and others. We will not go into each of these complicating factors other than to acknowledge their presence.

What are the results? What are the implications of our findings to the hospital administrator, the medical staff, or the nursing service? We found positive as well as negative results, some of which have no ready interpretation.

Briefly, this was our method: We observed for a week on the four medical and surgical units before the study started in order to obtain some data for a "normal" week. We charted the distribution of time each of the nursing personnel spent in various activities, that is, on direct patient care, on indirect care, and on other activities. We summarized the time spent by each of the nursing personnel with each patient in direct care. We also computed the time each member of the nursing staff spent at her own level on the study—level 3 is the head nurse level, level 2 is staff nurse level, and level 1 is auxiliary level. With this information, we tried to determine the ideal number of personnel which the auxiliaries and the professional nurses thought should be on the units.

THE FINDINGS

Here's what we found—that we didn't expect to find.

We expected that most nursing activities would be clearly defined and that a consequence of the experimental variations would be a crossing of the lines of activities. This would, of course, happen much less with the nurse's aides, who are not trained and are not allowed to carry out the more highly skilled and complex functions. On the other hand, it was anticipated that the staff nurses would carry on many of the nurse's aides' duties.

Although this pattern did follow, the unexpected finding is that when the floors were staffed with a large number of persons, three-fourths of whom were staff nurses, the "aide type" of work still remained pretty much with the aides. From the attitudes of the nursing personnel, one explanation may be offered. A number of nurses who received their training recently see themselves primarily as highly professional nurses. Professionalism to them is defined in terms of highly technical skills and the assumption of administrative, educational and supervisory responsibilities. Thus, this group perceives nursing as an aggregation of skills and responsibilities involving primarily indirect contact with patients.

We expected that when we introduced more staff nurses on the floors they would spend more time with the patients. Although this occurred with some of the nurses, most of them chose to do other things. This has serious implications. As a result of this, nurses have been accused of leaving the bedside or leaving the patient in favor of some other functions. Possibly, necessary work may be taking the nurse from the bedside.

With the advent of modern medicine, personalized care may need to be sacrificed to achieve the desired goals of recovery for the patient. The "horse and buggy" doctor has disappeared. In effect, the "horse and buggy" nurse is also disappearing.

We expected that when there was more personnel on the floors, especially more staff nurses, there would be more time for the personnel to accomplish each task and hence a less hurried and more satisfied feeling of a task "well done." What we did not expect is that the nurses were all in agreement that on the "high" situations, those with approximately five R.N.'s and two nurse's aides for an average patient census of 20, the extra time increased boredom and restlessness, and resulted in a much more tired feeling.

We attribute this to two factors: (1) On any nursing unit, there is only so much work to be done. Once these tasks are finished, it is difficult to conceive of any "extra" work to be done, unless a person wishes to be highly imaginative and creative. (2) We gather that a part of the education of the nurse incorporates the Protestant Ethic: keep busy, work hard, and save. Thus, work is viewed as a necessary thing and time out for reflection or even rest may be discouraged as "sinful." When a nurse is put into such a position, she encounters some psychological difficulties, resulting in a tired feeling"—not from overwork, but from looking for work.

Conversely, we expected when there were both fewer personnel and fewer staff nurses on the floors there would be much scurrying around and there would be more complaints. Instead, both staff and auxiliary nursing personnel expressed satisfaction with the amount of work they were able to accomplish. To be sure, they were tired and busy and some felt that the patients were not receiving adequate care. Nevertheless, the consensus was that the lack of personnel meant a challenge to get everything done and satisfaction was derived from this. It must be mentioned that most nurses felt that they could stand this for only a short time; if it continued as a regular policy it would be undesirable.

One week after the study ended, one of the units returned to its short staffing pattern (consisting of approximately one R.N. and three nurse's aides for an average patient census of 20).

So far as patients were concerned, the expected changes of attitude did not occur. The answers from patients regarding satisfaction with nursing care received were constant throughout the nine weeks, regardless of the ratio of staff nurses working on the floors or the number of personnel on the floors. Three explanations may be offered:

1. In some instances nursing personnel does not increase the amount of time spent with patients. This being the case, it would be logical to assume

that the patient is less likely to notice whether there is a large influx of nursing personnel. So far as he is concerned, he does not see the nursing personnel any more on these "high weeks."

2. The average length of stay of patients (757 of the 881 patients remained for two weeks or less) may be a reason why the patients are not more discerning regarding their care. If the patient entered as an acutely ill case, he may not be aware of the care given him. In any case, we suspect that the patient is much more concerned that he recovers, and this is compartmentalized in his thinking as being a separate problem from nursing care.

Thus, if a patient recovers within a relatively short period of time he has not had an opportunity to reflect on his care. The hospital remains for him a place where many people, in different attires, come in and out of his room, performing various functions, silently and efficiently. If the patient made a conscious effort to discover who these people are and relate them to the work they perform, he might attain some measure of understanding.

3. Patients identify themselves with the nursing personnel on the units. We found, in our study, that often patients hesitate to complain about their services because they feel that, since they are in a sense guests in an institution, they should not bite the hand that feeds them. Since the patient sees the nursing personnel on a fairly intimate basis during a sustained period, he is bound to discover many of the problems which the nursing personnel encounters. One of the problems which is accentuated is "shortage of personnel." If the patient hears the nurse's aides comment on this problem, as has happened on a number of occasions on the study units, he is likely to feel that one way to remedy this situation is to impress the investigator with this problem through the use of the questionnaire. Even though the patient may complain directly to the nurse, he may still feel that this should be viewed strictly as a "within the family" squabble. Thus, the patient is less likely to air any grievances to outside investigators unless he feels that the researcher is in a position to "correct" certain undesirable situations.

VARIABLES COMPLICATE RESULTS

We have already mentioned the "complicating factors" that need to be considered in the interpretation of the results. Similarly, these complicating factors also limit our readiness to present solutions. For instance, which proportion of nursing personnel would be best? The data on the present study would seem to indicate that the nursing personnel felt that approximately two R.N.'s and five nurse's aides for an average daily census of 20 was an ideal situation.

However, in a hospital situation, one would also have to consider the budget, the types of patients on the units and the severity of their illnesses, the number of patients on the units, or the personality of these nursing personnel. Each of these variables can call for a different staffing pattern.

For example, on one of the hospital units in our study, there was a head nurse who was very close to her staff members. She would help them perform innumerable nursing activities; she knew the patients; her relationship with the staff physicians was excellent. On this floor, then, she was not only able to carry out many of the nursing functions herself, but she was able to perform these efficiently and smoothly, since the staff cooperated with her. It would be conceivable that in this kind of a situation she might have less need of nursing personnel. This is a human variable. The other variables call for similar readjustments of the staffing patterns.

There are, however, certain other problems which are basic to each one of these variables. We can suggest only a few of these:

Patient-Centered Care. We hear a great deal of this now in patient or nursing care studies. I just recently read an article concerned with progressive patient care units. A group of hospital administrators discussed all aspects of the problems involved in setting up one of these units—finance, staffing and patient care. It seemed that when one looked at progressive patient care from a financial standpoint—a very real problem these days in running a hospital—a constant question came up: "Is it *worth* the hospital personnel's time to set up progressive patient care units?" What are the advantages? Does progressive care lower costs?

From a nursing standpoint, do P.P.C. units facilitate giving the best possible type of care to the patient? Can patients be transferred readily (and without too much emotional distress) from one unit to another as they progress satisfactorily? From the patient's standpoint, does he, as an ultimate "consumer" of medical and nursing care, progress at a more rapid rate? These are some of the practical questions which have to be answered. Yet, there is no doubt in the physician's or administrator's mind that care must be centered on patients.

Nursing Functions in Relation to the Patient. When care is to be centered on the patient, it is possible that nursing functions and nursing activities may have to be altered. I am not suggesting that the procedures should be altered or that new methods be devised. I am suggesting that the concept of these functions be shifted from one of "task orientation" to one of "patient orientation." In all hospitals, there are certain tasks which have to be carried out during certain times of the day. It is inconceivable that a hospital can function properly otherwise. On our study, some nursing personnel complained that certain nursing procedures have to be done at certain times. If now the emphasis is shifted toward "patient-centered" care, could these procedures not be given at some other times? Is it not possible that here we can receive cues from patients?

Communication Problems. If we are to receive cues from the patients, it would necessarily mean more direct contact with the patients. Direct contact can be interpreted in a number of different ways. A person can walk into a patient's room, perform several functions to aid the patient, and thus accomplish a number of "direct contacts." Yet a few minutes later, an investigator can ask this patient if he has seen anyone from the nursing staff and he may conceivably answer, "No." The patient, to all intent and purpose, has seen no one because he was not sufficiently impressed with the significance of these acts, or functions, which someone has just performed. Just a slightly different approach can impress this patient: a few spoken words, some questions to the patient, or some explanation of the functions performed. This would make the patient aware that someone cares.

Patient Awareness. This brings us down to the possible crux of the matter. If a patient is not aware of the significance of the care given, no matter how many hours we spend with the patient, how many big or small, important or unimportant, functions we perform for the patient, that patient may not perceive that any care is being given. He remains in isolation.

Thus, what I am leading to is this: When we speak of the proportion of graduate nurses needed, or the number of hours they spend doing this or that, we constantly speak of these things *in relation* to the patient. This relation with the patient can be conceived in two ways. He can be the "top man" on the totem pole, or hierarchy of care, or he can be submerged at the bottom, under the "system," as Howard Wooden uses this term in a recent article in *The Modern Hospital*.* If the patient is seen as a V.I.P. with the others in the hospital system supporting him, emotionally, physiologically and *totally*, the care he receives would be quite different from the type he gets if he were seen as a person who receives some of the services "at the convenience" of the nursing or medical or hospital staff.

The latter type of care is often misconstrued by the patient who may be justly bewildered by the fact that he has to pay more for his hospital service than he has to pay for hotel rooms. I am sure this is not worth repeating. However, put in the context of nursing or medical care, this is worth emphasizing. The patient is receiving unique services, some on the order of a hotel, but many more on the order of getting well. If the patient is at the top of the "care system," and the nursing, medical or hospital functions are subjugated to him, we may ultimately reach a Utopian hospital system when such questions as the right proportion of graduate to nonprofessional nurses needed, the patient's reaction to nursing care, or the correct number of people to be hired, may be raised only as secondary issues. The primary question, hopefully, would then be: "How can we organize our hospital, medical or nursing services to provide the best type of care for this patient?"

---

* Wooden, Howard: The System May Come Ahead of the Patient, *Mod. Hosp.* 91:99 (September), 1958.

The Language of the Hospital and Its Effects on the Patient

ANNA TERESA BAZIAK · ROBERT KNOX DENTAN

🖎   The writers would like to introduce their topic by quoting from an unpublished paper by their colleague and friend, Ida J. Orlando:

> An elderly patient, just arrived in the general ward of a modern hospital, is crying softly. While her sister helps her to bed, a harassed nurse rushes in, places a specimen bottle and several chart sheets on the bedside stand and immediately begins to write.
> "Do you have any jewelry with you?" asks the nurse.
> The patient moans and swallows hard, while the nurse sighs and wiggles her pen. "No," says the patient. "Oh, my God, help me." She covers her face with her hand, and moans.
> "Do you have any false teeth?"
> Still moaning, the patient shakes her head, then suddenly tries to grab a small bottle from her sister. "Give me my pills, please don't take them away."
> The sister jumps back, saying, "You know you can't keep them."
> "Yes, but when I have the pain, I have to wait too long. I know this place, I've been here eight times." The old woman is sobbing.
> "Now, you know you can't keep them here," interjects the nurse.
> "I told you so," the sister adds.
> "But I can't stand the pain. Oh, why doesn't God help me?"
> "Can you give me a urine sample?" asks the nurse.

From an anthropologist's point of view a hospital is a relatively isolated subculture. Doctors and nurses often live on the grounds; they go from place to place via underground tunnels; they eat, sleep and dance within the hospital; get their clothes washed at the hospital laundry; buy presents at the hospital gift shop; and often do not leave the hospital grounds for days at a time.

Reprinted with permission from the authors and *ETC: A Review of General Semantics*, Vol. 17, No. 3, September 1960, pp. 261-268; copyright held by the International Society for General Semantics.

Within hospital "culture," roles are strictly defined. The doctor is the dominant figure. He diagnoses symptoms and prescribes for his forty-odd patients. In hospitals these prescriptions are called "orders" and are entered in an "order book." The nurse is to carry out the doctor's orders. She is not even supposed to give a patient a hot water bottle without a written "order." A doctor or a nurse tends to refer to himself or herself as "we," which seems to be shorthand for "we, the Hospital." Last, the patient is to "cooperate"—another frequently used hospital term—to make it possible for doctors and nurses to function with a minimum of disturbance. The patient does not call himself "we." Requests made by the patient to the doctors and nurses are often called "complaints."

The contentions of this paper are (1) that instead of paying attention to the patient's idiosyncratic problems, which may stem from the new environment, the unfamiliar disease and the patient's past, doctors and nurses tend to *perceive* only certain features of the patient's condition, features which to an outsider may seem less significant than the ones which are ignored; (2) that this situation is the result of cultural and linguistic preconditioning.

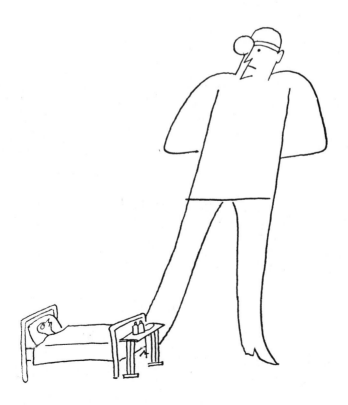

Doctors are frequently taught to think in terms of symptoms to be diagnosed. Doctors' language both reflects and constitutes part of this training. For many doctors, then, the patient is a symptom-vehicle, and such doctors perceive and respond to symptoms instead of patients.

For example, after an examination, a doctor calls to a passing medical student, "Come on in here, there's a finger you can do." The doctor begins to describe the symptoms in a voice inaudible to the patient, whom they both ignore.

"Hmmmm," says the student, with enthusiasm. "Where do you open it?"

The doctor answers, again inaudibly, and concludes "You get him all cleaned up. The only thing you need is a number eleven blade."

Then he goes away.

In this example the neglect of the patient as a human being is striking. Although both the doctor and the medical student make comments which probably upset the patient, neither speaks to him. This neglect is made even more striking by the doctor's reference to the patient as a "finger." Apparently, all that either responds to under these circumstances is this abstraction from the total patient.

Traditionally, the nurse is trained to be the doctor's "handmaiden." Furthermore, she tends to respond to the doctor's "orders" (which are actually prescriptions) as if they were commands; indeed, the doctor often expects her to respond this way. Thus the patient may become an object upon which "orders" are to be carried out. This depersonalization of the patient may be carried so far that he is called by room number or symptom. This linguistic habit, in turn, increases the anonymity of the patient. The diagram on the following page illustrates this semantic relationship.

In the example with which this paper opens, the nurse's apparently inappropriate responses result from her "orders" to "admit" the patient.

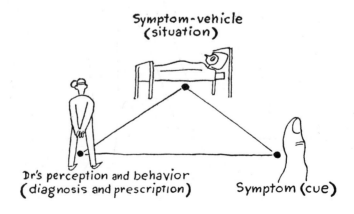

Symptom-vehicle
(situation)

Dr's perception and behavior
(diagnosis and prescription)

Symptom (cue)

Outside the hospital the nurse would probably have been sympathetic with the old woman's distress. Within the hospital, however, she responds to the "order" given her by her superiors, instead of to the patient. The nurse, therefore, ignores, *i.e.,* doesn't "perceive" any responses of the patient which cannot be used on the admission-form.

In another example, a nurse is reporting on a patient, characteristically called by room number. We quote again from the paper by Orlando:

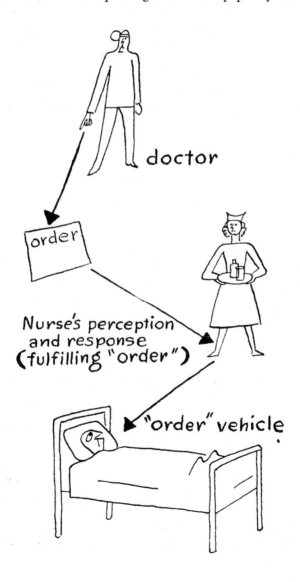

doctor

order

Nurse's perception
and response
(fulfilling "order")

"order" vehicle

"She has one more dose of repeat methergen to go."

The head nurse interrupts, "Did you give her her Seconal? It's no use, you know, because it takes such a long time to wake her up."

"I really had to shake her, too," answers the nurse.

To show that these inappropriate responses are the result of linguistic as well as cultural conditioning, take the example of Miss Reynolds.

Three nurses and an aide are sitting in a ward office. A light flashes on the signal board indicating that a patient is calling for attention.

NURSE NO. 1: Oh, brother, there's Miss Reynolds again.

NURSE NO. 2: What does she want now? She's had her morning care.

AIDE: I hate to go in. She'll keep me there an hour. She acts as if she can't lift a finger for herself.

NURSE NO. 1 TO NURSE NO. 3: You're new here. Would you mind going in? We get enough of her when you're not here.

NURSE NO. 3: All right.

(After having seen the patient, who was lonely, uncomfortable and in pain, Nurse No. 3 decided to try to change the attitude of the staff. She returned to the office.)

NURSE NO. 3: Poor Miss Reynolds. She has such a hard time getting out of bed. She seemed so weak. I had to support her with my arm when she walked. What's wrong with her?

NURSE NO. 1: Oh, she has metastatic carcinoma. She's been here for three weeks. I guess she does have some pain.

For three months, each time Nurse No. 3 came to the ward she asked if she might take care of Miss Reynolds. She followed this care by talking with the staff in this manner: "Miss Reynolds told me that she has no family. She said it makes being in the hospital especially lonely."

By the end of these three months, the behavior of the nurses toward Miss Reynolds had changed. They would fix her food in an attractive way, exercise more care in assisting her to move, bring her flowers from the rooms of discharged patients, and so forth.

What is striking here is that Miss Reynolds, the patient, has not changed at all, although the interpretant behavior of the staff has changed radically. This fact, it seems to us, indicates that the nurses were not responding to the flesh-and-blood Miss Reynolds, but to the word "Miss Reynolds" in a verbal context such as "Miss Reynolds is not *cooperative*." Since the phrase "Miss Reynolds" is phonemically unchanged, we are forced to the conclusion that it is the context of "*orders* which must be obeyed and with which Miss Reynolds does/does not interfere" that serves as the cue or sign for the nurses' interpretant behavior. Miss Reynolds is, phrase and person, irrelevant, except as a sign vehicle. But by manipulating the context in which the phrase "Miss Reynolds" occurred so that it no longer designated a situation in which obedience to "orders" was impeded but rather denoted a lonely, sick old woman, Nurse No. 3 was able to create a completely new interpretant behavior among the nurses.

Such a denotation would, outside hospital culture, be very likely to occur. The contention of this paper is not that the inappropriate behavior of nurses and doctors results from stupidity or inhumanity, but that it is conditioned by the subculture in which it occurs and by the language this subculture uses—a language in which prescriptions are "orders," patient's comments "complaints," and patients themselves numbers. Thus language is both the result and the cause of a situation in which sick people who come to an institution and take care of themselves are labeled "cooperative" and those who make demands on the personnel are labeled "uncooperative."

This sort of linguistic set-up seems to be an example of what Charles Morris calls "semiosis."[1] The doctors and nurses take account of the patient mediately, *i.e.*, by means of something else. Symptoms and "orders" are examples of what Morris calls "signs," insofar as doctors and nurses take account of the patient because of the presence of symptoms or orders. The patient is a "sign vehicle" and the behavior of the doctors and nurses is "interpretant."

The hospital is a very complex community. We have looked only at one aspect of this community and at how this aspect seems to inhibit the avowed functions of the hospital—namely, the meeting of a sick person's physical and emotional needs.

---

[1] Charles W. Morris, *Foundations of the Theory of Signs,* Vol. I, No. 2 (Chicago: University of Chicago Press, 1938).

Medical Vocabulary Knowledge Among Hospital Patients

JULIAN SAMORA · LYLE SAUNDERS · RICHARD F. LARSON

I'll tell you something, a good one on me. When my first child was born the doctor—like I told you I think it would be nice if they would reduce the language to where a person with hardly no education could understand these people; but me, I'm so frank myself that I tell them, "Look, let's knock this thing down and let's speak English to me because I don't know what the devil you're talking about." And they always have; the doctors I went to and those that seen my children have always been very nice about it. In other words, they knock it down to where it is just plain English to me. But this doctor kept coming in every day and asking, "Have you voided?" So I'd say, "No." So in comes the nurse with some paraphernalia that was scary. So I said, "What the devil are you going to do?" And she said, "I'm going to catheterize you, you haven't voided." Well of course I knew what catheterization was. I said, "You are going to play hell. I've peed every day since I've been here." I said, "Is that what he said?" And she said, "Of course, Rusty, didn't you know?" And I said, "Well, of course why didn't he just ask me if I'd peed? I'd have told him."

The doctor-patient relation is one that calls for the clear, precise, and complete transmission and reception of information. In arriving at a diagnosis and formulating a plan of treatment, the physician must elicit and use reliable information about the medical (and social) history of the patient. The patient, for his part, must understand what is asked of him and what is told to him if he is to cooperate fully with the physician in their common undertaking.[1]

---

[1] Kenneth R. Hammond, Fred Kern, Jr., and others, *Teaching Comprehensive Medical Care: A Psychological Study of a Change in Medical Education* (Cambridge: Harvard University Press, 1959), p. 40.

Reprinted with permission from the *Journal of Health and Human Behavior*, Vol. 2, 1961, pp. 83-92. This report is part of a larger study sponsored by the Russell Sage Foundation and conducted at the University of Colorado Medical School under the direction of Lyle Saunders, Associate Professor, Department of Preventive Medicine and Public Health.

Unfortunately, there are many barriers to ideal communication between medical practitioner and patient. These arise out of such factors as the physical inability of the patient to hear what is said to him; his psychological unwillingness to receive unpleasant information or to impart information about private matters; anxieties and inhibitions stemming from perceived status differences or from uncertainties about the clinical situation; and his inability to remember clearly past experiences or to formulate and relate what he does remember. Still other sources of communication difficulty are to be found in differences in what patients and physicians know about disease and about normal and pathological functioning of the body; in factors associated with social class or ethnic group membership; in the differing role expectations patients and physicians may have of themselves and each other; and in differences in ability to comprehend terms commonly used in medical discourse.

This paper is primarily concerned with one of these factors as it was found to operate in a particular medical setting. It reports findings that bear upon the ability of in-patients in a public general hospital to understand selected medical terms frequently used in that hospital (and presumably in others) in situations requiring communication with patients. It also attempts to isolate and make explicit some of the factors associated with observed differences in levels of understanding.

PROCEDURES

In a number of preliminary interviews with patients, a consistent finding was a generalized complaint by patients that they did not understand much of what physicians told them and that matters pertaining to their illness and its course were not explained to them in terms they could understand. These interviews suggested, among other things, that a problem in communication existed, one part of which related to the vocabulary used by physicians and other hospital personnel in conversations and interviews with patients.

To obtain a measure of the extent to which patients might be failing to understand the meaning of frequently used words, a vocabulary schedule was constructed as follows: From interviews with patients and from a knowledge of clinic and ward situations, the investigators compiled a list of terms believed to be in common use in conversations with patients. Four physician-patient interviews, of about an hour's duration each, were electrically recorded and transcribed. Using terms from these transcriptions, from suggestions made by medical personnel, and from the list already compiled, a combined roster of 230 words was developed. Nouns, verbs, and adjectives made up the bulk of the list. Care was taken to assure that words selected were not highly technical and were common enough in general lay usage to permit a good likelihood of their being known to many laymen.

A panel of eleven judges—two full-time physicians, two residents, and seven fourth-year medical students serving their senior clerkships—was asked to review the list and to indicate those words they would not ordinarily use in talking to their patients. All words that four or more panel members indicated they would not use were eliminated.

The remaining 208 words were used in the construction of a schedule with four scoring categories: (1) I do not know this word; (2) I recognize the word but have no clear understanding of what it means; (3) I recognize the word and have a fair understanding of what it means; (4) I have a clear and unambiguous understanding of the meaning of the word. Thirteen professional persons, all but one outside the field of medicine, went over this schedule and scored their own understanding. The results were scaled according to the Guttman technique and a new schedule prepared omitting all words that had not achieved 100 per cent reproducibility. The revised version, now including 131 terms, was given to a group of twelve nurses. A reproducibility of 98.7 per cent was found when the results were scaled.

A random sample of fifty words was drawn from the 131 terms surviving the preliminary screening.[2] These were used in the construction of a schedule for use with patients. Because it was felt that patients would have difficulty in giving definitions of words in the abstract, each of the terms was placed in a simple sentence.[3] And because patients were not expected to be facile in reading skill or in language usage, the schedule was designed to be administered and scored by an interviewer who would read each of the sentences, ask what the key word meant as used in that context, and record his judgment of the response. Pretests of the schedule indicated that reliability of the scoring was not good. Scoring categories were refined in a series of steps until, with the definitions included in footnote 6, an average agreement of 96 per cent was obtained in the scoring by two interviewers who independently scored a number of pretests. This was considered good enough for our purposes and no further revisions were undertaken.

It was not expected that many patients would be able to give technically acceptable definitions of the words. "High" scores, therefore, were given to

---

[2] The final fifty-word sample was checked against the results from the panel of eleven judges who had been asked to indicate if they would use certain words in communicating with patients. Three of the fifty words were checked as suitable for use by eight of the eleven judges; one word by nine judges; seven words by ten judges; and thirty-nine words by all eleven judges.

[3] E.g., Do you have a pain in your *abdomen*? Have you ever been *constipated*? How is your *digestion*? Have your *nasal passages* been clear? Let me feel your *pulse*. Take this medicine *orally*. Was the pain *persistent*? This will *relieve* the pain. I think you should *isolate* your child.

responses which, although technically inadequate, revealed that the respondent had such an understanding of the word that the intent of the communicator could be conveyed reasonably well when the word was used in context in the hospital ward or clinic situation. Scoring directions and procedures were such as probably to overestimate rather than underestimate the extent to which patients understood words put to them.

PATIENT RESPONDENTS

The 125 patients to whom this schedule was administered were selected by a sampling procedure from wards of the surgical-gynecological and medical services in a publicly operated general hospital.[4] Slightly more than half were native English-speaking white; the others were about evenly divided between Spanish-Americans and Negroes. All were old enough not to have been admitted to a pediatric ward; the modal age category was 25-34. Women outnumbered men 73 to 52. Twenty-four per cent had completed fewer than seven years of school; 55 per cent had been to school seven to eleven years; 21 per cent had a high school education or better.[5] When classified by the Hollingshead Two-Factor Index of Social Position, more than 90 per cent of the group fell in the lower two categories. This, then, was largely a lower class sample heavily weighted—as was the population of the hospital from which the sample was drawn—with Spanish-Americans and Negroes.

The schedule was administered to patients during morning and afternoon slack periods in the hospital routine. Ambulatory patients were taken to a private room; others were interviewed at their bedside. The illustrative sentences were read; the patient was asked for his interpretation of the key word; the response was scored immediately by the interviewer. In those instances where there was any doubt about how a response should be scored, the

---

[4] These 125 were part of a larger sample of 297 persons selected for extensive interviews from among those admitted during a 10-week period. Our experience indicates that it is virtually impossible to draw a sample of general hospital patients (for interview) that conforms rigorously to the requirements for randomness. Psychiatric, pediatric, nursery, and senile medical or surgical patients must be excluded, for obvious reasons. Some patients are too ill to talk when admitted and subsequently die or are discharged before they can be seen again. Of the 125 patients who responded to this schedule 102 (81 per cent), were selected by a technically adequate sampling process; 23 were selected by less satisfactory means that might have been biased slightly in favor of obtaining the more verbally facile patients as respondents. A comparison, using the Kolmogorov-Smirnov Two-Sample Test, of the D category scores of randomly selected respondents with those of respondents selected by less rigorous methods indicates that the differences are not significant at the .05 level.

[5] The median for the group falls in the 7-9 years of schooling category. This is about three years less than the median number of school years completed for the population of the city in which the patients lived.

patient's reply was written down and the scoring was later reviewed by the principal investigators.

Scoring instructions are listed in the footnote below.[6] It should be noted that even with a high degree of reliability of scoring, the distinction between categories B and C is not a sharp one. If these two are combined, there are three sharply distinguished levels of understanding: no understanding (category A); vague, ambiguous, or wrong understanding (category B and C); and reasonably clear and complete understanding (category D). Categories B and C are combined in all tables. The list of words used and the distribution of responses are shown in Table 1.

FINDINGS

No respondent gave an adequate meaning to all fifty words, and no single word was adequately defined by all respondents. The range of individual responses in the D category—i.e., those judged adequate for communication in the hospital ward or clinic situation—was from 11 to 47 words, with a mean of 28.9 and a median of 29 words. A quarter of the respondents (24.0 per cent) knew forty or more; an equal number knew twenty or fewer words. Four words (vomit, relieve, appointment, constipated) were known to more than 90 per cent of the respondents; four (tendon, terminal, malignant, nerve) were clearly known to fewer than 25 per cent. More than half the respondents failed to recognize four words (respiratory, malignant, secretions, cardiac) well enough to attempt any definition;[7] two-thirds or more of

---

[6] Directions for the scoring procedure were as follows:

Score A when, in the judgment of the interviewer, the response is such as to indicate that the respondent does not recognize the word and does not know any meaning for it. This score will usually be given when the respondent says that he does not know the word or when he is unable to say anything that might be construed as a definition.

Score B when, in the judgment of the interviewer, the response is such as to indicate that the respondent has an erroneous understanding of the meaning of the term. This score will be given when the response clearly indicates an erroneous understanding (e.g., the abdomen is the heart) or when the response is vague, incomplete, superficial, or ambiguous but contains enough of an element of error to lead to the conclusion that the respondent is "on the wrong track" in the definition or explanation he is attempting (e.g., "appendectomy means to rupture the appendix").

Score C when, in the judgment of the interviewer, the response is such as to indicate that the respondent recognizes the word but gives such a vague, incomplete, superficial, or ambiguous explanation that it can be reasonably doubted that he understands the term well enough for clear or full communication in the clinic or hospital situation (e.g., an abortion is a kind of childbirth).

Score D when, in the judgment of the interviewer, the response is such as to indicate that the respondent has a fairly clear idea of the meaning of the term and will be likely to understand it when it is used in context in the hospital or clinic situation.

[7] Ten or more of the panel of eleven judges had indicated that they would ordinarily use these words in conversations with patients.

TABLE 1. NUMBER AND PERCENTAGE OF CORRECT AND INCORRECT
RESPONSES TO FIFTY MEDICAL TERMS; NUMBER PATIENTS
RESPONDING TO EACH TERM—125

	CORRECTNESS OF RESPONSE					
	D. ADEQUATE		B. AND C. WRONG OR VAGUE		A. NO KNOWLEDGE	
MEDICAL TERM	NUMBER	PER CENT	NUMBER	PER CENT	NUMBER	PER CENT
Vomit	123	98.4	0	0.0	2	1.6
Relieve	120	96.0	5	4.0	0	0.0
Appointment	120	96.0	4	3.2	1	0.8
Constipated	116	92.8	6	4.8	3	2.4
Rash	110	88.0	10	8.0	5	4.0
Injection	108	86.4	5	4.0	12	9.6
Skull	107	85.6	13	10.4	5	4.0
Amputate	103	82.4	6	4.8	16	12.8
Persistent	101	80.8	15	12.0	9	7.2
Splint	100	80.0	11	8.8	14	11.2
Abdomen	100	80.0	9	7.2	16	12.8
Negative	90	72.0	17	13.6	18	14.4
Sterile	90	72.0	28	22.4	7	5.6
Symptoms	89	71.2	23	18.4	13	10.4
Reaction	88	70.4	22	17.6	15	12.0
Swab	87	69.6	26	20.8	12	9.6
Abortion	87	69.6	11	8.8	27	21.6
Mole	87	69.6	28	22.4	10	8.0
Pulse	86	68.8	37	29.6	2	1.6
Isolate	86	68.8	11	8.8	28	22.4
Nasal	80	64.0	14	11.2	31	24.8
Deformity	80	64.0	24	19.2	21	16.8
Fatal	79	63.2	32	25.6	14	11.2
Autopsy	75	60.0	29	23.2	21	16.8
Routine	75	60.0	34	27.2	16	12.8
Acute	75	60.0	22	17.6	28	22.4
Allergic	74	59.2	45	36.0	6	4.8
Cavity	73	58.4	24	19.2	28	22.4
Specimen	70	56.0	47	37.6	8	6.4
Sedative	68	54.4	22	17.6	35	28.0
Deficient	67	53.6	36	28.8	22	17.6
Germs	63	50.4	55	44.0	7	5.6
Intern	63	50.4	44	35.2	18	14.4
Bacteria	61	48.8	30	24.0	34	27.2
Cerebral	57	45.6	18	14.4	50	40.0
Nutrition	56	44.8	49	39.2	20	16.0
Digestion	54	43.2	63	50.4	8	6.4
Vitamins	51	40.8	67	53.6	7	5.6
Cardiac	43	34.4	9	7.2	73	58.4
Orally	43	34.4	57	45.6	25	20.0
Tissue	40	32.0	60	48.0	25	20.0
Dilate	40	32.0	43	34.4	42	33.6
Respiratory	38	30.4	24	19.2	63	50.4
Secretions	36	28.8	20	16.0	69	55.2
Appendectomy	35	28.0	28	22.4	62	49.6
Therapy	32	25.6	37	29.6	56	44.8
Nerve	28	22.4	80	64.0	17	13.6
Malignant	22	17.6	35	28.0	68	54.4
Terminal	16	12.8	60	48.0	49	39.2
Tendon	16	12.8	58	46.4	51	40.8
Total	3,608	57.7	1,453	23.3	1,189	19.0

the respondents did not know any of these words well enough for their responses to be scored in category D.

A Word About the Words

The particular words known or not known on this list are perhaps not important since it cannot be claimed that they constitute a representative sample of any universe of words used in hospital discourse. But they are words known to be frequently used in one hospital, and presumably used in others, so that it is illuminating to see how far from the intended meanings some of the responses are. Listed below are some selected terms with definitions as given in Dorland's *Medical Dictionary*[8] (in quotation marks), the question or statement used to elicit a response, and illustrative responses from scoring categories B and C.

The medical definition of *abdomen* is "that portion of the body which lies between the thorax and the pelvis." When presented with the statement "Do you have a pain in the abdomen?" respondents identified the abdomen as the sides, buttocks, back, uterus, heart, bladder, and the entire area below the waist.

Appendectomy is defined as the "surgical removal of the appendix vermiformis," but some respondents hearing it in the statement "An appendectomy is not serious," indicated that the term meant a cut rectum, sickness, the stomach, rupture of the appendix, a pain or disease, taking off an arm or leg, something contagious, something like an epidemic, something to do with the bowels.

The term *germs* (defined as "a microbe or bacillus") was put in the sentence "This sickness is caused by germs." Respondents variously defined the word as disease, dirt, something like diphtheria or typhoid, cells not functioning, like an infection, something in the body, something bad, something that causes a lot of things like sickness, things you can't hardly see, varmints that grow in the stomach, things that get on food and poison it.

Digestion, "the process or act of converting food into materials fit to be absorbed and assimilated," was explained in response to the stimulus question, "How is your digestion?" as appetite, normal elimination, swallowing, constipation, a sick feeling, your bowels, belching, whether food goes down all right, what you eat, food settling in the stomach.

Intern, "a medical graduate serving and residing in a hospital preparatory to his being licensed to practice medicine," was presented in the sentence. "The intern will take care of you." The term was identified as referring to an internist, a man nurse, a nurse helper, head of the doctors, drug store

---

8 W. A. Newman Dorland, *The American Illustrated Medical Dictionary,* 22nd edition (Philadelphia: W. B. Saunders Company, 1951).

man, same as an orderly, boys that help in the hospital, a medical student, a doctor's helper, a doctor with no degree.

"A cordlike structure which conveys impulses from one part of the body to another" is the medical definition of *nerve*. Confronted with the sentence, "This looks like a case of nerve injury," patients defined nerve as nervousness, veins, arteries, blood vessels, something that feeds the blood, like a bone, vessels in the body that circulate, something that goes to the heart, an elastic like thing, something like a pink worm, something like tissue in the body, something operated by the brain, something that keeps the body going.

"Let me feel your pulse," was the stimulus sentence for the term defined as "the expansion and contraction of an artery which may be felt with the finger." *Pulse* was identified as a bad hurt or sickness, a nerve, the pressure of nerves, temperature, a check for high blood pressure, too much fever, blood rushing through the nerves, something in the arm, a vein that shows how fast blood flows through the body, something that shows how the system is working, something that beats too fast or too slow.

And, as a final example, *respiratory*, "pertaining to the act or function of breathing," was presented in the sentence "Have you had any respiratory diseases?" and received responses indicating that it was thought to mean dangerous, in the arms and legs, heart, venereal, resulting from one's work, piles, an arrested case, a sickness in which you sweat and have hot and cold flashes, tiredness, and recent.

Each Patient Responded to All Words

Each of the 125 patients interviewed responded to the entire list of fifty words, thus giving a total of 6,250 responses. About three fifths of these (57.7 per cent) were scored in category D, indicating knowledge judged adequate for communication in the clinic situation. In about one fifth (19.0 per cent), the respondent could not—or would not—attempt any statement of meaning; the other fifth was about evenly divided between responses that indicated an incorrect understanding (10.5 per cent) and those that were so vague or ambiguous as to leave doubt about the degree of understanding (12.8 per cent).

In the information available about the patient-respondents there were four factors thought to have some possible association with variation in performance on the vocabulary schedule. These were sex, age, amount of formal education, and ethnic group membership.[9] Distribution of scores by sex of the respondent is shown in Table 2.

Analysis of variance in the distribution of the response in category D resulted in an F value which is not significant at the .05 level of confidence.

---

[9] No intelligence or personality test scores were available for this population.

TABLE 2. NUMBER AND PERCENTAGE OF CORRECT AND INCORRECT
RESPONSES TO FIFTY MEDICAL TERMS BY SEX OF RESPONDENT

| | CORRECTNESS OF RESPONSE | | | | | | |
| | D. ADEQUATE | | B. AND C. WRONG OR VAGUE | | A. NO KNOWLEDGE | | |
SEX	NUMBER	PER CENT	NUMBER	PER CENT	NUMBER	PER CENT	TOTAL
Males	1,487	57.2	602	23.1	511	19.7	2,600
Females	2,121	58.1	851	23.3	678	18.6	3,650
Total	3,608	57.7	1,453	23.3	1,189	19.0	6,250

To test further the association between sex and performance on this vocabulary schedule, comparisons, using the Mann-Whitney test, were made of the distribution of category D scores among Spanish-American males and females, Anglo-Saxon males and females, and Negro males and females with comparable amount of formal education, i.e., years of school completed. A series of six such comparisons yielded no significant differences. Our general conclusion was that we were unable to find in our data any evidence that the pattern of category D responses of females to this vocabulary schedule differs from that of males when ethnic group membership and amount of education are controlled.

When the responses are grouped by the age of the respondent, a negative relationship is revealed (Table 3).

Analysis of variance of the category D distributions shown in Table 3 yields an F value which is significant at the .05 level of confidence. The younger the respondent, the more likely it is that he will have a fairly clear idea of the meaning of the words; the older, the more likely it is that he will

TABLE 3. NUMBER AND PERCENTAGE OF CORRECT AND INCORRECT
RESPONSES TO FIFTY MEDICAL TERMS BY AGE

| | CORRECTNESS OF RESPONSE | | | | | | |
| | D. ADEQUATE | | B. AND C. WRONG OR VAGUE | | A. NO KNOWLEDGE | | |
AGE GROUP	NUMBER	PER CENT	NUMBER	PER CENT	NUMBER	PER CENT	TOTAL
15–24	831	61.6	260	19.2	259	19.2	1,350
25–44	1,460	63.5	514	22.3	326	14.2	2,300
45–64	835	53.9	392	25.3	323	20.8	1,550
65 and over	482	45.9	287	27.3	281	26.8	1,050
Total	3,608	57.7	1,453	23.3	1,189	19.0	6,250

not recognize the word or will give an incorrect or an ambiguous or vague response. Since common sense would seem to indicate that, everything else being equal, advancing age would give more familiarity with commonly used verbal symbols, an explanation of the apparent association between age and vocabulary performance was sought through further analysis. One finding was an expected inverse relation between age and amount of formal education. More than 60 per cent of the respondents 65 years of age or older had fewer than seven years of schooling. By comparison, only 4 per cent of those aged 15-24 had this little. There was an inverse correlation of $-.40$ between age and years of school completed, and a comparison of the age distribution of respondents with nine or fewer years of schooling with that of respondents with ten years or more yielded a statistically significant finding (chi square test; $P < .001$) that persons 45 years of age and older in the population from which this sample was drawn are more likely to have less formal education than persons aged 15-24. Comparisons of the distribution of category D scores, using the Mann-Whitney U Test, were made for all respondents aged 25-44 and 45 or over, with 7-9 years of school; for Anglos[10] in these two broad age categories with 7-9 years of school; and for Spanish-Americans with fewer than 7 years of school.[11] No significant differences were found. We conclude, therefore, that the observed differences in performance reported in Table 3 are probably due largely to differences in educational level between older and younger people in this population and that age *per se*, when not related to ethnic group membership or amount of formal education, has no consistent influence on performance on this vocabulary schedule.

A definite relation between amount of formal education and vocabulary performance is shown in Table 4. Calculation of a variance ratio for the distribution of category D scores (with 12 or more years of school completed combined into a single category) yielded an F value significant at the .01 level. This expected relation holds for all age groups, both sexes, and all of the three ethnic groups represented among the respondents. The higher the formal education of the respondent, the more likely he was to give a response that could be scored in category D; the lower the formal education, the more likely he was to give a response that indicated lack of recognition of the word or inability (or unwillingness) to define it. This is, of course, an obvious finding. What was not expected was the relatively low category D scores of respondents with a fair amount of formal education. A third of the responses of those with 10-11 years of educational experience were such that

---

[10] This is a term common in the Southwest to designate the numerically dominant, English-speaking white population. In this study it refers to all respondents who were not definable as Spanish-Americans or Negro—with the exception of one Japanese-American.

[11] These were the only categories in which numbers were large enough for meaningful comparisons to be made.

TABLE 4. NUMBER AND PERCENTAGE OF CORRECT AND INCORRECT
RESPONSES TO FIFTY MEDICAL TERMS BY NUMBER OF YEARS
OF SCHOOL COMPLETED BY RESPONDENTS

| | CORRECTNESS OF RESPONSE | | | | | | |
| | D. ADEQUATE | | B. AND C. WRONG OR VAGUE | | A. NO KNOWLEDGE | | |
YEARS OF SCHOOL COMPLETED	NUMBER	PER CENT	NUMBER	PER CENT	NUMBER	PER CENT	TOTAL
Under 7	567	37.8	401	26.7	532	35.5	1,500
7–9	1,096	56.2	455	23.4	399	20.5	1,950
10–11	972	64.8	357	23.8	171	11.4	1,500
12 (high school graduate)	777	74.0	195	18.6	78	7.4	1,050
13–15 (1–3 yrs. college)	118	78.7	26	17.3	6	4.0	150
16 (college graduate)	78	78.0	19	19.0	3	3.0	100
Total	3,608	57.7	1,453	23.3	1,189	19.0	6,250

they could not be scored as indicating adequate understanding of the terms tested; a fourth of the responses of high school graduates were similarly deficient. A part of this poor showing may be due to inadequacies in the scoring technique even though pre-test reliability checks were high and every schedule was checked by at least two investigators. But even allowing for substantial error in scoring technique, performance was poor enough to suggest that a good deal of what is said in a hospital and clinic to patients of average or even better educational background may not be clearly understood.

Table 5, giving the distribution of responses by ethnic groups, reveals that the performance of Anglos and Negroes was very similar but that Spanish-Americans gave fewer category D responses and proportionately more category A responses. Analysis of variance of category D responses among the three groups yielded an F value significant at the .01 level. To test whether this observed difference was valid or whether it resulted from concealed differences in the characteristics of Spanish-Americans and other groups in the sample, further analyses were undertaken. All Spanish-Americans in the sample had completed eleven or fewer years of school. Specific comparisons (with the Mann-Whitney U Test) of category D score distributions of Anglos and Spanish-Americans with fewer than seven years of school, 7-9 years of school, and 10-11 years of school showed that both young (age 15-44) and old (age 45 and over) Anglos consistently and significantly had "higher" scores than their Spanish-American counterparts.

TABLE 5. NUMBER AND PERCENTAGE OF CORRECT AND INCORRECT
RESPONSES TO FIFTY MEDICAL TERMS ACCORDING TO
ETHNIC BACKGROUND

| ETHNIC GROUP | CORRECTNESS OF RESPONSE | | | | | | |
| | D. ADEQUATE | | B. AND C. WRONG OR VAGUE | | A. NO KNOWLEDGE | | |
	NUMBER	PER CENT	NUMBER	PER CENT	NUMBER	PER CENT	TOTAL
Spanish-American	616	41.1	414	27.6	470	31.3	1,500
Anglo-American	2,103	62.8	713	21.2	534	15.9	3,350
Negro	868	64.3	300	22.3	182	13.5	1,350
Other	21	42.0	26	52.0	3	6.0	50
Total	3,608	57.7	1,453	23.3	1,189	19.0	6,250

Not only are the Spanish-Americans likely to do less well—that is, to understand clearly fewer terms—than Anglos of comparable age and level of education but, as numerous other studies have also shown, Spanish-Americans on the average are likely to have completed fewer years of formal schooling than Anglos and (in this study) Negroes.[12]

SUMMARY AND CONCLUSION

This research was concerned with a small but important part of a highly complex process—communication between patient and medical personnel in the hospital or clinic setting. It investigated a single aspect of that process, *i.e.,* the ability of patients to understand the meaning of certain verbal symbols commonly used in conversations with patients about their illness, its course, and its treatment. It presents evidence indicating that the level of comprehension is somewhat less than perfect and that there are variations associated with such factors as educational background, ethnic group membership, and age. Because of difficulties inherent in the attempt to define and sample a universe of words used in hospital-clinic discourse and a universe of hospital patients, it cannot be claimed that either the word sample or the patient sample is, with any known degree of probability, representative of a larger population. Generalization beyond the immediate respondents and the specific words used is, therefore, hazardous and, possibly, unwise. But, without such generalization, the research becomes pointless since these respondents have long since gone from the hospital, and nothing is known

---

[12] As indicated above, no Spanish-American in the sample had more than 11 years of schooling. By contrast, 24 per cent of the Anglos and 37 per cent of the Negroes had completed 12 or more years of school.

about the exact extent to which our sample words were used in attempts to communicate with them when they were hospitalized.[13]

In compiling words for our schedule, an attempt was made to bias the selection in favor of words that might be frequently used, that might collectively be appropriate for a wide range of illness conditions, and that might reasonably be expected to be found in the vocabularies of the majority of laymen. It was thought that this would give more conservative findings, on the assumption that if words such as these were not well understood, the more esoteric, more technical, less familiar terms would be even less likely to be comprehensible to patients.[14]

There was bias also in the characteristics of the patient-respondent group that could be expected to influence performance on a vocabulary test. All were sick enough to warrant hospitalization and some, at the time of interview, may have been under the effects of medication.[15] All were patients in a public hospital, which means that, in terms of the admission policies of that hospital, they were defined as medically indigent.[16] Their formal education, as indicated by median years of school completed was lower than that of the population of the city in which they lived. Substantially larger proportions were Spanish-American or Negro than is true for their city, their state, or the nation as a whole. As measured by the Hollingshead Two-Factor Index of Social Position, more than 90 per cent were in the lowest two social classes and nearly two-thirds in the lowest class. These, then, were not people who could be expected to have a high degree of verbal facility. But, on the other hand, in terms of such characteristics as low social class status, minimal education, and ethnic group membership, they are not unlike a good many millions of Americans who, at one time or another, find reason to seek medical care and thus come into interaction with clinic and hospital personnel.[17]

---

13 A weakness of research such as this is that, while it tells us something of the ability of patients to understand the terms included, it does not give information on situations in which these words were actually used. Physicians using these or similar terms may be highly sensitive to possible hiatuses in communication and may use supplementary or alternative terms to close the gap. Or they may be relatively insensitive to the degree of comprehension of patients and may use these or similar terms without being aware of all the instances in which comprehension is deficient. Undoubtedly both circumstances occur. Our subjective impression is that the latter is not unusual, particularly with relatively nontechnical words that laymen might be expected to know.

14 This point of view does not, of course, take account of the possibility that physicians may be more careful in the use of technical or "difficult" terms and may take more pains to be certain of being understood when such terms are used.

15 It must be remembered, however, that hospital and clinic personnel typically talk with people who are sick and frequently on medication.

16 For a more detailed description of some of the characteristics of the population of this hospital, see Hammond and Kern, op. cit., Ch. 4-5, pp. 24-59.

17 The U.S. Bureau of the Census estimates that there were over ten million foreign born in the United States in 1950, many of whom must have been reared in homes where other than English was spoken, and that in 1952 there were more than forty-

A question could be raised about the necessity of adequate communication between patients and those who treat them in hospital and clinic. Certainly no one has demonstrated that those patients who understand everything that is said to them get well faster or more certainly than those who do not. Perhaps, if the goal of medicine is the diagnosis and treatment of disease, the quality of communication between practitioner and patient makes little difference so long as an adequate medical history can be obtained and the necessary cooperation of the patient in doing or refraining from doing certain things can be assured. But if the goal is more broadly interpreted, if the concern is with the person who is sick and the purpose is to relieve, reassure, and restore him—as would seem to be increasingly the case—the quality of communication assumes instrumental importance, and anything that interferes with it needs to be noted and, if possible, removed.

The present research suggests that in any instance of practitioner-patient communication there is the possibility of misunderstanding or non-understanding on the part of the patient due to vocabulary deficiency, and that when the patient is one with little formal education, or a member of an ethnic group that has preserved a language other than that used in local medical discourse, or a person who can be identified as coming from a low social class environment, the probability of poor understanding or misunderstanding is increased. Since literally millions of Americans have and will continue to have these characteristics, the potentiality for impaired communication may be large. Practitioner-patient communication, even under the best of circumstances, is rendered difficult by the tremendous and probably increasing differences in conceptualization and knowledge of normal and pathological processes that exist between professionally trained persons and even well informed laymen. With less well informed laymen, the risks of communicating incorrectly or not at all are even greater.

In his interviews in "Regionville," Earl Koos concluded that much of the dissatisfaction felt by the people he talked to with respect to their relations with physicians was the result of a lack of communication between physician and patient. A comment from one of our subjects appears at the beginning of this paper; let one of Koos's speak at the end:

> Nobody should blame the doc if he doesn't fix them up right away—or maybe never. But maybe things would be better if the doc understood us, and if we always knew what the hell he was driving at—and not in big words either.[18]

---

four million people, fourteen years of age and older, with eight or fewer grades of school completed. U.S. Department of Commerce, Bureau of the Census. *Statistical Abstract of the United States, 1957* (Washington: Government Printing Office, 1957), pp. 32 and 111.

[18] Earl Koos, *The Health of Regionville* (New York: Columbia University Press, 1954), p. 77.

Some Social Functions of Laughter

A Study of Humor in a Hospital Setting

ROSE LAUB COSER

☙   Laughter is a peculiarly human trait. Animals do not laugh—*vide* the interesting German idiom *tierischer Ernst* (animal earnestness). No wonder that this distinctively human activity has preoccupied philosophers ever since antiquity and that psychology and especially psychoanalysis, following Freud's lead, have devoted much attention to its interpretation.[1] Yet there have been few attempts at a sociological analysis of humor. The literature contains mainly discussions of specific types of humor in some social settings[2] but hardly any generalizations about the social functions of humor.[3] The relative neglect of humor and laughter on the part of sociologists is the more surprising since, as many a philosopher has remarked, laughter is a peculiarly social activity.

Laughter, like all other expressions of emotions, as well as most other physiological reactions, is regulated by society. It is expected to remain under control: "mad laughter," "hysterical laughter," are disapproved. This is to say that laughter is socially patterned, like yawning, for example; but it is not so much that which makes laughter similar to other physiological reactions but rather what makes it dissimilar from them that requires sociological inquiry.

Laughter, unlike many other human activities, occurs—or is expected to occur—only within patterns of interaction. This seemingly most spontaneous

---

[1] See the bibliographical article by J. C. Flügel (12).

[2] Of outstanding importance is, of course, Radcliffe-Brown's work (27). Other anthropologists, among them Margaret Mead and Gregory Bateson (3), have also dealt with joking relationships and comic representations. Some sociological writings have also appeared on the subject (2, 7, 8, 22, 24).

[3] On some social functions of humor, see the writings of Blau (6), Burns (9), and Fox (14).

Reprinted with permission from the author and *Human Relations*, Vol. 12, No. 2, 1959, pp. 171-182. This is a revised version of a paper read at the meetings of the Eastern Sociological Society, New York, March 1956. The author is indebted to Warren Bennis for a critical reading of this paper.

means of individual release and self-expression is not expected to be used by a person who is alone. The man who laughs or chuckles to himself is looked at as "probably crazy." He is granted an exemption from this stigma only if it can be observed that he responds to the symbolic stimulus of an interactive pattern, as when he reads a comic book or responds to a comic incident on a movie screen.[4] Laughter, like language, is supposed to function within a communicative relationship and the man who laughs to himself, like the man who talks to himself or the man who hoards his goods or his daughters, is considered an asocial man. He who laughs in isolation calls forth a social disapproval that may be compared to the disapproval that greets the miser or the incestuous father. Laughter must be shared; it is socially defined as a prime part of the interactive process, of the give and take of social life. As Francis Jeanson has remarked: "Even your joys must be quoted on the market, you are not allowed a satisfaction which is not listed on the exchange—and if you refrain from saying why you laugh and if the reason is not apparent, you will soon be told that "you laugh like an idiot [that is, to go back to the root sense of the term, like a peculiar, a dis-sociated man]." Jeanson continues: "Your laughter is supposed only to express the reactions of the 'collective consciousness': in any other case it is absurd to the extent that it signifies maladaptation" (20, p. 152).

To laugh in the company of others presupposes a minimum of common "definition of the situation." Those who refuse to join in common laughter are frowned upon, they are "bad sports"; on the other hand, if an invitation to laugh is not accepted by the group, the incipient humorist feels "out of place." In laughter one must share and share alike.

To laugh, or to occasion laughter through humor and wit, is to invite those present to come close. Laughter and humor are indeed like an invitation, be it an invitation for dinner, or an invitation to start a conversation: it aims at decreasing social distance. What Levi-Strauss has said about the social meaning of an exchange of table wine among strangers seated at the same table in a French restaurant applies to the uses of humor: "The partner who had the right to maintain reserve is called upon to give it up; . . . cordiality demands cordiality. . . . There is no possibility of refusing the neighbor's offer . . . without appearing insulting. Moreover, the acceptance of the offer authorizes another offer, that of conversation. Thus a number of minute social bonds are established in the offering and an obligation in the receiving. And there is still more. The person who begins the cycle has taken the initiative, and the greater social ease which he has proved becomes an advantage for him. However, the opening always carries with it a risk, namely that the

---

4 Even in the marginal case of a person laughing because he sees a stranger stumble, the laughter establishes an interactive relationship with a symbolic other in that he rejoices over his own good fortune in comparison with the victim.

partner will answer the offered libation with a less generous drink . . ."
(23, pp. 84-94).

Laughter always involves an element of reciprocity. This is why it would
be impossible to analyze the functions of laughter without discussing humor,
that is without discussing what elicits laughter. Thus Bergson, who entitles
his famous essay *Laughter*, proceeds to analyze the comic. Humor and laughter are intrinsically linked because a situation is defined as humorous by the
laughing response that it elicits. "The comic," writes Baudelaire, "the power
of laughter, lies in the man who laughs, not in the object of laughter"
(4, p. 370).

Hence, humor and laughter can be understood only in terms of the common concerns of the participants. "To understand laughter," writes Bergson,
"we must put it back into its natural environment, which is society, and above
all must we determine that utility of its function which is a social one . . .
Laughter must answer to certain requirements of life in common. It must
have *social* signification" (5, pp. 8-9; emphasis in the original).

From what has been said so far it would appear that different degrees or
frequencies of laughter, and different types of humor, prevail in different
types of group structure. It is well known that different nationalities as well
as ethnic groups have their peculiar types of humor. There is Jewish humor,
British humor, Irish humor. Certain types of humor are peculiar to particular
status positions: there is the humor of the underdog as well as the humor of
the top dog. Specific types of humor flourish under different political conditions: there is totalitarian humor as there is democratic humor.

A social group or subgroup, as it is differentially located within the social
structure, produces and sanctions variant forms of humor. And since, within
particular groups, structures of authority and systems of role allocation differ,
the specific types of interaction that accompany such variations will also
encourage specific types of humorous interaction. The present paper will
explore in detail some of the social mechanisms of humor in one subgroup of
a complex organization: the ward patients of a general hospital.

The writer has been engaged recently in a study of the social structure of
a hospital ward. Although this study was primarily concerned with other
problems, it has been possible to make a series of observations on the use of
humor and jocular talk within this setting which lend themselves to the
formulation of some hypotheses. The interpretations presented here are
meant as suggestions for stimulating further research.

This report will be limited to jocular talk among patients, i.e., among
peers, and will not discuss any humor between patients and staff; it has to be
remembered that humor across status lines may well take other forms and
have other functions than humor among status equals.

During daily observations in the ward for a period of three months, the researcher was impressed by the jocular tone of conversation among patients. Although some patients were more gifted than others in highlighting comic elements of their experiences, most of them, when they were together in the sitting-room or when they were conversing in the ward, tended to fall into jocular conversation. Much of their jocular talk consisted of jocular griping. The humorous intent was discernible in the tone of voice, in facial expression, but above all in the laughing responses that it elicited. If much of what will be quoted will not appear humorous to the reader, this will be evidence for the main point of this paper, namely that humor is an expression of the collective experience of the participants, and receives response only from those who share common concerns.

Jocular talk and laughter of hospital patients can be understood in reference to three main characteristics: anxiety about self, submission to a rigid authority structure, and, related to this, adjustment to rigid routine.

Hospital patients are likely to be subject to a high degree of insecurity and generalized anxiety. As Michael M. Davis has stated in his introduction to R. Rorem's book, to the sick person ". . . the hospital is a battlefield between life and death, the focus of intense anxieties and hopes" (28, p. vii). The very fact of hospitalization is an indication that there is some measure of danger. Patients report:

> "I'm not afraid of being alone in the hospital, but it's just the uncertainty."

> "I was very apprehensive. I was frightened to death. I didn't know what to expect."

> "[A good doctor is] a good speaker to you who explains you very good, explains everything what happens to you and what's going to happen, that's what I call a good doctor."

The insecurity of patients not only derives from their physical condition but is enhanced by the peculiar type of authority relation to which they are submitted. A patient's loss of control over his body is matched by his loss of control over his physical environment and over his own actions. Everything is planned for him—his meals, his intake of medication, etc. Even his body temperature is no longer his concern, but that of nurses who insist on removing the thermometer immediately after its use. The total control by hospital staff is justified in terms of a sick person's helplessness and lack of competence (25, pp. 439-446).

To patients the authority of the hospital staff seems to be unlimited. Whereas in the society at large people are under the authority of one set of persons for a limited amount of time, say from nine till five, a patient has to submit to the authority of hospital staff twenty-four hours a day. He is under continuous supervision and his full day is scheduled for him.[5]

Authority relations in the hospital are symbolized by the sharp contrast in dress: while patients are deprived of most body symbols—not only of clothes but also of other intimate belongings such as jewelry—which constitutes a loss of identity of the social self, the staff, nurses as well as doctors, dispose of elaborate body extensions for the sake of status recognition and role symbolization.

Related to authority relations is the strict routine of the hospital. It would seem that hardly anywhere is the term "routinized emergency," which Everett C. Hughes has coined (19), more applicable than to the hospital. "In many occupations," says Hughes, "the workers or practitioners deal routinely with what are emergencies to the people who receive the services." For the staff the term points to the functional importance of discipline in emergency situations. But since the definitions of "emergency" and "routine" emerge from the staff,[6] a patient is soon impressed with the fact that he is a "routine case," and senses that many of the hospital's rules and regulations may be extrinsic to his own treatment, that they serve to maintain the organization as a going concern.

The patient's need of security, their low position in the hospital hierarchy, and the need to preserve their moral self against the pressure of physical routine—these are three main aspects of the status of patients in a hospital. Though it is true that these three factors are not peculiar to hospitals only but may be variously distributed in society, they seem to occur simultaneously and perhaps in a more dramatic way in organizations set up to deal routinely with the emergency of physical threat.

The following example, a patient's jocular report of a significant event in the ward, will illustrate the combination of the three themes:

> "Did you hear what happened yesterday? I'm telling ye, it was a riot, the funniest thing. There were two Mrs. Broseman admitted here yesterday with the identical first name. So, Mrs. Broseman from our ward [i.e. medical] was sitting here with us, and up comes Dr. B. [from the surgical ward] and asks for Mrs. Ann Broseman. Out she goes. When she walks to the left to the medical ward, he says, 'No, this way, please,' and takes her to the other side to give her a physical. In the meantime, the nurses in the

---

[5] For a brilliant statement of these authority relations and of the split between staff and patients, see Erving Goffman's work on "Total Institutions" (17). For a formulation of the problem of patients' deprivation of decision-making, see the remarks by Leo W. Simmons and Harold G. Wolff (29, pp. 176-187).

[6] Cf. ". . . The institutional plant and name come to be identified by both staff and inmates as somehow belonging to staff, so that when either grouping refers to the views or interests of the 'institution,' by implication they are referring to the views and concerns of the staff" (17, p. 7).

medical ward were looking for Mrs. Broseman. They were all excited and worried because they are responsible for the patients, you know. Well, finally they got her. She was raving mad and red as a beet. She came here for high blood-pressure in the first place. Well, it must have gone sky-high after that!"

The patient who reported the incident reinterpreted it in such a way that it became stripped of its threatening aspects. This recalls Freud's observation that humor serves as a means of allaying anxiety: "The principal thing is the intention which humor fulfils. Its meaning is: 'Look here! This is all this seemingly dangerous world amounts to. Child's play, the very thing to jest about'" (15, p. 220). The humorous reporter modified reality by denying the objective justification of the fears common to all, namely that some confusion in administering medication might occur. By making the story sound funny and by implicitly contrasting, through ridicule, the plight of the victim to the good luck of those present, this patient implied that such fears are not grounded in reality, that even if a confusion occurs it is simply "the very thing to jest about."[7]

Moreover, the jocular wording of the report provided an opportunity for talker and listeners to get back at the nurses.[8] Note that the nurses and not the patients were "excited and worried." Such a reversal of roles is a frequent element in comic representations, as Bergson has shown.[9] This type of humor is referred to by Freud as "tendency wit" which "is used with special preference as a weapon of attack or criticism of superiors who claim to be in authority" (16, p. 699).

The main "funny" element of the story, however, consists in the confusion resulting from a mechanical way of dealing with individual persons. Bergson speaks of the comic element contained in the "complete automatism . . . in the official, for instance, who performs his duty like a mere machine." The story illustrates his point, that an incident is comic "that calls

---

[7] On the safety-producing functions of humor, see also the writings of Donald Hayworth (18) and Renée Fox (14).

[8] This is a frequent device. It is a type of "rebellion" that promises immunity from retaliation by the "powerful," which is especially important in a dependency situation. To give one other example: Patient at the eve of a repeated operation, taking bobby pins out of her hair: "I may as well do this now. They'd do that to me tomorrow anyhow. This keeps me one step ahead of the nurses." The four patients present laugh heartily.

[9] Bergson has stressed the fact that reversal of roles is a frequent element in comedies (5, p. 95). The psychoanalyst Ludwig Jekels (21) remarks that whereas in tragedies the theme is usually the hostility of the son against the father, in comedies the theme is reversed: the father is being deprived of his "fatherly" attributes and invested with the weaknesses of the son. Gregory Bateson (3) writes about a reversal of roles in the ceremonials of primitive tribes, through buffoonery for the man and magnificent ceremony for the woman, in a society which glorifies masculinity in everyday life and assigns a passive role to women.

our attention to the physical in a person when it is the moral side that is concerned" (5, pp. 90-91).

This type of humor, then, serves as a means of warding off danger; as a means of rebellion against authority; and as a relief from mechanical routine. It is important to note that these themes are conveyed to persons who have the same worries and anxieties and that the humorist invites the listeners to join with her in a "triumph of invincibility."

The very process of communication, moreover, consists in the jocular talk through which the speaker conveys information: the other patients are told, in this story, that the nurses protect patients because "they are responsible, you know," and "they finally got her." Again, there is reassurance that there is no real danger; this time the security comes, according to the report, from the social organization of the hospital. Thus the jocular report is, as Donald Hayworth has pointed out, a "communication to other members in the group that they may relax with safety" (18).

In her jocular report, this patient *taught* the other patients, through jocular interaction with them rather than through a moralizing speech, to adapt to hospital society. Thus, in addition to its *safety-producing function*, jocular talk serves the *socialization* of patients. This is even more obvious in cases where the use of humor permits the transformation of individual complaints into collective pleasure.

The need to abstain from complaining was well expressed by one patient:

> "I never complain. What good would it be anyhow? No use complainen . . . Got to take things as they are. Take life as it is. Some people magnify things. Others make them smaller. That's the better way."

This patient stated that she intentionally "makes things smaller," and indeed in her jocular talk with other patients she fashioned reality herself, *for* herself and *for* the other patients as well. Conversations like the following are rather typical for the ward:

> "I couldn't sleep all night. The lady next to me had a nightmare and was shrieking. Across the hall there was one who had gotten a needle and she yelled that the ceiling came down, I'm telling ye. So, I walked out to have a smoke and there in the television room there was the family of one who had died across the hall. They were crying and lamenting. I'll be glad to get home to get some rest. If I stay here longer, I'm going to get sick."
>
> Patients laugh, nod, exclaim "Yeah," "That's how it is." Another patient joins in: "Yeah, just like me, I came in as a lion and am going out as a lamb. I came in for three days, have been here for two weeks now."
>
> Third patient: "Sure, you can't get no rest. At 6 o'clock they wake you up. So I thought I'll sleep after breakfast. I dozed off,

and there I hear the doctor: 'Are you sleeping?' Of course I said, 'Not anymore.' I went to sleep after they left, so the nurse comes up with a pill."
Everybody laughs.

In this conversation there are some jokes that have become standard in hospital life: that in the hospital you get sick, that you cannot get any rest; the story of the nurse who wakes you up to give you a sleeping pill is not a new one. These jokes are part of the hospital folklore. They all imply rebellion against the routine,[10] against the "mechanical encrusted upon the living," and against the staff who on the basis of their authority may intrude any time they wish on the privacy of the patient. It is to be noted also that shrieking patients and laments over death are stripped of their threatening quality.

Again, the content of the jocular talk consists in the three themes that were stated at the start. But there is more: the mechanism consists in transforming a personal experience into one that can be shared by all. *The jocular gripe is the collective expression of an individual complaint.*

Peter Blau, in his recent *Dynamics of Bureaucracy*, observes that complaints are nearly always made to a single person whereas jokes are often told to a group (6, p. 92). What Blau says about jokes applies also to the jocular gripe. What is more, the jocular gripe performs the functions of both complaint and joke, but differs from both.

A patient told the observer: "Dinner was no good, what I cook is better." Ten minutes later, in the sitting-room, she told the other patients:

> "Those hamburgers today were as hard as rocks, if I'd bounced them against the wall they'd come right back" (breaks out in laughter about her own good joke and other patients join in).

The contrast between these two negative statements is remarkable.

(i) The patient talked about herself when she was alone with the observer, but when several patients were present she chose to transform her personal experience into a general one. Her humorous image let all participate imaginatively in the appraisal of the meat's quality, while in her remark to the observer she had pointed to her own superior cooking ability as a basis for judgment.

(ii) The image the patient used permitted all to join in liberating laughter. It is not necessary here to labor what has become obvious since Freud's writing on the subject, namely that this feeling of liberation consists in a release of tension and aggression (16, pp. 733 ff.). But the comparison

---

[10] The following remarks of patients provide additional illustration of this type of jocular talk: "All night patients in, patients out, nurses running around. At home a sick man can get some rest." Or again: Patient A, opening the newspaper: "They shot the President of Panama." Patient B: "They go on shooting these days just like they shoot needles into you. It's true, all they do is shoot needles into you, a dime a dozen."

between the complaint and the jocular gripe can be carried a step further by drawing upon one other insight by Freud in his analysis of humor: "What is fine about [humor] is the ego's victorious assertion of its own invulnerability" (15, p. 217). In the complaint the patient admits his vulnerability; in the jocular gripe, as in humor generally, he overcomes it and allows his listeners to participate in his triumph over weakness. In addition to the humorist's triumph over his own weakness—the peculiar quality of gallows humor— there is here the added gratification in the *collective* character of the triumph.

The jocular gripe is peculiarly fit as a mechanism of adaptation to the hospital for it helps patients to regain their identity through collective triumph over their weakness and at the same time to release their grudges in "substitute complaints."

(iii) The liberating effect of joined laughter consists also in the consensus that it brings about in a brief span of time.[11] Stanton and Schwartz point out that real consensus brings with it an element of delight about its achievement (31, p. 196). They join Bergson, who saw that the liberating amusement indicates a feeling that "only we" know what it means. It strengthens the boundaries between the group of laughters and the outsiders (5, p. 6), between the patients and those who are in authority, doctors and nurses. One only has to think of the annoyance that overcomes us sometimes when we hear people laugh in the next room, a feeling of being "left out." Thus not only do the patients achieve consensus, but through this consensus nurses and doctors, who otherwise have access to the most intimate parts of the patients' bodies, are denied access.

(iv) Jokes and jocular talk are the fare of sociability. As a patient said, "We are full of jokes. My sister asked me, 'How do you feel?' I said, 'I'm enjoying myself; we're chatting around; it's a pleasure.'" Personal complaints are tabooed on the ward because, as Simmel remarked, "the purely and deeply personal traits of one's life, character, mood and fate must . . . be eliminated as factors in sociability. It is tactless . . . to display merely personal moods of depression, excitement, despondency—in brief, the light and darkness of one's most intimate life." When Simmel goes on to say that in sociability "each individual ought to have as much satisfaction . . . as is compatible with [the] satisfaction on the part of all others" (29, pp. 46-47), he seems to mean that each participant must present his piece of conversation in such a manner that it becomes meaningful to all other participants.

The patient who complains considers himself more important than others and thereby violates the "democratic structure of sociability" of which Simmel speaks. Corroborative evidence comes from a patient who said: "There's always one who's crabbing. He thinks he's better than others, but he isn't

---

11 Cf. "The joke is a shortcut to consensus" (9, p. 657).

more than a patient. A patient is a patient in the hospital . . . Even when you're a doctor and you're a patient, you're just another patient."

Unlike the complainer, the patient who invites others to laugh with him creates or strengthens the feeling of equality in the participants. Hence jocular griping brings about a social relationship in its simplest and purest form: that of reciprocity. There are many different ways of saying the same thing, depending on the social situation; one only has to consider the difference in implication between "I cannot sleep" and "a hospital is no place to rest." Although both phrases denote the same experience, the first is, in Piaget's terms, an egocentric statement that does not take account of the point of view of the other person (26).

The jocular gripe differs not only from the complaint but to some extent from the joke also. Like all jocular talk, it is more akin to humor in that it contributes more than the pure joke to the reinterpretation of events and to the solidarity of the participants. Fowler's differential definition may serve well here: whereas the joke has its comic quality in the surprise element of the punch line and makes a demand upon the intelligence of the listener, the humor contained in jocular talk is based on observation of actual events and relies on the sympathy of the listener (13, p. 241). Unlike the pure joke, jocular talk, especially the jocular gripe, is based on shared experience; it unites the group by allowing it to reinterpret together an experience that previously was individual to each. Although, like the joke, it permits all to join in laughter which in itself strengthens social cohesion, it cannot be resorted to in the complete absence of social cohesion for it presupposes a common experience between speaker and listener that is the basis of the sympathy that it elicits. A patient's different accounts of the same experience—one to those who are "in the know" and another one to a newcomer—will make this clear:

> Patient, to a group of women in the sitting-room, all of whom had been in the ward for several days, at least, and who were griping about the commotion on the ward: "They never let you sleep here. One thing you can't get is sleep. At 6 o'clock it's temperature, at 6.30 it's blood pressure, at 7 it's washing and at 7.30 it's breakfast, and so it goes all day. They never leave you alone. Not even right after my operation. Four nurses would stand around me and come up all the time asking, 'Do you feel all right?' 'Do you have any pain?' 'Do you want a pill?' 'Do you want some water?' when all you want is sleep."
> Other patients nodded, smiled, and laughed.

A little later that same afternoon, the same patient sat in the sitting-room again, and also present was a newcomer, admitted a few hours previously.

> Newcomer: "I wonder what they're going to do to me."
> Patient: "They're really nice here, you know. Like after my

operation, four nurses were standing around me asking if I wanted something and they kept coming asking if I was in pain or was there anything I wanted. I didn't want anything, but it felt good just the same, to know they care. You don't have to worry around here."

The newcomer might have been more perturbed than relieved had she learned that "they never leave you alone," for she could not have interpreted this patient's gripe in the same way as the initiated. To participate in jocular talk one has to have overcome one's worst fears and be somewhat detached, and what is more, participation in jocular talk presupposes some common experiences about which consensus is sought. Jocular talk and especially jocular griping is not being shared with a stranger.

In summary: unlike the joke which calls for a listener, the jocular gripe calls for a participant. It transforms a personal experience into a collective one; by generalizing it and making it the property of all, the individual sufferer is "dispossessed" of his own suffering. This type of behavior stresses the equality of all patients within a social structure otherwise characterized by its rigid hierarchy; it brings about consensus and strengthens group identification among persons whose relationships are only transitory.

The different accounts that a patient gave about her experience with nurses after her operation raises the problem of the role of the jocular griper.

Though it is obvious that in her serious reassurance of the newcomer the "veteran" patient had acted as an agent of socialization, she acted in a similar role when talking in jocular fashion to the initiated. There is reason to believe that this patient enjoyed the care and reassurance of the nurses when she woke up after the operation, and that she somehow "put up an act" in her jocular criticism of hospital routine. There is, indeed, a performance quality in jocular talk. In Flügel's words, "at least one of the most important functions [of laughter] is to attract the attention of our fellow beings and to elicit an appropriate reaction from them" (12, p. 730). Just as in an artistic creation,[12] there is a make-believe element: the term "make-believe" expresses well the bond that the act creates between speaker and listener (1, p. 153). Moreover, as Freud, Baldwin, and others have suggested, make-believe gives a sense of exaggerated self.

The self-aggrandizement of the speaker, far from being egocentric, is a means of establishing a bond with his audience. When the patient was griping in humorous fashion about the nurses' busyness around her, she did not merely overcome her own fear and wretchedness, which must have overwhelmed her when waking up from the operation, and she did not only

---

[12] Cf. "The funny story is an artistic thing even as is the novel, the movie or the drama . . ." (18, p. 379).

oppose the institutionalized, routinized care that she was given. She also exaggerated her own self with regard to the other persons in the audience. Not only did she make an assertion of invulnerability, but she adopted toward her listeners, as Freud remarked, "the attitude of an adult towards a child, recognizing and smiling at the triviality of the interests and sufferings which seem to the child so big. Thus the humorist acquires his superiority by assuming the role of the grown-up . . . while he reduces the other people to the position of children" (15, p. 218).

It is to a large extent through jocular griping that a patient assumes the role of a socializing agent with respect to other patients. Bergson's remark, "the humorist is a disguised moralist" (5, p. 28), is appropriate here. In her account of her waking after the operation, this patient acted as a socializing agent in two ways. With the newcomer she manifestly took the role of adult toward a child; with the initiated she concealed her socializing role in a performance that had, at the same time, an "equalizing" function in bringing about collective pleasure and elation in consensus about common experiences.

So far some functions of jocular talk for the participants have been considered as well as the role of the jocular griper. It will now be seen that jocular griping performs integrative functions for the social structure of the ward.

The tendency to reduce complaints through the taboo enforced by the patients themselves and through their substitution by jocular griping, helps to shape the behavior of patients according to the expectations of doctors and nurses, and is thus an integrating elements among these three groups in the ward. The patients themselves, by teaching and helping each other to suppress complaints through laughter, help to enforce the norms of the hospital community. Through laughter, "we internalize a community attitude toward the self. We learn in great laughter that it is possible to love those we laugh at, as well as those we laugh with" (11, p. 54).

Moreover, by referring in jocular fashion to incidents that ordinarily would call forth complaints, the patients effect what Bergson calls a "corrective for an imperfection" (5, p. 87). The undesirable situation is being remedied, in the minds of those who are exposed to it, through its humorous interpretation. The patients themselves, by bringing about a change in the definition of the situation, transform the undesirable into the harmless, the frightening into amusement, and thereby make the hospital ward acceptable *as it is*.

This points to a possible dysfunctional consequence of humor: by effecting a "corrective for an imperfection" only in the *perception* of the patients, an unsatisfactory situation may remain unaltered and continue to be a source of concern.[13] The early waking of patients is one example that stands for many.

Humor is a "safety-valve," i.e., it provides institutionalized outlets for hostilities and for discontent ordinarily suppressed by the group. Thus, as Lewis A. Coser has remarked, it reduces the "pressure for modifying the system to meet changing conditions." "Wit may not bring about a change in the relations between one person and another, especially if the target of the aggressive wit is not aware of the source and intention of the witticism . . . [Wit] may afford expression to the weaker member without changing the terms of the relationship" (10, pp. 48 and 43 respectively).

In conclusion: humor allows the participants, in a brief span of time and with a minimum of effort, mutually to reinterpret their experiences, to entertain, reassure, and communicate; to convey their interest in one another, to pull the group together by transforming what is individual into collective experience, and to strengthen the social structure within which the group functions. Whereas Freud has pointed to the *psychic economy* that humor makes possible for the individual (15, 16),[14] the contribution it makes to *social economy* should be stressed—a contribution that should not be underestimated in groups whose membership is continuously changing, and especially in the transient little subgroups that are formed for short spans of time each day in wards and sitting-rooms. In such a shifting and threatening milieu, a story well told, which, in a few minutes, entertains, reassures, conveys information, releases tension, and draws people more closely together, may have more to contribute than carefully planned lectures and discussions toward the security of the frightened sick.

---

[13] Cf. "[Humor] transforms reality without any efficacious material intervention and even makes such intervention unnecessary. In this respect the social function of laughter in modern societies is comparable to that of magic in pre-literate societies" (32, p. 166).
[14] On this point, see also Victoroff's work (32, Ch. V).

REFERENCES

1. Baldwin, James, *Mental Development*. New York: The Macmillan Co., p. 153, 1897.
2. Barron, Milton L., "A Content Analysis of Intergroup Humor." *Amer. Sociol. Rev.*, Vol. 15, pp. 88-94, 1950.
3. Bateson, Gregory, *Naven*. 1936.
4. Baudelaire, Charles, "De l'essence du rire." In *Curiosités Esthétiques*, Paris: Calmann-Levy, II, 1884.
5. Bergson, Henri, *Laughter*. London: Macmillan & Co., 1911.
6. Blau, Peter, *Dynamics of Bureaucracy*. Chicago: University of Chicago Press, 1955.
7. Bradney, Pamela, "The Joking Relationship in Industry." *Hum. Rela.*, Vol. 10, pp. 179-187, 1957.

8. Burma, John H., "Humor as a Technique in Race Conflict." *Amer. Sociol. Rev.,* Vol. 11, pp. 710-715, 1946.
9. Burns, Tom, "Friends, Enemies and Polite Fiction." *Amer. Sociol. Rev.,* Vol. 18, pp. 654-662, 1953.
10. Coser, Lewis A., *The Functions of Social Conflict.* Glencoe, Ill.: Free Press, 1956.
11. Duncan, Hugh Dalziel, *Language and Literature in Society.* Chicago: University of Chicago Press, 1953.
12. Flügel, J. C., "Humor and Laughter." In Gardner Lindzey (ed.). *Handbook of Social Psychology.* Cambridge, Mass.: Addison-Wesley, Vol. 2, pp. 709-734, 1954.
13. Fowler, *A Dictionary of Modern English Usage.* Oxford: Clarendon Press, 1952.
14. Fox, Renée, *Ward F-Second and The Research Physician.* Unpubl. Ph.D. Dissertation. Harvard University, 1953.
15. Freud, Sigmund, "Humour." In *Collected Papers.* London: Hogarth Press, pp. 215-221, 1950.
16. Freud, Sigmund, *Wit and Its Relation to the Unconscious.* New York: Moffat Yard, 1916.
17. Goffman, Erving, *On the Characteristics of Total Institutions.* To appear in the Proceedings of the Symposium on Preventive and Social Psychiatry, Walter Reed Army Institute of Research, Washington, D.C., 15-17, April 1957 (Mimeo.).
18. Hayworth, Donald, "The Origin and Function of Laughter." *Psychol. Rev.,* Vol. 35, pp. 367-384, 1928.
19. Hughes, Everett C., "Work and Self." In John H. Rohrer and Muzafer Sherif (eds.), *Social Psychology at the Crossroads.* New York: Harper, pp. 313-323, 1951.
20. Jeanson, Francis, *Signification humaine du rire.* Paris: Editions du Seuil, 1950.
21. Jekels, Ludwig, "Zur Psychologie der Komoedie." A. J. Storfer (ed.), *Almanach des Internationalen Psychoanalytischen Verlags,* pp. 190-198, 1927.
22. Klapp, Orrin E., "The Fool as a Social Type." *Amer. J. Sociol.,* Vol. 54, pp. 135-141, 1948, and Vol. 55, pp. 157-162, 1949.
23. Levi-Strauss, Claude, "The Principle of Reciprocity." In Lewis A. Coser and Bernard Rosenberg (eds.), *Sociological Theory.* New York: The Macmillan Co., pp. 84-94, 1957.
24. Obrdlik, Antonin J., "Gallow's Humor—A Sociological Phenomenon." *Amer. J. Sociol.,* Vol. 47, pp. 709-716, 1942.
25. Parsons, Talcott, *The Social System.* Glencoe, Ill.: Free Press, 1951; London: Tavistock Publications, 1952.
26. Piaget, Jean, *The Moral Judgment of the Child.* Glencoe, Ill.: Free Press, 1948.
27. Radcliffe-Brown, A. R., "On Joking Relationships" and "A Further Note on Joking Relationships." In *Structure and Function in Primitive Society.* Glencoe, Ill.: Free Press, Chapters IV and V, 1952.
28. Rorem, C. Rufus, *The Public's Investment in Hospitals.* Chicago: University of Chicago Press, 1930.

29. Simmel, Georg. *The Sociology of Georg Simmel.* Trans. Kurt H. Wolff. Glencoe, Ill.: The Free Press, 1950.
30. Simmons, Leo W., and Wolff, Harold G. *Social Science in Medicine.* New York: Russel Sage Foundations, 1954.
31. Stanton, Alfred H., and Schwartz, Morris S. *The Mental Hospital.* New York: Basic Books, 1954; London: Tavistock Publications.
32. Victoroff, D. *Le rire et le risible.* Paris: Presses Universitaires de France, 1953.

The Schizophrenic No-Society

ROBERT SOMMER · HUMPHRY OSMOND

Social scientists have described mental hospitals as societies, communities, neighborhoods, and cultures which, like the same forms of social organization found in the outside world, have grown out of the common shared life of the group. Among the more familiar models used by the various writers who have applied this social concept to the patient population are the school, the general hospital, the nursery, and the prison. Whether these terms can appropriately be used to describe all types of mental hospitals and all kinds of patients, we believe, remains to be determined. In this paper we shall examine their appropriateness with reference to long-stay wards in a large state hospital.

Most of the studies that have been made of the social life of mental patients have been made in private sanitaria or teaching and research centers. How far the findings relate to the large state hospital is therefore open to question, for, although all mental hospitals have some features in common, there are differences between the large public hospital and the private sanitarium that cannot be ignored.

Furthermore, the comparatively few studies of this type that have been made in large public hospitals have almost all been made on admission wards. Since the social life on admission wards differs greatly from that on

Reprinted by special permission of The William Alanson White Psychiatric Foundation, Inc., holder of the copyright. This study appeared originally in *Psychiatry*, Vol. 25, No. 3, August 1962, pp. 244-255 and was aided by grants from the Commonwealth Fund and the Department of Health and Welfare, Ottawa.

long-stay wards, as many studies have shown, the findings here may not have relevance for the long-stay wards. An obvious difference is that, on admission wards, the patient population is a transient one, with patients continually being admitted and discharged; the nurses and doctors are the only stable factors in the ward population. On the long-stay wards, in contrast, it is the patients who remain stationary while the doctors and nurses change. Compared with the long-stay wards, moreover, admission wards have more staff and better treatment, a different population composition, and an active and spontaneous social life among patients. Every sociometric study of mental hospital wards has shown that there are more friendships on the admission wards than on the long-stay wards. Since admission wards comprise less than 10 per cent of the patient population in most mental hospitals, it is clearly important to develop models that apply to the long-stay wards.

In the paper presented here we shall examine some models now commonly used for these long-stay wards that house most patients in public mental hospitals. Following the practice recommended by Johnson, we use the term "long-stay" to describe patients who have been in the hospital two years or longer. In effect this means that we shall be mainly concerned with schizophrenic patients, a residual population left over from several decades of admissions. Morgan and Johnson call them "the psychiatric failures."[1] These are the two out of ten admissions who do not leave the hospital within a year. They form that corps of hospital patients, stabilized by tranquilizers and receiving little in the way of active psychiatric treatment, who have settled into a passive but acceptable adjustment to routine. Simply because of their numbers they are the greatest challenge to psychiatry.

Many of the models now used for hospitals and wards seem to us inappropriate or even misleading, while others apply only to a minority of hospitals. This indicates, we believe, the importance of knowing the extent to which the concepts of the social scientists can be transposed to the mental hospital. Because some writers have assumed without question that people who live together on mental hospital wards for a long period of time must form groups, societies, and cultures, we suspect that social organizations which do not exist have sometimes been carefully described. For example, Von Mering uses the method of ideal types to delineate the Fringers, Sneaky Petes, and High Priests of the ward in the same way that he would map out a South Sea society.[2] He overlooks an important difference, however, between the ideal types used in such a society and those in a mental hospital. In any society the ideal types are usually recognized by the members them-

---

[1] Norman C. Morgan and Nelson A. Johnson, "Failures in Psychiatry: The Chronic Hospital Patient," *Amer. J. Psychiatry* (1957), 113:824-830.

[2] Otto Von Mering and Stanley H. King, *Remotivating the Mental Patient*; New York, Russell Sage Foundation, 1957.

selves, but Von Mering never suggests that the patients are aware of the
Fringers, Sneaky Petes, and High Priests as such or that they confer these
titles on one another. The fashionable phrase "therapeutic community" provides another example of the ambiguous and imprecise sense in which these
sociological terms are being used today with reference to the mental hospital.
Some writers suggest that it is the patients themselves who form these communities, while others stress the importance of creating therapeutic communities *for* the patients. But surely, both for theoretical and practical purposes, it is necessary to distinguish between a social order created and
maintained by the staff and one that develops spontaneously among the
patients.

The development of suitable models for the long-stay wards of the mental
hospital is of more than academic interest, we believe, for effective remedial
measures cannot be taken unless the sociological ingredients of the ward are
understood. In our search for such models we shall first examine the evidence
for the existence of societies, communities, and cultures on these wards,
using as a starting point some representative definitions of these terms.

EVIDENCE FOR THE EXISTENCE OF A PATIENT *SOCIETY*

Mental hospitals contain many of the ingredients essential for a society—
a population composed of both young and old people, with men and women
in almost equal proportion, and counterparts within the hospital itself of
almost all jobs found on the outside. The physical arrangements on the long-
stay wards of these hospitals would also seem to be conducive to a flourish-
ing patient society. Patients spend most of their time together in large day
rooms, dormitories, and dining rooms, and the staff in most hospitals now-
adays eagerly encourage patient interaction. Whether these patients do, in
fact, form a society is the question that we shall consider here. We must,
therefore, at the outset establish some working definition of a society. The
following are fairly representative definitions of the term.

> A society consists of all the individuals and groups that have
> some significant number of common expectations.[3]

> Any group or number of human individuals who cultivate
> acquaintance and mental agreement, and who, knowing and enjoy-
> ing their like-mindedness, are able to work together for common
> ends.[4]

> A group of individuals of any species, living in a community,
> in mutual intercourse with one another and cooperating in the

---

[3] Arnold M. Ross, *Sociology: The Study of Human Relations*; New York, Knopf,
1956; p. 32.
[4] Franklin H. Giddings, *Inductive Sociology*; New York, Macmillan, 1909; p. 6.

various activities of the community; sometimes used in a general and abstract sense of the essential factors underlying and constituting social organization and community life.[5]

Society itself may be defined as a vast network of mutual agreements.[6]

A social system of this type, which meets all the essential prerequisites of long-term persistence from within its own resources, will be called a society.[7]

These definitions all emphasize cooperation and mutual understanding as determining characteristics of a society. This, in itself, rules out the long-stay wards in the mental hospital. There is little spontaneous cooperative activity among schizophrenic patients. There are no organized revolts, and attempts to escape are almost always made by single patients. When a patient attacks a nurse, other patients usually protect the nurse and do not assist their fellow patient. A further reason for doubting that the aggregate of patients can properly be called a society is the fact that patients' status symbols, such as parole cards and canteen privileges, all derive from the staff and not from interaction between patients. This is also true, as we noted earlier, of the "ideal types" used by several anthropologists, which are really social roles assigned by the staff. Since there is no evidence that they are accepted or even recognized by the patients, it would be more logical to think of these ideal types as people who occupy marginal roles in the staff society rather than as members of a patient society. Mental hospitals differ significantly from prisons in this respect. In prisons, criminals are often known by such titles as Big Shot, Scarface, Killer, or even the King of Tramps or the Queen of Criminals. These titles are conferred on them by other criminals in recognition of their authority, courage, guile, wealth, or ferocity and are often used even outside the prison. In marked contrast to this, the Kings and Queens, Napoleons and Cleopatras of mental hospitals give themselves these distinctions. If other patients recognize them at all, it is only with derision for such "crazy talk." Neither staff nor patients look upon such people as leaders.

In fact, except on admission wards, leadership among mental patients is noticeably absent, unless one is observing special institutions for psychopaths and alcoholics. Whatever leadership seems to exist on long-stay wards is that established by staff rather than arising from spontaneous social activity among patients. In significant contrast to this situation, John Vaizey's

---

[5] James Drever, *A Dictionary of Psychology*; Harmondsworth, Middlesex, England, Penguin Books, 1952; p. 270.

[6] Eugene L. Hartley and Ruth E. Hartley, *Fundamentals of Social Psychology*; New York, Knopf, 1958; p. 16.

[7] Talcott Parsons, *The Social System*; Glencoe, Ill., Free Press, 1951; p. 19.

account of life in a children's orthopedic hospital shows that the children, although confined to bed and immobilized in plaster casts, formed gangs with leaders who made many major decisions on the ward.[8] The hospital administration was forced to heed these leaders, not from any particularly enlightened concern for the mental health of the children, but because the ward could not work without them.

The fact that, compared with prisoners, patients have no economy of their own is further evidence that a patient society, similar to the type of social organization found in prisons, cannot be said to exist. In considering this evidence, of course, one must distinguish between canteens provided by the hospital or prison management and enterprises run for profit by the inmates themselves. There is active trading and selling of commodities among prison inmates. But "merchants" are few and far between in the hospital and do not seek out their customers; a new inmate here has a very difficult time in finding the sources of supply among his fellow patients. Since the few patients who sell tobacco and sundries charge about half the price these commodities cost in the hospital canteen, our nurses believe that only the less intelligent patients indulge in such trading.

Even in the economy maintained by the staff, there is a tremendous difference between the prison and the mental hospital. Prison work is rewarded on a rational though often meager basis, with a clear relation between effort and remuneration. The rewards are explicitly stated and are known by most prisoners. It is taken as a matter of course that every prisoner will work if he is physically able. In contrast, work assignments in mental hospitals are usually given on a haphazard basis, and reward when it exists is often equally haphazard. Long-stay patients form the hard core of institutional workers (in this hospital we found that the employed patients have stayed an average of eighteen years). Perhaps one difference between work conditions in the hospital and in the prison is that psychiatric patients do not organize to make demands. The cadre of reliable workers in mental hospitals is, in fact, composed of the least privileged class of patients. They often work long shifts for seven days a week without complaining. In contrast, it is not uncommon for prison riots to develop when the inmates feel that they are used unfairly. Another observable difference is that while prisoners themselves often make considerable effort to learn a trade or master a useful skill, such spontaneous interest is rarely seen in mental hospitals; patients have to be encouraged and cajoled to undertake constructive work.

Mental patients often have money, sometimes plenty of it. But it does not circulate among inmates as money does in jail. One patient in this hospital carries nearly a thousand dollars around with him. He does not, how-

---

[8] John Vaizey, *Scenes from Institutional Life*; London, Faber and Faber, 1959.

ever, use his money to gain comfort, favors, status, or better treatment for himself. He has made no attempt to bribe the staff to give him a better bed, a softer pillow, or a special room removed from his neighbors; nor has he tried to bribe his way out, although with his ample funds he could easily hire a car and get to another province where the Saskatchewan committal laws do not obtain. He has not bought the services of other patients in a domestic or sexual way, and he has not bought extra food, clothing, or furniture for himself in the nearby town. In marked contrast to a prison, where everything from minor comforts to drugs, drink, and sex is available at a price, there is very little financial dealing between patients in a mental hospital. Prisoners, as McGrath notes in his account of his own prison experience, are quickly made aware of a need for money.[9] A prison guard had told him that if he should ever return to prison, he should be sure to bring in enough money to last the sentence; otherwise he would be very uncomfortable and would end up "in a convict's grave." Patients, on the other hand, spend their money at the hospital canteen and seldom complain about its prices and fare.

If further evidence is needed that the concept of a society cannot be appropriately applied to the way of life found on the long-stay wards of the mental hospital, there is the fact that patients have very little interest in one another. Patients who have lived together on the same ward for many years do not even know each other's names; sociometric studies have shown that only a handful of reciprocated friendships occur; occupational therapists have compared patients doing craftwork to seven or eight people playing solitaire. Sociologists have suggested that the schizophrenic's capacity for role-taking is impaired.

Given these circumstances, one can hardly envisage that the mutual agreement or common expectations necessary for the formation of a society would develop. It becomes even more difficult to see why the concept of a patient society has been employed for so long.[10]

EVIDENCE FOR THE EXISTENCE OF A PATIENT *COMMUNITY*

Maxwell Jones introduced the term "therapeutic community" to describe his special unit for unemployables, mostly psychopaths and character dis-

---

9 Ed McGrath, *I Was Condemned to the Chair*; New York, A. L. Burt, 1934; p. 52.

10 In a penetrating analysis of the organization of mental hospitals, Etzioni questions the appropriateness of the term "small society." However, he does not explore the social organization (or lack of it) among patients. See Amitai Etzioni, "Interpersonal and Structural Factors in the Study of Mental Hospitals," *Psychiatry* (1960), 23:13-22.

orders.[11] Jones has been scrupulously careful in limiting his claims for the usefulness of the community approach to this sort of patient and has never suggested that it would help chronic schizophrenic patients. In recent years, however, the term has become fashionable so that huge mental hospitals and their large wards full of chronic schizophrenic patients are freely called therapeutic communities. The frequent discussions on this topic are usually devoted to considering whether a particular regime is therapeutic, while little attention is paid to a question which is at least as important, whether it is a community. In the recent volume edited by Denber, Brill refers to Kirkbride's hospital as "a truly therapeutic community," while Fink states categorically that "all hospital aggregates are communities and the therapeutic element is a matter of degree."[12] In an article intended to define the term "therapeutic community" Wilmer writes, "The hospital is conceptualized literally as a form of community with its special culture and sub-cultures."[13] But surely two very different questions are involved here and must be clearly distinguished: first, whether mental hospital staffs create a therapeutic regime for their patients and, second, whether these patients themselves form an actual community.[14] Since it is the second of these questions with which we are immediately concerned, we shall begin our consideration of it by presenting the following representative definitions of the term community.

> A community is described in terms of competition, symbiosis, and the division of labor by which it gains sustenance from its environment. . . . The characteristic primitive community consists of a small clearly defined group of individuals, relatively independent of other communities for the goods required by the prevailing standard of life.[15]

> A community is a number of people living in one place and working together for certain common ends.[16]

---

[11] Maxwell Jones, *The Therapeutic Community*; New York, Basic Books, 1953.

[12] Henry Brill, "Historical Background of the Therapeutic Community," pp. 3-15, and Max Fink, "Discussion of Dr. Gralnick's Paper," p. 162, in *Therapeutic Community*, edited by H.C.D. Denber; Springfield, Ill., Charles C Thomas, 1960; pp. 10 and 162.

[13] Harry A. Wilmer, "Toward a Definition of the Therapeutic Community," *Amer. J. Psychiatry* (1958), 114:824-833; p. 824.

[14] Cameron's concept of "the paranoid pseudocommunity," which he defines as "the patient's organization of his own reactions into a structure without social validity," is outside the scope of this paper since it is a phenomenological view of the patient's private world, while we are concerned with the actual ward situation and the social scientist's conception of it. See Norman Cameron, *The Psychology of Behavior Disorders: A Biosocial Interpretation;* Boston, Houghton Mifflin, 1947; p. 438.

[15] Everett C. Hughes, "Institutions," Chapter 27, in *New Outline of the Principles of Sociology*; New York, Barnes and Noble, 1946; p. 248.

[16] George A. Lundquist and T. N. Carver, *Principles of Rural Sociology;* Boston, Ginn, 1927; p. 208.

Members of a species living in close proximity having some sort of organization; some authors maintain that there is no community without shared interests wide enough to include their lives. It is also a group of persons, whether or not in physical contact, who are aware of themselves as sharing a common ideology, interests, property, etc., or the fact of sharing something in common.[17]

On the basis of these definitions, the determining characteristics of a community may be assumed to be communal work and a division of labor, both having as their purpose the gaining of sustenance from the environment. The fact that all the necessities of life are provided for patients by the hospital is in itself almost enough to preclude the existence of a patient community. Interdependence of function—which on the outside means that the baker buys his meat from the butcher, who consults the lawyer, who buys gas from the garageman, and so on *ad infinitum*—is not found in the mental hospital, where one patient's labor is rarely seen to have any relationship to the well-being of others. Many writers even maintain that the practice of patients working in the hospital should be discontinued since it is both uneconomic and untherapeutic. They believe that the staff could perform the work themselves in less time than it takes to supervise the patients to whom the jobs are assigned. From the standpoint of the patients, the work is degrading, meaningless, and unremunerative. Since the necessities of life are provided by the hospital, and any division of labor is set by the staff and not by the patients, it seems to us that essential features of a community are lacking in mental hospitals.

At Montrose Veterans Hospital social psychologists found that the bulk of interactions on long-stay wards took place between staff and patients; those between patients were largely confined to borrowing cigarettes and securing a light.[18] Because the necessities of life and the recreational needs are all provided by the hospital, smoking is one of the few areas in which patients can reinforce one another. In contrast, there is considerable cooperative activity in prisons. Prisoners can punish and reward each other in innumerable ways—through an active grapevine which sends messages and contraband articles, through homosexual gratification, and through social pressures and ostracism. As Goffman points out, there is no kangaroo court in mental hospitals.[19] A patient who steals from or assaults fellow patients does not have to worry about organized retribution from patients; instead, he will probably be put into seclusion by the staff.

---

[17] Horace B. English and Ava Champney English, *A Comprehensive Dictionary of Psychological and Psychoanalytical Terms*; New York, Longmans, Green, 1958; p. 100.

[18] Leonard Solomon and others, "A Method for the Systematic Analysis of Social Interaction on a Ward of Chronic Schizophrenics," paper presented at the 1958 meeting of the American Psychological Association, Washington, D.C.

[19] Erving Goffman, "The Moral Career of the Mental Patient," *Psychiatry* (1959) 22:123-142.

It is clear that the generosity of the hospital in providing for its inmates does nothing to facilitate the development of cooperative activity. On the other hand, there is still no evidence that communities develop more readily in deprived hospitals where food and other necessities are in short supply.

EVIDENCE FOR THE EXISTENCE OF A PATIENT *CULTURE*

Several authors discuss the mental hospital culture, implying by their use of the term that any large number of people living together must form a culture. While this may be true for well people, it cannot be assumed to be equally true for schizophrenic patients. We shall use the following definitions of culture as a measuring stick in attempting to determine whether a patient culture can accurately be said to exist on the long-stay wards of the mental hospital.

> Culture consists in patterned ways of thinking, feeling, and reacting, acquired and transmitted mainly by symbols, constituting the distinctive achievements of human groups including their embodiments in artifacts; the essential core of culture consists of traditional ideas and especially their attached values.[20]

> The sum total of the arts, science, social customs and educational aims of the people, regarded as an integrated whole.[21]

> Culture is that complex whole which includes knowledge, belief, art, morals, law, custom, and many other capabilities and habits acquired by man as a member of society.[22]

> Since "culture" is an abstraction commonly agreed to refer to the products, knowledge, tradition, skills, and beliefs that are shared by a group of people and passed on from generation to generation, its very existence is predicated on the functioning of communication.[23]

Several of these definitions base the existence of a culture on communication and shared symbols. Hall, an anthropologist, is explicit about this, saying that "interaction lies at the hub of the universe of culture, and everything grows from it."[24] (He uses the term "infraculture" to describe the activity that preceded culture and gives territoriality as an example of an infra-cultural activity. In this context it is interesting to note that many

---

[20] See Rose, footnote 3; p. 33.
[21] See Drever, footnote 5; p. 56.
[22] E. B. Taylor, *Primitive Culture* (7th ed.); New York, Brentano's, 1924; p. 1.
[23] See Hartley, footnote 6; p. 16.
[24] Edward T. Hall, *The Silent Language*; Garden City, N. Y., Doubleday, 1959; p. 62.

patients *do* have territories on their wards and will, as Pace has observed,[25] become acutely disturbed if anyone takes their favorite chair, table, or corner.) There is a dearth of interaction on long-stay wards, as every study of these wards has shown, and this in itself may stunt the development of a patient culture. There is also evidence that patients do not use the same symbols. The importance of a common symbolism in the development of a culture has been stressed by many writers. Ogburn and Nimkoff, for example, assert that the speaking and understanding of a language "was the big event that helped to make the culture of man so magnificent an achievement compared with that of the lower animals."[26] In our work with the Word Association Test, we found that the associations of the schizophrenic are not only different from those of normal persons, but also differ from the associations of other schizophrenics.[27] Mental patients do not possess a special language, as do convicts, school children, and army recruits; rather, each patient has a private language. Thus the prerequisites to the development of a culture—communication and shared symbols—are lacking on the long-stay wards of the mental hospital.

Further support for the idea that there is no culture on mental hospital wards comes from the comprehensive *Inventory of Social and Economic Research* published by the Health Information Foundation. This lists several dozen studies by social scientists on life in mental hospitals. While there are a few studies of *attitudes* of mental patients among them, there are *none* of their mores, folkways, or norms. If, as it is reasonable to suppose, this omission is due to the fact that these norms, folkways, and mores either do not exist on the mental hospital ward, or are so rudimentary and attenuated as to be hardly worth recording, then the mental hospital "culture" is unlike any other.

The fact that hospital folkways, customs, or language diffuse so little is further indication of the weakness and poverty of the patient culture. In prison, new guards soon take on the mannerisms of the convicts. Prison authorities often remark on the short time it takes a guard to talk like prisoners. One former prisoner told us that even the children of the guards talk "con language." This is in striking contrast to the mental hospital, where the only special terms are those used by the staff and later taken over by the patients (for example, parole, ECT, OT, and so on). Since one of the characteristics of culture is that it spreads into adjoining areas, the fact that nothing radiates out, although not conclusive evidence of its absence, casts

---

[25] Robert E. Pace, "Situational Therapy," *J. Personality* (1957), 25:578-588.

[26] William F. Ogburn and Meyer Nimkoff, *Sociology*; Cambridge, Riverside Press, 1946; p. 26.

[27] Robert Sommer, Robert Dewar, and Humphry Osmond, "Is There a Schizophrenic Language?" *AMA Arch. General Psychiatry* (1960), 3:665-673.

doubt upon the vigor or even the existence of a viable patient culture. Customs, songs, and legends do not diffuse from hospital to hospital. But in prison, the same songs are sung in many parts of the country. Work songs from Georgia chain-gangs will be heard in Northern prisons, for example, and prison poems and legends make similar migrations. Dramatic evidence for diffusion are the waves of riot and destruction which sweep American prisons periodically. Prison staffs and penologists know that a riot in one prison is likely to be followed by riots in others. This does not happen in mental hospitals.

As a final point of evidence that the patient population cannot be accurately said to have a culture, we present in the accompanying table a comparison of the mental hospital and the prison in regard to the nine culture elements listed by Clark Wissler as the "universal patterns and irreducible minimums of culture."[28] The mental hospital, it can be seen, is deficient in all nine of these elements.

CULTURE ELEMENTS IN MENTAL HOSPITAL AND PRISON

ELEMENTS OF CULTURE*	MENTAL HOSPITAL	PRISON
(1) Speech, language, writing systems, and so on	Very little conversation, even though encouraged by staff. No special hospital language, although some patients have private language.	Flourishing conversation and sending of notes, despite prohibitions and penalties. Special language in all prisons; some glossaries available.
(2) Material traits—food habits, shelter, transportation and travel, dress, utensils, tools, weapons, occupations and industries	All material needs met by hospital staff. No weapons or tools. Inefficient occupations and industries, done mainly as therapy.	Most material needs met by prison, but to an inadequate degree (actual hunger, poor heating, poor ventilation, and so on). Prison provisions supplemented and sometimes replaced by active trading and bartering of commodities, prison cells, bedding, and so on. Ingenious weapons and tools. Inefficient industries ("make-work" ventures) except for contract labor.
(3) Art—carving, painting, drawing, music, and so on	Individual productions. No mental hospital folklore, songs, style of art. Childish and uninteresting newspapers.	Prison songs, poems, legends of famous criminals and escapees. Well-written and near-professional newspapers.

---

[28] Clark Wissler, *Man and Culture*; New York, Crowell, 1923; p. 74.

CULTURE ELEMENTS IN MENTAL HOSPITAL AND PRISON—(*Continued*)

ELEMENTS OF CULTURE*	MENTAL HOSPITAL	PRISON
(4) Mythology and scientific knowledge	None passed on. Individual delusions.	Heroes, legends of famous criminals, shared superstitions about release and other events. Knowledge of how to fashion knives, keys.
(5) Religious practices, ritualistic forms, treatment of sick, treatment of dead	Organized religion very weak. Some individual worship and religious delusions. No formal death ceremony. Physical illness treated by staff. Burial of dead done by staff.	Religion and church service very important. Death ceremony at executions; legend of ending in "a convict's grave." Physical illness treated by staff. Burial of dead done by staff.
(6) Family and social systems — forms of marriage, methods of reckoning relationship, inheritance, social control, sports and games	No family life even though members of same family may be in one hospital. Little status differentiation by patients, but a fairly important one by staff. No inheritance. Sports and games initiated and led by staff.	Homosexual mating system flourishes. Highly organized communication network. One status hierarchy established by staff and another by inmates. Some inheritance of good job, bunk, possessions, and so on. Few sports and games, but flourishing where present.
(7) Real and personal property, standards of value and exchange, trade	All material needs supplied by staff. No trade with outside. Incidentals purchased from staff canteen. Tobacco sometimes used as a medium of exchange.	Some material needs supplied by staff, but supplemented by active barter and money economy. Currency in large supply continually changing hands. Exchange of commodities and currency between inmates and illicitly with guards. Trade at prison canteen and with outside merchants.
(8) Government, political forms, judicial and legal procedures	Most disputes settled by staff. Patient government organized and maintained by staff but weak and ineffectual; also dominated by admission ward alcoholics and psychopaths. No leaders among patients. Punishment for offenses by staff.	Trials and kangaroo courts conducted by inmates. Competition for power by rival factions. Flourishing stool pigeons who are, however, often put on trial by convict court and killed. Leaders of factions and gangs; designated spheres of authority. Punishment by staff or inmates.
(9) War	Individuals become disturbed. No organized protest or escapes.	Collective disturbances, riots, gang wars, mass escapes.

* According to Wissler; see footnote 28.

THE CONCEPT OF A *NO-SOCIETY*

Now that we have rejected the concepts of a patient society, a patient community, and a patient culture, what remains? Simply that mental patients live as an aggregate of discrete individuals. Long-stay wards are inhabited by ghostly figures who, like the crew of the Flying Dutchman, are able to walk through one another without leaving a trace. More than fifty years ago Sir Francis Galton gave an excellent description of this:

> There is yet a third peculiarity of the insane which is almost universal, that of gloomy segregation. Passengers nearing London by the Great West Railway must have frequently remarked upon the unusual appearance of the crowd of lunatics who take their exercise in the large green enclosure in front of the Hanwell Asylum. They almost all, without exception, walk apart in moody isolation, each in his own way, buried in his own thoughts.[29]

Woodson, an alcoholic who spent several months in a mental hospital, observes much the same thing:

> There are no wholesale attempts at breaking out of an insane asylum. The mental condition of insane patients seems to preclude entirely their cooperating in escape attempts. They act alone. They keep their plans, if they are able to plan, entirely to themselves. They do not act in concert in anything; they are completely individualistic.[30]

We believe there is more evidence to support the idea of a no-society than there is for the other concepts we have discussed. The present tendency in psychiatry to apply such terms as society, community, and culture to the patient population can often be traced to social scientists who have carried over these concepts from normal society into the mental hospital. Some social scientists believe that people living together *invariably* form societies and cultures. For example, in discussing prisons Sykes writes,

> Such aggregates enduring through time must inevitably give rise to a social system—not simply the social order decreed by the custodians, but also the social order which grows up more informally as men interact in meeting the problems posed by their particular environment.[31]

Jacobs and Stern state,

> Any aggregate of persons who live in a community, no matter

---

[29] Sir Francis Galton, *Inquiries into Human Faculty and Its Development*; London, J. M. Dent, 1943; p. 46.

[30] Inmate Ward Eight (W. W. Woodson), *Behind the Door of Delusion*; New York, Macmillan, 1932; p. 81.

[31] Gresham Sykes, *The Society of Captives: A Study of a Maximum Security Prison;* Princeton, Princeton Univ. Press, 1958; p. xii.

how small it may be, possess a heritage of culture elements which always numbers in the tens of thousands.[32]

Leslie White makes the following generalization,

> Every member of human society is of course always subjected to socio-cultural stimulation from the members of his group. Whatever a man does as a human being, and much of what he does as a mere animal, is a function of his group as well as of his organism. Any human act, even in its first expression in the person of a single individual, is a group product to begin with.[33]

The authors of statements like these, it seems to us, can never have seen or even imagined aggregates of the type found on the long-stay wards of the mental hospital. Undoubtedly many, if not all, of the patients housed on these wards were members of societies and cultures before they ever became schizophrenics, but they have lost this membership in the process of the illness. To continue to regard them as members of societies and communities on the basis of their premorbid membership is like regarding a corpse as a living human being.

Although no-societies are found in places other than the mental hospital—for example, on buses, trains, airplanes, and perhaps even in general hospitals and hotels for transients—the mental hospital is unique in the persistence of a no-society among people living together over long periods of time. We know from a large number of autobiographies that social relations flourish in the terror of the concentration camp, the heat and privation of Devil's Island, and even in the physical isolation of solitary confinement in prisons. Schizophrenia has accomplished what no tyranny, no inhumanity of man to man, has ever been able to do—it has kept people from communicating with one another.

We do not believe that the lack of social organization on the long-stay wards of the mental hospital is primarily the fault of hospital architects or psychiatrists. When social scientists criticize mental hospitals for the obstacles they place in the way of patient communication, psychiatrists are all too ready to cry *mea culpa*. It is true that large mental hospitals are often badly designed, uncomfortable, squalid, and understaffed. But even under greater obstacles than these, other aggregates of human beings have been known to develop a vivid social life. In concentration camps and in prisons under the old "silent system," inmates talking to others have been beaten and starved; yet even under these conditions they have managed to communicate with each other by learning to talk without moving their lips or by using a code

---

[32] Melville Jacobs and B. J. Stern, *General Anthropology*; New York, Barnes and Noble, 1952; p. 113.

[33] Leslie A. White, "The Concept of Culture," *Amer. Anthropologist* (1959) 61:227-251; p. 244.

for tapping out messages with their fingers. Almost every autobiography of concentration camp and prison inmates mentions how communication flourished under the very eyes of the guards. It is surely more probable then that the lack of social organization on the long-stay wards of the mental hospital is an attribute of the most common illness found there than a consequence of hospital conditions. Though there is undoubtedly a need to improve both present hospital architecture and treatment regimes, we believe that societies, communities, and cultures will not begin to develop until a cure for schizophrenia is found or social scientists start studying the special characteristics of human aggregates that do not possess common symbols and cannot place a high premium on communication. We believe that, essentially, the following characteristics of the patient population are responsible for the lack of social organization on these long-stay wards: (1) Deficient role-taking; (2) unstable perception reflected in a loss of perceptual and conceptual constancy; and (3) private symbols and a private language. In addition, there is the fact that the necessities of life are provided by an outside agency.

Another characteristic of the no-society is the absence of any carry-over of relationships to the outside. No relationships exist, in fact, to make such a carry-over possible. This may help explain the lack of social organization among former mental patients. Clubs for ex-patients usually last through only a few meetings unless they are guided and directed by outside authorities. There is no prominent national organization of ex-patients or any form of national convention.[34] Considering the number of former patients living outside, this is remarkable. The ex-convict, on the other hand, can either rejoin the culture of crime or take out membership in a branch of the John Howard Society. The ex-alcoholic can take his place at the bar again or join Alcoholics Anonymous. In any event, ex's of almost any variety go from one society to another. But those persons who have resided together in a no-society—whether it be a bus, train, hotel, or mental hospital—will continue on their separate paths afterwards.

This lack of a hospital culture may explain something that puzzled us in our reading of books written by ex-patients and ex-prisoners. After we had read five or six accounts of prison life, the rest of them seemed to us dull and repetitious. This was not true of the accounts of mental hospital life. Each

---

[34] Recovery, Inc., may be an exception to this, but the recent article by Wechsler states that half the membership sampled had never been hospitalized and the typical member was a middle-class, middle-aged married woman with at least a high school education, which does not suggest this to be an organization of former schizophrenics. The author also emphasizes the difference in size and influence between Recovery, Inc., and Alcoholics Anonymous. See Henry Wechsler, "The Self-Help Organization in the Mental Health Field: Recovery, Inc., A Case Study," *J. Nervous and Mental Disease* (1960), 130:297-314.

of them, we found, was interesting and said something new. (Our wives and colleagues who read many of the books experienced the same reaction to them.) The fault did not seem to lie with the prison authors who, generally speaking, possessed more literary talent than their hospital counterparts. A better explanation is that the prison authors were all dealing with essentially the same material. The same prison songs, legends, and customs are known everywhere. In fact, the frequency with which prison authors encountered one another and mentioned the same famous criminals was striking. At least a dozen of them referred to Oscar Wilde's "Ballad of Reading Gaol," for example. While the prisoner describes a common culture, the mental patient writes about a private world. This world is unstable, unpredictable, and Kafka-like. The prison world is only too predictable to its inmates. For the reader this means that, while five books by ex-prisoners can tell him all about the prison world, fifty autobiographies of ex-patients do not nearly exhaust the private worlds of the mentally ill.

An unthinking acceptance of the view that the mental hospital can be compared with the prison or the school prevents one from recognizing and studying a unique situation. We have seen several cases where the wrong kind of model interfered with clinical practice. This happens frequently in discussions of group activity and group therapy, which are haunted by the persistent belief that because several people are doing the same thing, it must automatically become a group activity. For example, an occupational therapist may think that her seven patients making baskets around a table constitute a group. With mental patients this can be a grossly mistaken belief. Anyone who has ever seen seven patients sitting at a table doing craftwork must question whether, in terms of the spontaneous interactivity that exists among them, they conform to accepted definitions of a group. The correct sociological term for these patients is an "aggregate," and the best methods for working with groups are not necessarily the most suitable ones for aggregates. A more appropriate model than the group for describing the situation of seven patients and one occupational therapist would be the schoolroom class. In a classroom one person tries to develop relationships with many different individuals of different status. It would probably clarify roles to call the occupational therapist or nurse an "instructor" rather than a "group leader."

Incorrect models for a hospital ward can easily lead to that stereotyped perception which, ignoring the silence and inertness of the long-stay ward, attends only to the few transient interactions which occur. There are specific instances in which investigators have attached more importance to three transient conversations in a crowded day room than to the silence of the other fifty patients. Obviously, the investigator who looks for interaction will find it, and this is precisely why the use of an appropriate model for the mental hospital is so important. We believe that the social scientist who uses a no-society for his model will make more meaningful and more realistic observations than one who assumes that human beings invariably form societies when they congregate in one place for long periods of time.

The fact that there are no societies, communities, or cultures in mental hospitals does not mean that the anthropologist and sociologist have no function in these hospitals. But it does mean that, if they are to serve a useful function here, they must adapt themselves to the unique situation of human aggregates that do not combine in any form of known social organization, and they must determine for psychiatry how societies, communities, and cultures can be developed from such aggregates. The performance of this important task, and not the description of social entities that do not exist, is the province of the social scientist. The reluctance of some social scientists to accept the fact that people can live together without any form of social organization is illustrated by our encounter with an anthropologist whose field experience has been extensive. He described our hospital as "an acultural culture—a place without a story. It has no culture heroes, no continuity, no traditions. . . . The mentally ill are not myth-makers. Perhaps they do not need to be; their whole lives are mythological." We feel that he was on the right track but that there is still a big difference between thinking in terms of an "acultural culture" and no culture at all. (To describe a mental hospital as an acultural culture strikes us as a delightful absurdity; it is like describing an automobile as a nonequine equine.)

The long-stay ward in the mental hospital challenges many of our assumptions about the social life of human beings. Where else are so many people gathered together for decades with so few and such tenuous social relationships? It is possible that the smaller mental hospitals now being planned, which will be mainly or entirely open, will provide better soil for organized patient social life than the large, isolated mental hospitals now do. If this happens, societies and communities and cultures must be expected to develop on the long-stay wards of these hospitals. But until this level of social organization has been achieved, or a cure for schizophrenia has been found, we believe that a preoccupation with forms of patient organization that exist only in fantasy cannot advance either the theory or practice of psychiatry. It is only in terms of a no-society, we propose, that the social ingredients of the long-stay wards that house the large majority of all patients in mental hospitals today can be understood; and it is only when these ingredients are understood that effective remedial measures can be taken.

Section 5

Doctor, Nurse and Patient: Role and Status Relationships

INTRODUCTION

🎜 In the previous sections of this book we have concentrated on the process of patient care with the patient as the center of attention. We have been concerned with the interpersonal dynamics of patient care and its socio-cultural context. In this last section we shift to the main patient-care functionary: the nurse. Six articles deal with different aspects of the nurse's role and her relationships with other members of the health team. In our first article Mauksch describes the social context within which the student nurse learns her professional role. He raises some important questions concerning the latent as well as the manifest consequences of existing methods of recruiting and educating student nurses. He also explores the conflict for the novice nurse produced by the different definitions of the nurse's role expounded by the school of nursing and the general hospital. The next selection, by Corwin, studies this conflict between the ideal "professional" role and the "bureaucratic" role that the nurse finds once she has left the student role and becomes a practicing nurse. The paper by Malone, Berkowitz and Klein elaborates further this conflict between professional and bureaucratic roles of the nurse. These authors identify some alternative responses by the nurse to role-conflict situations. In their interviews with the out-patient department nurses the physician was often mentioned as a source of the nurse's frustration. The next selection, by Rushing, concentrates explicitly on the resolution of one nurse-doctor role conflict situation. He identifies two components of the nurse's role: (1) caring for the patient, and (2) helping the doctor to help the patient. At times, these psychiatric nurses told Rushing, the doctor may order something for the patient that seems contraindicated by other things that the nurse knows about the patient. Such a situation activates the latent conflict between the patient-helper and the doctor-helper nurse roles. Nurses reported different ways of resolving this conflict. Of special interest is the use of "manipulative deference" to influence the doctor to modify the order. This tactic was used to influence the doctor to change his order so that it is no longer in conflict with what the nurse understood to be best for the patient. In Merton's article we note some similarities between the doctor-nurse and RN-LPN relationships as well as one very important difference. Merton also gives a general theoretical overview of the function of status for the individual and for the system as a whole. The final article, by Segal, is based on interviews and self-administered questionnaires given to nurses in a mental hospital. Segal points out that these nurses, in addition to conflicts in role definition, were affected by incongruity in their own status in relation to the patients' status. The patients in this hospital were rather wealthy and thus the ordinarily higher status of the nurse within the hospital was incongruous with their lower status in the extra-hospital status hierarchy. Segal also reports variations in the nurses' definitions of their own role from one ward to the other and from one time of day to the other. We can expect that comparable shifts in the care received by patients also occurred.

All of these variations and conflicts in the definition of the nurse's role have consequences for patient care because of their impact on the nurse's interaction with the patient. As we have mentioned before, in connection with patient behavior, one of our basic propositions is that a person's behavior in a situation depends on his definition of that situation. And one of the most important aspects of the person's definition of a situation is his definition of his own role. Thus it can be seen that both the nurse and the patient are caught in some very similar dilemmas. Just as the patient discovers incongruity between the "sick" role and the hospitalized "patient" role, so also does the student nurse discover conflict between her "professional" role and the "bureaucratic" role that she is asked to perform in the hospital. Many patient-staff communication problems are consequences of communication problems between nurses, doctors and other staff members. For example, problems stemming from status differences between nurse and doctor may be resolved, as Malone, *et al.*, and as Rushing point out, by avoiding communication with the patient. We have already seen the detrimental effect that this course of action can have on the patient. The nurse's choice of "manipulative deference" in communicating her special knowledge of the patient to the doctor when that knowledge contraindicates a particular order by the doctor, may in the long run also be an extremely dysfunctional method for meeting the patient's needs. And delegation of administrative duties to the professional nurse along with delegation of actual bedside care to "subprofessionals" must be reversed before any change in the basic training of professional nurses for improved communication skills can have any direct impact on the patient. Thus, study of patient, nurse and doctor roles and the role relationships within the medical setting are essential for ultimate improvement of patient care.

Becoming a Nurse: A Selective View

HANS O. MAUKSCH

🗨 Becoming the member of a profession, or learning the skills of an occupation, is not simply the exposure of the novice to institutional forces which shape him to fit the mold. It is, rather, a process of multidimensional interaction between the newcomer and the occupational system, taking into account other roles and behavior affecting either the occupational model or dimensions of applicant selection.

In this paper, I wish to examine some of the factors which appear to be important agents in affecting the development of the young woman[1] who enters a school of nursing. The data in this paper are based on a study conducted in a large school of nursing associated with one of the major general

---

[1] For the purpose of this paper, we concern ourselves exclusively with the female applicant to nursing. Although there is some increase in males entering nursing, the numbers are still very small and the data too scant to warrant any extension of the conclusions offered here to the males entering this profession.

Reprinted with permission from the author and *The Annals of the American Academy of Political and Social Science*, Vol. 346, March 1963, pp. 88-98.

hospitals in a midwestern metropolis. These data were obtained through formal interviews with 108 nurses and student nurses, through counseling, conferences, and contacts with students and graduate nurses over a period of ten years, and through observation and participation in the hospital and in the school of nursing. It must be emphasized that the data derive from a hospital school of nursing; there are indications that a number of the processes delineated here may not be typical of those encountered by students who enter a collegiate program of nursing.

FIRST IMPRESSIONS

> Oh, I know that nursing means hard work. I will have to work hard and be on duty nights and weekends and they will be very strict. I intend to do just what they tell me.[2]

Like the high school senior who made this statement, the young woman who enters the average diploma school of nursing expects to work hard and to be subjected to considerable discipline. She anticipates few early rewards and little prestige, at least in the beginning. She does expect, however, to be quickly "made" into a nurse. Her highly focused and long harbored desire to be a nurse and her conviction that nursing represents the acting out of many "natural" qualities make the student eager to begin taking care of patients. She is frequently a girl who is impatient with theory, impatient with classroom content, particularly if it is not directly related to nursing.

> I was furious about all the classes. I came to take care of patients and I found myself cramming anatomy and physiology. I was only interested to get on the wards.

The student nurse is confronted with a twenty-four-hour cycle which tends to reaffirm the message "you are now a nurse—you are a nurse at all times." The school, the hospital, and the residence are physically within one structure or at least adjacent. The school of nursing itself is almost exclusively the territory of nurses. Even within the hospital, the communication system effectively maintains a wall between the nurse and all others.[3] The student shares her waking and her sleeping hours with others who have similar goals and identical experiences. The full impact of the new role is, of course, sharpened and communicated by the fact and symbolism of the uniform, by the teaching of the nursing instructors, and by the policies and rules of the school of nursing. This development of a nursing identity is furthered by the label given to the nurse by all others from the beginning of her learn-

---

[2] All quotations used in this paper are from the 108 interviews with graduate nurses, student nurses, and applicants to schools of nursing.

[3] A. F. Wessen, "The Social Structure of a Modern Hospital" (unpublished Ph.D. dissertation, Yale University, 1951).

ing experiences. The uniform as a device of social visibility serves here, as it does with the police and the army, as a means of creating in-group identification by means of out-group imposition.

If one were to seek a theme for the most significant early learning experiences, one could characterize these first experiences as a shift of identity from self to role. This is not only symbolized by the formal subject matter of the curriculum culminated by the courses called "professional adjustment" but is more effectively accomplished by the transfer of many phases of life from individual responsibility to the realm of professional behavior. Such personal matters as grooming and social graces, manners and morals are evaluated as professional qualities. Fingernails and hairdo, waist and weight are now the province of school rules. The student learns that, unlike other citizens, she should not even take simple medicines like aspirin at her own discretion, because this is self-medication and, therefore, unprofessional. Most importantly, the range of behavior and attitudes from personal faith and feeling to professional skills and relationships is subsumed under the domain of the nurse's role.

To the extent to which personal behavior becomes professional domain, an important element of social control is introduced. When rules of conduct become criteria of professional quality, they can take precedence over problems of substance.

> It's no use. I go to the nursing office and make my complaints. I make suggestions. What am I told? I don't behave professionally. Not a word about the things I want to talk about—just that I didn't behave professionally.

The early and forceful emphasis on "professional behavior" serves several functions. It is an effective introduction to the general occupational phenomenon that failures in role behavior are more severely censured than technical mistakes.[4] This pattern, because of the visibility, symbolic content, and external pressures, is highly emphasized in nursing, because role failure reflects on the nursing community rather than on the individual. For the new student, this early transfer of self-preservation from ego to role serves as an effective device for protection and guidance because, in her early experiences on the patient unit, she is less confronted with technical skills than with the impact and sorting of new experiences.

THE IMPACT OF REALITY

It is a widely held tenet in schools of nursing that girls enter nursing to do nursing and that, therefore, "we have no right to keep them away from

---

[4] Everett C. Hughes, "Mistakes at Work," *The Canadian Journal of Economics and Political Science,* Vol. 17 (August 1951), pp. 320-327.

the patient." Accordingly, the experiences of the student nurse differ importantly from the novice in other occupations. The young lawyer, the young teacher, and the young physician have had opportunity to become formally as well as informally acquainted with the norms of their occupation, with the role as fashioned by their school community before they are exposed to the reality. The impact described as reality shock[5] is a crucial point in the career of most professionals. This reality shock is uniquely structured in the case of nursing. Before the school has had an opportunity to provide a theoretical basis, before the novice knows the skills or feels comfortable wearing the mantle of her new role, she is taken to the ward. There she meets a reality for which preinstitutional expectations are her only preparation. And the reality is different in flavor and impact. This uncushioned leap from childhood fancy to stark reality assumes greater proportions when seen in the context of the concurrent involvement in the tug of war between education and service, between the standards of the classroom and the practices of the ward.

THE ADOLESCENT DILEMMA

Even though less dramatic than other aspects of the early experiences of the nurse, one of the most profound impressions on this young woman is what one might call "role aging." Nearly all of our interviews contain some reference to the shock of realization, that—all of a sudden—one is seen not only as an adult but as actually superordinate to adults. This confrontation with adulthood occurs at a time when the eighteen-year-old does not yet consider herself as an adult but has also rejected the adolescent self-image. She is in that no man's land where the need for parental support alternates and conflicts with rejection of dependence on parental authority. It is at this point in life that this teen-ager is placed on the patient-care unit and expected to take care of real adults.

Although they had expected to take care of sick people, and had even viewed the nurse's role as that of a nurturant mother, very few of these girls had fully faced the impact of the helplessness and the seeking of support by these sick adults. They are hit with a double blow, because the feelings of occupational inadequacy and role insecurity only serve to sharpen ambivalence about assuming a place in the adult world.

> I wanted to crawl into a little hole. These people looked so big
> and old to me. They just could not be so sick. I was sure that they
> all thought, "What is this little girl doing here?"

---

[5] Miriam Wagenschein, "Reality Shock: A Study of Beginning Elementary School Teachers" (unpublished Master's Thesis, Department of Sociology, University of Chicago, 1950).

> It does not matter how young and green you are. When you wear this uniform a woman who could be your mother calls you over and says, "You're a nurse and so you'll understand. . . ." And then she'll tell you problems she wouldn't share with anyone else.

The formal course content in most diploma schools of nursing provides much of the technical knowledge of nursing but few conceptual tools to help the nursing student to understand her own reactions and the dynamics of the relationship between herself and the patient. The prevalent technique which serves to organize attitudes and responses is the reliance on "professional behavior." As used under these circumstances and as transmitted to the student, professional behavior—dignity, defense, distance—is a device for coping with otherwise threatening situations. More importantly, this interpretation of the term "professional" sets limits to the concurrent teaching theme "to be cheerful," to "reassure the patient," and to care for the "whole patient."

Many students resort to their private repertoire for coping with adults. Some of them coax the adult male into conformity by means and devices they might have used in asking their father for the family car, or, with younger men, by semiflirtatious techniques. The writer suspects that nurses' preference for male patients over female ones can partly be explained by the fact that the young girl has skills in successful relationships with young and old men which can be imported into the hospital situation, but experiences with her mother and other females cannot be transferred as easily nor as successfully.

CONTACT WITH THE PATIENT

One realization of the difference between dream and reality frequently occurs when the student nurse witnesses the first physical examination or other procedures with real, live patients.

> I was shocked at myself. I wondered whether I was in the right place. I came into nursing to help people, but I shuddered when I watched the doctor handling this man. It was unpleasant. It made me crawl.

This student expressed a common reaction to first contacts with the procedures of the hospital. To witness manipulation of the human body, felt to be inviolable and whole, or to see the unpleasant sights of tubes and dressings can make the novice ask herself, "What am I doing here? Did I make a mistake to come into nursing?" Although this writer recalls many times when he wanted to flee a patient's bedside, he never felt this to be a failure on his part. A nursing student, however, sees the dreams of her childhood, the commitment to her career crumble as she faces the impulse to run.

A similar reality confronts the novice as she learns that she has to modify her attitudes toward the rules of modesty, so deeply ingrained in the teaching of Western society. Although classroom instruction stresses proper and constant draping of the patient, the reality of the floor and the peculiarities of ongoing work do not always permit implementation of these rules. The short hospital gown makes it impossible to prevent exposure; many procedures require it.

In coping with situations which involve a partial or total exposure of the private parts, the nurse has the task not only of controlling verbal behavior but also of controlling those feelings which usually are communicated to the other or, at least, are felt to be communicated. Likewise, when aware of discomfort on the part of the patient, she feels that she is excepted to cope with the subjective feeling of the patient. Of this, there is frequent resentment.

> Who did she think she is. She acted as if this were the worst that could happen to her. I catheterized hundreds of women, but such fuss. . . . She made me all confused. How about my feelings?

ILLNESS AND DEATH

Sooner or later, the student has to learn to face death and to accept it as one of the inevitabilities of patient care. Although death is a dreaded experience, anticipated with a certain amount of reluctant eagerness to have this thing over with, it often differs in impact from what has been anticipated by the nurse herself. Very frequently, the death which is most vividly remembered is not the first one, but one which had significance because of the circumstances under which it occurred. It may have involved a patient with whom the student became friendlier than with others, it may have been an unexpected death, it may have been memorable for some other reason.

> I do not even remember the first death. We had a lot of them during my probie period. The case I remember was a woman with whom I became very friendly. She was like an aunt; we did not expect her to die. She did. I cried for days.

Two factors are involved. This death was unexpected, and the nurse had become "friendly" with the patient. The potential presence of death, accordingly, can serve as a force which teaches the nurse to keep emotional distance.

> The first time a patient died on me, well, it was shortly after my probie year, and I remember I cried about it because, well, it's your first experience with death. That's the trouble: I get attached to people.

Death, according to this statement, would not have been "the trouble" if emotions had been kept in check. Actually, the interviews contain many assertions that death is not an undue stress, that it can be accepted.

This general attitude is in contrast with the difficulties observed in coping with some of the previously mentioned aspects of patient care. Primarily, death had been expected; it is part of the lore of nursing. The tug of war between adolescent status and adult role is subtle; it is neither foreseen nor can it always be recognized when it occurs. The actual responses to patient contacts could not be anticipated. Secondly, death is an institutional risk which the nurse shares with others, but problems of modesty and of relationships with people are defined as private problems. Death is fairly freely discussed. The informal structure of the patient-care unit and the primary group of the student body serve as a means of support as well as a guide for adjustment and reaction to death.

ADDITIONAL REALITY FACTORS

The student nurse who had dreamed of being needed for soothing the fevered brow of the grateful patient learns very quickly that her relationship with patients is not as simple nor as direct as she had anticipated. Patient care does not always involve willing acceptance on the part of the patient, nor is the nurse always able to render all the services that the patient wants. The student learns very quickly that patients have anxieties and demands for which she is neither trained nor enabled to cope. Even though in the first period of her education she is protected from the total system of the patient-care unit and assigned only to few patients at a time, she learns that patients compete with each other for her time and that she must learn to apportion her time and organize her day in terms of the dictates of the organizational pressures—rather than according to patients' needs.

It does not take the student nurse very long to find out that the community of those who care for patients is far from being well integrated, unanimous, or cohesive. The first conflict to which she is exposed is the dichotomy between the School of Nursing and Nursing Service. The clinical instructor who, at least in the first period of education, serves as her main guide and teacher is frequently but a tolerated outsider in the sphere of the nursing-service organization. The conflict between those who want to "get the work done" and those who try to teach the student nurse good patient care rests not only on the usual cleavage between the practitioner and the educator but is expressive of the pressures and stresses under which nursing proceeds. In spite of the protective shielding by the instructor, the student learns early that the nurse on the patient-care unit is caught in the dilemma of conflicting authorities and conflicting demands on her time.[6] Before she

[6] Harvey I. Smith, "Two Lines of Authority Are One Too Many," *The Modern Hospital*, Vol. 84 (March 1955), pp. 59-64; Hans O. Mauksch, "It Defies All Logic—But a Hospital Does Function," *The Modern Hospital*, Vol. 95 (October 1960), pp. 67-70.

knows the skills of her job, before she feels comfortable in wearing the mantle of her new role, she meets the dichotomy between the teaching situation in the laboratory and the ongoing practices on the ward.

> I tried very hard to follow the procedures I was taught and then I watched this senior student. She did it all wrong and then she turned to me and said, "Don't watch me or you'll get into trouble with your instructor."

This young student had to face the realization that her theoretical foundations did not provide the final answers, but she sooner or later will learn to associate short cuts with climbing in status.

Although the student probably entered a school of nursing primarily to be of service, she also, as a normal adolescent, may have dreamed of an exciting social life with young physicians and other males from the hospital community. This young woman faces, however, a peculiar, walled-off world in which segregation by social label and social status also involves segregation by sex. Fred Davis describes eloquently the impact of this experience on girls who, after two years of college, move into the nursing phase of their program.[7] Although the student in a diploma program may not have the same conflicts as the student in the collegiate school, the data of this study confirm Davis' findings that the social life in the school of nursing not only tends to emphasize and retain adolescence but actually causes partial return to an earlier latency period during which the boys were outsiders and approaches to them were fraught with insecurity and reluctance. Much of the social life of the student nurse is an expression of a complex of socially difficult situations. Leaving the residence is more like the soldier going on pass than the free and easy movement in the college community, even though the formal rules may be similar.

Like Fred Davis, this author has been impressed by the number of nursing students expressing difficulties in their relationships with boys, frequently after earlier, more successful experiences. A parallel and not unrelated development in the school of nursing is the emergence of close ties and relationships. The common fate, the closed bonds, the enforced sharing of experience, all serve to develop a primary-group context within which individual experiences become common property. Particularly because individual crises and problems tend to threaten carefully guarded common thresholds and fears, any error in medication, any failure in class, or even trouble with the boyfriend becomes a threat to the group rather than a mere personal experience. Should a student withdraw from the school, the ripples of dismay can be observed like those on a lake into which a stone has been thrown.

---

[7] Fred Davis and Virginia Olesen, "Initiation into a Woman's Profession: Identity Problems in the Status Transition of Coed to Student Nurse," *Sociometry*, March 1963.

Davis reports of the closed and intimate pairing off that occurs, and, again, his observations fully parallel mine. Will future personal and professional relationships with the opposite sex show consequences of this single-sex culture in which contact with the male all too frequently means the physician up on the pedestal or the patient down in bed?

CHARACTERISTICS OF THE NOVICE

The events described here do not operate on a random aggregate of young people. There is an increasing body of data suggesting that selective factors tend to bring a certain kind of person into an occupation, particularly an occupation which is fraught with symbols and social meaning as is nursing.[8] Thus, we must be concerned not merely with the social forces of the educational process but also with the characteristics of the newcomer to nursing. From an extensive study of the self-image of nurses and of their perception of the typical nurse, we will offer here merely a very brief summary.[9] The data showed that the three study populations of graduate nurses, student nurses, and of high school students about to enter nursing were nearly identical in profile but that they were different from a comparison group of female college students in several important personality dimensions. They expressed significantly greater needs for affiliation, nurturance, and succorance. This finding supports the widely held impression that the young woman joins nursing because "she wants to be with people," "she wants to help people," and "she wants to be needed." This area of apparent conscious motivation and seeking satisfaction for perceived needs was to be expected. These findings are corroborated by Table 1, showing the selection of descriptive statements about nursing from the interviews.

Less expected but even more pronounced were the findings that the study populations, although almost identical with each other, varied to a considerable, statistically significant degree from the college population by a strongly felt need for social controls and security. Table 1 does not reveal this dimension at first glance. The feeling that nursing provides security,

---

[8] Leslie Navran and James C. Stauffacher, "The Personality Structure of Psychiatric Nurses," *Nursing Research*, Vol. 5, No. 3 (February 1957), pp. 109 ff.; Rose K. Goldsen, "Factors Associated with the Selection of a Career in Nursing," Paper read at the 52nd Annual Meeting of the American Sociological Society, Washington, D.C., August 28, 1957.

[9] Hans O. Mauksch, "The Nurse: A Study in Role Perception" (unpublished Ph.D. dissertation, University of Chicago, 1960). In this study, graduate nurses, student nurses, and prenursing applicants responded to the Activities Index (self-descriptive) and the Professional Characteristics Inventory (typical nurse). Coding and analysis according to Henry A. Murray's needs scheme were based on the assessment approach reported in Stein, Stern, and Bloom, *Methods of Personality Assessment* (Glencoe: The Free Press, 1956).

TABLE 1. ATTRIBUTES OF THE NURSE OCCURRING IN 108 INTERVIEWS

THEME	FREQUENCY
Nursing provides an opportunity to do things for people	86
Nursing provides an opportunity to be with people	44
The nurse is respected	35
Nursing offers a limited, realistic goal	27
The nurse can take care of troubles	25
Nursing is a science and part of the medical world	22
The nurse's appearance is glamorous	20
Nursing is something tangible	15
Nursing provides new experiences	14
The nurse has a responsible position	14
Nursing provides security	13
The nurse is loved	13
The nurse is efficient	13
A nurse can always get a job	13
Nursing is a good preparation for marriage	11
A nurse is intelligent	11
A nurse is always needed	10
The nurse is a professional person, is among "better people"	10
Nursing is close to a religious activity	10

protection, and a *safe* means of gaining certain desirable social results emerged as a pattern only after careful analysis of the interviews. The following, admittedly facile description of the girl entering nursing is offered here as a typology suggested by the data and serving as a basis for the thesis of this paper. This young woman seeks entry into a hospital school of nursing strongly motivated to seek companionship, motivated to prove herself by being needed and by serving her ideals of helping others. This need to help others may have a religious, maternal, or libidinal basis. It is usually strongly developed and a genuine motivating force. At the same time, this person is greatly concerned about the risks involved in exposing herself to failure, to troubles, to threats. She would like to be close to people but prefers to avoid final and ultimate responsibility. She seeks the warmth and gratification of the maternal role without fully having to raise the child; she longs for contact with the opposite sex while fearing the consequences of her sexuality. She wants to move upward within the social scale but prefers a secure limited climb to the risks of wide open mobility. For this person, to be a nurse is more than merely the aggregate of gratifying tasks and ascriptions such as listed in Table 1. Nursing offers her a synthesis of her predominant motivating forces in that it suggests the fulfillment of the primary desire to engage in nurturant, helpful activities within the limits of protected, secure, and prescribed bounds.

If we return to the experiences of the nursing student described in the earlier pages, can we regard them now as random problems of learning or do they relate meaningfully to the pattern of expectations and needs which have been asserted to be characteristic of nurses? The same areas which were described as the leading motivational forces in the young nurse can be discovered as the leading themes of the social reality within which nursing is learned.

In the individual entering nursing, the conscious motivation to help people and to be with people is harnessed and modified by a more subtly located and less consciously manifested set of needs which dictate caution, care, and controls. The manifest content of the curriculum and the philosophy of the school of nursing are generally patient-centered and patient-directed. The efforts to help the young student to give good patient care are sincere and represent genuine efforts to assist the student to be patient-oriented. But the experiences reported in this paper serve as the subtle, less manifest, and unintended reality factors which forcefully tell the novice to "be careful, don't go too far; find refuge and security behind the uniform and the dignity of your professional model." The bureaucratic structure of the nursing world, the risks of getting into trouble with either patient, head nurse, or physician emphasize the same lesson. This writer has been impressed with the widespread and not always tacit recognition that the proverbial enthusiasm and patient orientation of the freshman student give way to an attitude among seniors that "to get away with doing least is best." That this happens to the idealism in other professions is well known,[10] and that it serves the function of reality orientation must not be forgotten. To what extent could unharnessed enthusiasm and involvement with the patient survive in the face of the drama of death and disease and, even more so, vis-à-vis the apparently simple but yet so difficult reality of having to divide one's time between many patients, many tasks, and many radically different situations? The nurse has to move from the bedside of the dying patient to the room of the recuperating one and is expected to show the appropriate mood in both situations. The very detachment which enables her to select and display the appropriate relationship for each patient can, if not carefully developed, result in the aloofness of routine. The modern hospital, an urban institution with its crowded, heterogeneous, large population of patients who today rapidly move through the hospital, represents a unique challenge to patient-care orientation: how to provide intimate, personalized, understanding relationships despite the fleeting nature of interpersonal contacts which actually occur. As Georg Simmel pointed out, great frequency and brevity

---

[10] Howard S. Becker and Blanche Geer, "The Fate of Idealism in Medical School," *American Sociological Review*, Vol. 23 (February 1958), pp. 50-56.

of interhuman stimulation itself will breed a blasé response as a means of psychological survival.[11]

In observing the entire matrix of learning experiences for any profession, the novice is usually given the sword as well as the shield: he is taught the techniques and skills needed to practice, and he is equipped with the defenses he needs to function. In the preceding pages, some of the factors which teach the reality aspects of nursing were selected for presentation. The question to be raised is not about the merits of these limit-setting experiences but, rather, about the balance of those forces and the relationship between the kind of nurse these forces produce and the aims and trends of the profession.

There are several reasons why it seems to this author that a hard look at the induction process of nurses is warranted.

Initiative versus Safety

We have described the factors which demonstrate that the novice in nursing is exposed quickly to a set of hard-hitting reality factors which include the concurrent exposure to theory and practice as well as the necessary profound readjustment of learned modes of behavior. We have argued that the reality forces are pitched against childhood dreams rather than against a theoretical foundation. We have, furthermore, suggested that the student learns quickly that there is risk attached to extending oneself or in getting involved. When such experiences meet well-rooted theoretical teachings and professional ideals, they result in adjustment and adaptation to reality. However, when these forces represent the shattering of childhood images they provide the taste of failure, of self-doubt, of timidity. We would raise the question whether the timing and organization of these reality factors may, as a consequence, tend to discourage the development of leadership, of initiative, of the willingness to experiment among those who go through these experiences associated so frequently with the education of the nurse.

Security versus Purpose

We have suggested that there may be a fascinating convergence between the social forces operative in the socialization of nurses and the apparent needs pattern of the entrants into this profession. This raises the important question of the impact and consequence of the interaction of such complementing forces. The same reality experiences which, if viewed purely from an institutional point of view, serve as the necessary orientations and limit-setting experiences may assume different proportions if seen within the framework of the ongoing needs of those who are exposed to these expe-

---

[11] Georg Simmel, "The Metropolis and Mental Life," in Kurt H. Wolff, *The Sociology of Georg Simmel* (Glencoe: The Free Press, 1950), pp. 409-424.

riences. If it is true that the people who enter nursing seek, in addition to their desire to help people, also the controls and security of a highly structured environment, will not, then, the opportunities for such protection and bureaucratization of function serve both as a limit to their primary purpose and as a substitute for their original motivation? In other words, will the opportunity to remain safe and to maintain a precarious but protected balance between the demands of the physician, the hospital, and the patient outweigh the risks of getting involved in the challenges of direct patient care for which they originally came but which spell self-exposure and the possibility of making mistakes?

The educational as well as the organizational reality must be viewed with an assessment of the novice in mind in order to strengthen, develop, and protect those motivating forces which brought her into nursing as an opportunity to give care and in order to control and to limit those needs which tempt the novice to retrench and to seek safety.

Administrator or Clinician

Occupations are institutions undergoing constant change. They change as their function and technology change, as status, scope, and aims alter.[12] Few fields have been observed to be in flux as much as the health professions. Among them, nursing has been engaged in a serious process of self-examination, of exploring its optimal scope and place, and of experimenting with various modes of educating the newcomer. This paper suggests that changes in the practitioner cannot be accomplished solely by recasting the formal educational process but by exploring the total network of socializing forces which fashions the novice.

There have been a number of studies investigating differences in role orientations of nurses.[13] One can summarize the various available models by suggesting that the traditional conception of nursing as the nurturant mother surrogate has given way to several possible alternatives. The approximation of the healing function, the attempt to serve as the physician's assistant, is not a collective trend but, rather, can be seen as the occasional model for individual nurses. The current debates seem to show nursing at the crossroads between accepting the co-ordinating function of unit management within the hospital structure and the emergence of the patient-care

---

[12] Rue Bucher and Anselm L. Strauss, "Professions in Process," *American Journal of Sociology,* Vol. 66 (January 1961), pp. 325-334.

[13] Robert W. Habenstein and Edwin A. Christ, *Professionalizer, Traditionalizer, and Utilizer* (Columbia, Missouri: University of Missouri, 1955); Sam Schulman, "Basic Functional Roles in Nursing: Mother Surrogate and Healer," in E. Gartly Jaco (ed.), *Patients, Physicians and Illness* (Glencoe: The Free Press, 1958); Ronald G. Corwin, "Role Conception and Career Aspiration: A Study of Identity in Nursing," *The Sociological Quarterly,* Vol. 2 (April 1961), pp. 69-86.

oriented nurse clinician.[14] This latter trend represents a move toward clinical rather than administrative service within the social organization of patient care. It is not within the scope of this paper to discuss these alternatives and their implications, but it is of relevance to those who are concerned with the trends in this profession to raise a question about the direction in which the novice is moved by the realities of the educational process. Nursing is largely taught within the structure of a nursing-service organization. It is communicated as the performance of policy-based, required practices and acts. Clinical orientations and personal professional responsibility, it seems to me, are most effectively taught through the existence of strong and meaningful role models among the teachers and among the practitioners with whom the novice functions. The study on which this paper is based revealed only few instructors who actually served forcefully in this capacity.

One cannot afford to disregard the subtle and yet forceful factors which, in a sense, serve as a counterbalance to the formal, educational program. They are of particular importance in a field in which human crises must become routines, in which otherwise frightening experiences must serve as professional challenges. To the social scientist, these problems are of particular interest not because they are unique to nursing but because the extreme nature of the nurse's job sheds a sharper light on stresses in professional socialization.

---

[14] For this concept, I am indebted to Miss Frances Reiter, Dean, Graduate School of Nursing, New York Medical College, Flower and Fifth Avenue Hospitals, New York.

The Professional Employee: A Study of Conflict in Nursing Roles

Ronald G. Corwin

A STUDY OF ROLE CONFLICTS IN NURSING

⚶ The career is a process of transformations in status. Of primary signifi-cance in the assumption of new status is the grasping of new conceptions, particularly of role, which create transformation in the relevant perceptions and beliefs. Most transformations are so mundane they go unnoticed, but occasionally an incident of great conceptual and personal significance is encountered. At these turning points fundamental terminological and status shifts occur, reclassifying and reassessing the job—indeed, the self.[1] Gradua-tion from a vocational training program and the commencement of career is such a turning point. Contradictions inherent in the occupation are encountered with new relevance at graduation. These create pressures of work not fully imagined by the student from his perspective.

There are several reasons why contradictions within the structure of work are felt more intensely after graduation. Perhaps most obvious is the abstract nature of conceptions of role, themselves. At best, conceptions are

---

[1] Everett C. Hughes some years ago emphasized that the career consists of a series of statuses and offices which tend to become fateful "turning points" in the person's career as the social structure becomes increasingly rigid ("Institutional Office and the Person," *American Journal of Sociology*, XLIII [November 1937], 404-409). Strauss makes extensive and systematic use of the concept of turning point, proposing that development of personality be viewed as a series of related transformations of concept (see Anselm Strauss, *Mirrors and Masks: The Search for Identity* [Glencoe, Ill.: Free Press, 1959], p. 92).

Reprinted from Corwin, Ronald, "The Professional Employee: A Study of Conflict in Nursing Roles," *American Journal of Sociology*, Vol. 66, 1961, pp. 604-615, by permission of the University of Chicago Press. Copyright 1964 by the University of Chicago.

This investigation was supported by Research Grant GN-4647 from the National Institutes of Health, United States Public Health Service, Marvin J. Taves, principal investigator. The author is indebted to Professor Roy G. Francis for suggesting many of the ideas developed here and to Professor Taves for advising on the research.

images—in a sense, fantasies—which set the ideal; they cannot provide a totally realistic picture of the career. Largely because of the inevitable discrepancy between concept and experience, conceptions of role learned in training schools do not comprehend the full complexities of work experience. Consequently the refining and modifying of ideal standards of conduct is an almost inevitable adjunct to the career. In short, the transcendent character of language always distorts the full range of work demands.

For another reason, the initial job is often fraught with contradictions: Staffed by non-practicing specialists and teachers, training schools are at least partially removed from the occupation. Now, teaching, involving as it does the necessary justification of the teacher's own self-conception to her student audience, normally involves rhetorical persuasion and hence a certain amount of deception. Teachers, like parents, are easily tempted to project their fantasies, ideals, and aspirations upon their students. By stressing ideals, the teacher's hope for a better world lives on in the possibility of future implementation by students; their own aspirations may be attached to the careers of others. So those who teach may easily tend to fuse their conceptions of what ought to be with their conceptions of what exists. This is especially so when teachers are not practitioners. Probably no other occupational group works so consistently under the dominant influence of one institution as teachers do: teachers are unique in being practitioners who work in the same institutional setting in which they were trained from childhood.

Merton observes that medical schools act as guardians of values basic to the effective practice of medicine. Their job is enabling the medical man to live up to the expectations of the professional role long after he has left their sustaining environment. He concludes that "once they have entered upon their own practice some of these physicians will find themselves working under conditions which are far less conducive to ready conformity to these norms."[2] Hughes makes similar observations about nursing: "The nurses who educate nurses cherish the most consistent opinions as to who does and who should perform a given task. In the manner of teachers they are dogmatic. Removed to some degree from reality, they may preach an idealized version of hospital work."[3] Discrepancies between ideal and practice are systematically incorporated into the organization of work, full awareness accompanying the passage from the school's climate of values to that of work.[4]

---

[2] Robert K. Merton, "Some Preliminaries to a Sociology of Medical Education," *The Student Physician* (Cambridge, Mass.: Harvard University Press, 1957), chap. i.

[3] Everett C. Hughes, "The Making of a Physician: A General Statement of Ideas and Problems," *Human Organization*, Winter, 1956, pp. 21-25.

[4] See, e.g., Arnold M. Rose, "The Adequacy of Women's Expectations for Adult

Finally, sensitivity to occupation contradictions increases after graduation, which forces shifts in students' allegiances to school and hospital. Contradictions within nursing are in part a consequence of conflict of interests between the nursing faculty and hospital staff over control of the student's classroom and clinical experience. Teachers must share students' time and allegiance with hospital supervisors; justifications of the school and hospital are pronounced by each group; conflicting demands are made on the student. But the student is not neutral, for while he is in school his destiny is controlled by the teaching faculty. It is they who tend to command his loyalty just as it is the nursing principles stressed in school which hold his interest.

At the same time, the student is a transient who has little occasion or motive to develop immediate allegiance to the hospital. But with graduation he becomes one of its responsible office-holders. At this point, the conflicts between the teachers' versions of the occupation and those of practitioners gain new intensity: old loyalties are threatened and new are demanded as the graduate adapts to another power structure. It is in this setting that the inherent cross-pressures are encountered in full strength. The cross-pressure between school and hospital creates both conflict between alternative roles and discrepancies between ideal conceptions of the role and perception of the reality.

BUREAUCRATIC VERSUS PROFESSIONAL ORIENTATION

But what idealized version is preached in professional schools, and how does it differ from reality? It is apparent that there is not one but at least three dominant conceptions of nursing—an office, a profession and a calling.[5] These provide alternative identities for the nurse who is at the same time a hospital employee (or a bureaucrat), a responsible, independent professional, and a public servant (when in a religious or humanitarian context).

Roles," *Social Forces*, XXX (October 1951), 69-77; and Mirra Komarovsky, "Cultural Contradictions and Sex Roles," *American Journal of Sociology*, LII (November 1946), 184-189. Also, Ruth Benedict suggests several cultural discontinuities which are probably felt most severely by the adolescent upon graduation from high school ("Continuities and Discontinuities in Cultural Conditioning," pp. 522-531 in Clyde Kluckhohn, H. A. Murray, and D. M. Schneider [eds.], *Personality in Nature, Society and Culture* [2d rev. ed.; New York: Alfred A. Knopf, Inc., 1953]).

[5] A more extensive summary may be found in my unpublished Ph.D. thesis, "Role Conception and Mobility Aspiration: A Study in the Formation and Transformation of Nursing Identities" (University of Minnesota, 1960), chap. ii; and in my unpublished manuscript, "Role Conception and Mobility Aspiration: A Study of Identity in Nursing." Habenstein and Christ call three similar, though not identical, types of nurses the "professionalizer," the "traditionalizer," and the "utilizer" (Robert A. Habenstein and E. A. Christ, *Professionalizer, Traditionalizer and Utilizer* [Columbia: University of Missouri Press, 1955]).

Each identity provides a different source of loyalty—to the local administration, to professional principles and associations that transcend the local place of employment, and to the patient. There is reason to believe that the three ideal conceptions of nursing involve incompatible demands. Potential conflict is particularly evident between the professional and the bureaucratic conceptions of role.

Because bureaucratization and professionalization constitute major trends which happen to be occurring concurrently, there is a common tendency to fuse their identity in analysis as well as history. But, precisely because of this, dilemmas are created. Therefore, they should be distinguished.[6] Bureaucracy and profession, as ideal types, seem to differ fundamentally in at least three characteristics: degree of standardization of tasks and procedures, degree of authority permitted, and relationship to organizational means and goals, that is, efficiency and standards. Each of the three may be visualized as a continuum progressing from the highly bureaucratic at one extreme to the highly professional at the other.

First, because the routine task is the basic standardizing unit, it assumes greater prominence in the bureaucratic than in the professional organization. The bureaucrat is specialized in some phase of administrative routine; the professional is primarily concerned with a vast and expanding body of knowledge, knowledge which may even occasionally challenge the fundamental assumptions of the practice. As a result, where the bureaucrat stresses the categorical and routine elements of his client's situation, the professional focuses on his unique problems. Standardization also makes for emphasis on files and records, thereby safeguarding continuity and stability; but the professional's stress on unique problems and decision ideally lends importance to variety and change.

Second, the bureaucrat has less authority than the professional has. Bureaucratic principles require elaboration of rules and sanctions in order to insure predictability, hence efficiency; but professional service to clients is guaranteed by the special capacity of the professional to solve problems.[7]

Finally, the professional's stress is on goals, while the bureaucrat is hired to carry out procedures. In the task-oriented environment, visible forms, such as record-keeping, are convenient criteria for rewarding per-

---

[6] F. Stuart Chapin, *Contemporary American Institutions* (New York: Harper & Bros., 1935), pp. 311, 316; also Roy G. Francis and Robert C. Stone, *Service and Procedure in Bureaucracy* (Minneapolis: University of Minnesota Press, 1956), chap. xi.

[7] Of course, the bureaucrat has authority to make decisions. But, in the sense that being a "good bureaucrat" means knowing the rules and enforcing them properly, the decision is often to interpret the rules literally when dealing with the public. In fact, because of the bureaucrat's emphasis on predictability, literal application of rules often seems to be an ethic of his work (see Robert K. Merton, "Bureaucratic Structure and Personality," in *Social Theory and Social Structure* [Glencoe, Ill.: Free Press, 1957], pp. 195 ff.).

formance. But stress on bureaucratic efficiency is in contrast to the profession's central purpose, the maintenance of standards and values.

Because the client's welfare is not necessarily equivalent to the welfare of the organization, professional and bureaucratic principles provide competing sources of loyalty. Professional standards are sometimes compromised for efficiency and the association's prestige.[8]

Of course, these ideal types do not exist in pure form; nor are the characteristics necessarily exclusive and contradictory. Nevertheless, there is the suggestion of potential conflict because of incompatible alternatives.

But this is not all. They not only conflict between themselves, but both bureaucratic and professional conceptions interfere as well with the traditional nursing values embodied in the conception of the service role. Professionalization has shifted attention and energy from the patient to a maze of technical duties and to a range of activities designed to raise professional standards, which include committee work, reading and contributing to professional journals, and attendance at meetings. Similarly, as nurses have become hospital employees with careers and identities inseparable from their office, they have been rewarded for such skill in administration as in the maintenance of charts and records and ordering. In this sense the professional and bureaucratic conceptions, requiring as they do duties which remove the nurse from contact with patients, are largely responsible for a basic dilemma of nursing: while nurses are supposed to want contact with the patient, they are rewarded for values and skills which do not require it.

In summary, these three ideal conceptions of nursing, referred to here as "bureaucratic," "professional," and "service," can be held simultaneously and in varying degrees by any one individual or group and often seem to prescribe conflicting programs of behavior.

FROM SCHOOL TO WORK

The latent conflict among dominant conceptions of the nursing role arouses suspicion that the disparity between school and the "reality" of which Hughes speaks is, in this case, partially a disagreement between school and hospital over allegiance to professional and bureaucratic principles. For, while bureaucratic principles define the role of the graduate nurse within the hospital, they are probably less crucial in defining the role

---

[8] Nurses often complain that they are reprimanded for not giving patients equal time, thereby reducing the efficiency of their work routine. On the one hand, a professional ethic requires that special attention be given to patients with unique problems, but, on the other hand, the necessity of accomplishing a daily routine seems to require the use of "assembly-line" organization. Nurses who spend time with patients often feel they are considered to be loafing by their immediate superiors and some of their peers.

of the student in the educational institution, partially removed as it is from the hospital. Then, passage from school to hospital is a discontinuous turning point at which the professional ideals stressed in school are sometimes dramatically confronted with the bureaucratic principles which operate the hospital.

Theoretically, what seems to be involved is a change from student *status* within an educational institution to the *office* of nurse in the hospital bureaucracy.[9] While a status is a position which rests on institutional prestige, an "office" is a responsible position of authority within an association. It is the formal distribution of rights and obligations; the proportion of administrative duties assigned to an office varies directly with its rank. The student's status relationships with peers and supervisors are broadly defined, mainly by the educational and medical institutions, but the office of nurse is more narrowly prescribed in the specific organization as well. In the office the full array of administrative, professional, business, and other institutions which constitute the organizational principles converge and are comprised in the course of daily routine. Offices are thus stages for the drama of conflicts in roles.

While the institutions and associational norms usually supplement one another, it is, nevertheless, often apparent that the achievement of an *organization* is not equivalent to *institutional* success; in fact, the survival of an organization often requires that it compromise fundamental values under pressures from the outside.[10] It is in the office of nurse rather than in the status of student nurse that bureaucratic and professional principles converge and conflict most seriously.

The scope of the student's perspective of the nursing career is fundamentally different from that of the graduate staff nurse in several ways. In the first place, their perspectives on hospital routine may easily differ. The student, relatively unspecialized as yet, has direct contact with a variety

---

[9] Of course, "office" has its functional orientation, and professional "status" has its bureaucratic aspects; the difference is one of relative emphasis. The distinction between "status" and "office," outlined by Kingsley Davis in *Human Society* (New York: Macmillan Co., 1949), pp. 88-89, rests on McIver's distinction between "institutions," which provide the principles of organization, and "association" of persons who are pursuing a common course regulated by the institutions (Robert McIver, *Society, Its Structure and Changes* [New York: Farrar & Rinehart, Inc., 1936], pp. 15-16). Hughes outlines the connective between institutions and office: listing the two essential features of institutions as mores or formal rules and people acting collectively in offices, he points out that the first element represents consistency; the second, *concert* or *organization*. He insists that the dynamics of institutional processes may be best understood in terms of these two features (see Robert E. Park [ed.], *An Outline of the Principles of Sociology* [New York: Barnes & Noble, Inc., 1939], pp. 283-288).

[10] This is an underlying theme in Philip Selznick's book, *Leadership in Administration* (Evanston, Ill.: Row, Peterson & Co., 1957), chap. i.

of hospital situations, personnel, and supervisors, besides having the benefit of an over-all perspective on the profession emphasized in many nursing programs. Contrast this with the routinization characteristic of the specialized graduate nurse, functioning not only as a surgical nurse but as a "rotating" or "scrub" surgical nurse; a perspective of her relationship to the total organization is not inherent in the office itself. Thus, the over-all aims and goals of the organization can easily become buried in a maze of specialized tasks. As Anderson states it: "The hours are not as lengthy, apparatus is more complicated, treatments are more time consuming, but nursing is still done largely on a job basis. It is strange that this should be so when nursing is such an intimate service."[11]

The emphasis on tasks also contrasts with the stress which schools normally place on the student. For, to the extent education implies changing personal attitudes, the personal opinions, independence, and individuality of the prospective nurse are emphasized in school. But in a large-scale organization personnel are not encouraged to express their opinions or personalities so much as to adjust themselves to a well-established policy. A dethronement of self-importance may easily result from full-scale encounter with this ideally depersonalized, task-oriented environment.

Consider also the amount of responsibility for decisions in the professional nursing role as defined by the school of nursing and hospital administration. In the nursing program the nurse's intellectual capacity as a decision-maker, her responsibility for patient welfare, and her leadership potential are emphasized. But on hospital stations much of the work may be even more standardized and the rules more arbitrarily constraining than expected.

As a net result, conflicts of loyalty between the nursing profession and the hospital easily emerge. The nurse is in part a daily record-keeper and follower and enforcer of the hospital rules and red tape which often seem irrelevant to her professional function. It may be difficult for the new graduate to understand what is professional about filling out six legal forms for each patient admitted and completing pages of detailed charts and reports each day; but the hospital requires a degree of conformity and loyalty to its rules and procedures to assure continuity and predictability.[12] On the other hand, the student has less responsibility for ordering, filling out forms, and filling them out properly. She encounters hospital regulations as a transient worker rather than a responsible office-holder; and, even when she does encounter the administrative bureaucracy, it is

---

[11] B. E. Anderson, "Some Paradoxes in Nursing," *Teachers College Record,* LIV (January 1953), 211.
[12] *Ibid.*

likely to be dismissed as an inconvenience unique to that school or hospital rather than an inherent part of nursing.[13]

Of course, students are not completely unaware of the bureaucracy, for they not only hear about it but sense it from their own experience. Even so, its influence is easily ignored wherever the integral functions of nursing are stressed. Briefly, *role-taking*, that is, anticipatory socialization, is always incomplete—the practical reality of bureaucracy is completely realized only as the graduate's career unfolds and she begins to play out her role.

But to assert that the bureaucratic conception is sanctioned most rigorously in the hospital is not to imply that all schools necessarily stress the professional role and play down the bureaucratic role to the same extent. The degree of conflict experienced at graduation will depend a great deal on the existing relationship between school and hospital.

There are two principal types of nursing education: "degree" and "diploma" programs. Teachers and administrators of the diploma program are normally practitioners on the hospital staff; the student's program and curriculum are often designed and regulated by the hospital administration. The diploma program is, in fact, *part* of the hospital. On the other hand, the degree program is a collegiate program, which, while it is affiliated with the hospital, maintains some independence from it in its separate administration and faculty. Curriculum and work programs, while often jointly designed with the hospital, are at least occasionally controlled by the school granting the degree, creating conflicts of interest for the time and loyalty of students. The bureaucratic conception is less appropriate in the collegiate program, while the professional conception flourishes there.

Hypothesis.—Not only because of the abstract nature of the conception of role learned in school, but also because of differences in value climates between training schools and the work experience, graduation constitutes a turning point in careers at which inherent occupational contradictions become manifest. The professional conception of role upheld by nursing schools is in principle opposed to crucial aspects of the hospital bureaucracy. Upon graduation, as the student's status merges with an administrative office, professional and bureaucratic principles converge, producing conflict in roles. Graduates of degree programs are especially vulnerable to the resulting conflict because of the program's independence of hospital administration.

The validity of the hypothesis seems to rest on answers to three ques-

---

[13] Becker and Geer conclude from their study that medical students confine their disillusionment about medical ideals to cynicisms toward the school situation: they remain idealistic about their profession but become cynical about their school activities (Howard S. Becker and B. Geer, "The Fate of Idealism in Medical School," *American Sociological Review*, XXIII [February 1958], 50-56).

tions underlying it: (1) Do bureaucratic and professional conceptions of role conflict? (2) Are there systematic differences in the organization of roles produced by diploma and degree programs? (3) Do discrepancies between ideal roles and perceptions of the reality increase after graduation?

For this study 201 staff nurses, 23 head nurses, and 71 junior and senior student nurses, all with either diploma or degree training, were selected from seven hospitals and four schools of nursing in a midwestern metropolis. They responded to questionnaires consisting of three Likert-type scales designed to assess bureaucratic, professional, and service role conceptions. Items representing the basic themes of each concept were stated as relevant hypothetical situations.[14] For example:

> Some graduate nurses try to put their ideas about good nursing into practice even when it means breaking hospital rules and established procedures.
>
> 1. Responsible staff nurses *should* put their ideas into practice even if it means going against the rules.
> 2. At my hospital staff nurses *do* put their ideas into practice even when it means going against the rules.

The scale of the bureaucratic conception of the role consists of six items which include such characteristics as punctuality and strict following of rules. Eight items pertaining to the professional role include a commitment to knowledge as the basis of a profession and the ability to use judgment and power to make decisions about nursing procedures. The eight items pertaining to the service conception of role include the desire to do "bedside" nursing and to serve humanity. By checking one of the alternative responses ranging from "strongly agree" to "strongly disagree," respondents indicated the extent to which the situation *should* exist in nursing. The arithmetic sum of responses weighted from 5 (strongly agree) to 1 (strongly disagree), constitutes the total scale score for each of the role conceptions of each respondent.

Conceptual *modification* of the role is inferred from comparisons of mean scores on the role-conception scale of graduate and student nurses. Since these data were drawn from separate populations, they do not directly pertain to changes in individuals over time; but cross-sectional data will provide some insight into the process of disillusionment.

Role *discrepancy* is the extent to which an ideal conception of role

---

[14] Each item was pretested for internal consistency. Discriminatory power was measured for each item by computing critical ratios between upper and lower quartiles based on respondents' total scores for each scale. Only items reaching the 5 per cent level of significance were retained. Several items were also omitted on the basis of criticisms of respondents, who were given opportunity to criticize items for ambiguity and relevance.

is perceived to be impracticable. The discrepancy score is the difference between the respondent's statement of what *should be* the case (ranging from "strongly agree" to "strongly disagree") and his perception of what is *actually* the case for each statement in the same scale (also ranging from "strongly agree" to "strongly disagree"). The arithmetic sum of differences between weighted responses to normative and reality perceptions for each statement in the scale constitutes the respondent's mean discrepancy score for each scale.[15]

Role *organization* refers to the relative allegiance which an individual or group expresses to the bureaucratic and professional roles, considered jointly. The scores on the professional scale and those on the bureaucratic scale were divided at the mid-points of the respective distributions, and each respondent was classified as either "high" or "low" on both scales. A "high" scale score indicates a high degree of acceptance of the principles constituting the scale. Respondents were then classified into four groups on the basis of their combined professional and bureaucratic conceptions of role: (1) high professional–high bureaucratic, (2) high bureaucratic–low professional, (3) low bureaucratic–high professional, and (4) low bureaucratic–low professional.[16]

Do bureaucratic and professional role conceptions conflict?—If bureaucratic and professional conceptions do prescribe opposing programs of action, then persons who subscribe strongly to both, simultaneously, should sense more discrepancy between their ideal conceptions and the actual opportunity to fulfil their roles in practice than do persons subscribing to one or both with less enthusiasm.

On the basis of this assumption, and considering the evidence, the question must be answered affirmatively. Bureaucratic and professional conceptions of role, jointly held, prevent adequate fulfilment of either role. For example, respondents who simultaneously hold high bureaucratic and high professional conceptions generally express greater discrepancy in the bureaucratic and professional roles than do those who have adopted other styles of role organization (Table 1, totals). Not only that, but the smallest discrepancies in role are consistently found among personnel who simultaneously hold low bureaucratic and low professional role conceptions. Similar patterns are found for all three roles among both student nurses

---

[15] E.g., a "strongly agree" response to the normative part of a statement is given a weight of 5, while a "disagree" response to the descriptive part is given a weight of 2. The discrepancy score is 3.

[16] In another context, Reissman identified the four combinations of bureaucratic and professional conceptions dealt with here. He labeled them: (1) functional bureaucrat, (2) specialist bureaucrat, (3) service bureaucrat, and (4) job bureaucrat (Leonard Reissman, "A Study of Role Conceptions in Bureaucracy," *Social Forces,* XXVII [March 1949], 305-310).

TABLE 1. BUREAUCRATIC-PROFESSIONAL ROLE ORGANIZATION AND MEAN
BUREAUCRATIC AND PROFESSIONAL ROLE DISCREPANCY
OF NURSING PERSONNEL

DISCREPANCY ROLE	ROLE ORGANIZATION*									
	HB–HP		HB–LP		LB–HP		LB–LP		F	d.f.
	Mean	N	Mean	N	Mean	N	Mean	N		
Student Nurses										
Bureaucratic	3.62	17	2.25	16	1.54	18	0.54	20	8.10†	3/70
Professional	5.62	17	2.13	16	4.38	18	1.00	20	5.85†	3/70
Service	4.46	17	3.75	16	4.62	18	2.46	20	0.99	3/70
Graduate Staff Nurses										
Bureaucratic	3.79	61	3.18	42	1.17	42	1.50	57	5.87†	3/201
Professional	5.18	61	1.95	42	6.17	42	1.75	57	55.9‡	3/201
Service	2.57	61	2.05	42	1.74	42	0.83	57	2.74†	3/201
Head Nurses										
Bureaucratic	2.0	4	3.33	11	2.60	5	1.00	3	0.96	3/22
Professional	5.75	4	2.83	11	6.20	5	4.00	3	3.20†	3/22
Service	0.38	4	2.16	11	2.70	5	1.00	3	0.70	3/22
Total Sample										
Bureaucratic	3.45	82	3.00	69	2.43	65	1.15	80	7.7†	3/295
Professional	5.39	82	2.14	69	2.43	65	1.68	80	40.6‡	3/295
Service	2.71	82	2.44	69	2.76	65	1.38	80	2.42†	3/295

* HB–HP = high bureaucratic–high professional; HB–LP = high bureaucratic–low
professional; LB–HP = low bureaucratic–high professional; LB–LP = low bureaucratic–low professional. High means indicate high role discrepancy.
  † Significant at .05 level.
  ‡ Significant at .01 level.

and nurses when they are considered separately (although the pattern is not
evident among head nurses).

A low bureaucratic–high professional style results in relatively greater
professional discrepancy than do high bureaucratic–low professional conceptions of role (particularly among graduate nurses), while these two
styles have contrary effects on bureaucratic discrepancy. Even a slight
allegiance to the opposing role frustrates the dominant one.[17]

As also expected, strong allegiance to professional and bureaucratic
roles retards fulfilment of the service conception of role, at least among

---

[17] But in the case of head nurses it is significant that high professional conceptions
have consistently high discrepancies regardless of bureaucratic allegiance. As personnel
move up the administrative hierarchy, demands of the job itself may increasingly interfere with the professional role. Their personal conceptions of the bureaucratic role
do not seriously modify the underlying conflict between their jobs and professional
fulfilment.

TABLE 2. TYPES OF BUREAUCRATIC-PROFESSIONAL ROLE ORGANIZATION
ADOPTED BY DEGREE AND DIPLOMA NURSES*

NURSES' TRAINING	ROLE ORGANIZATION								
	HB–HP		HB–LP		LB–HP		LB-HP		
	No.	PER CENT	No.	PER CENT	No.	PER CENT	No.	PER CENT	TOTAL No.
Degree	12	39	2	6	12	39	5	16	31
Diploma	53	27	51	26	35	18	55	28	194
Total	65	29	53	24	47	21	60	27	225
$\chi^2 = 12.6$			d.f. $= 3$				$p < .01$		

* For explanation of headings see n. to Table 1.

graduates with high bureaucratic conception. Again, among graduates, simultaneously strong allegiance to both roles is the most depriving, while low conception of both roles is least depriving for the total sample as well as staff nurses.[18]

Are there systematic differences in the style of role organization produced by diploma and degree programs?—Since the way roles are organized affects deprivation in role and therefore, presumably, the intensity of conflict, knowledge of the conceptual organization characteristic of different training programs will provide a basis for speculating on the relative disillusionment encountered among their graduates.

Degree nurses maintain high professional conceptions more frequently than do diploma nurses (Table 2), combining them with either high or low bureaucratic conceptions. This simultaneous allegiance to both roles suggests the intensity of conflict they must encounter.

---

[18] Since the ideal score is a component of both the independent and the dependent variables, there is a theoretical possibility that the high professional discrepancy score for the high professional–high bureaucratic group could be explained by the high ideal score. If this were true, two conditions would exist. First, all groups would perceive the same reality. However, on an analysis of variance, the reality scores between the groups are significantly different. This indicates that the role conception influences the perception of reality:

	MEAN SCORES					
	HB–HP	HB–LP	LB–HP	LB–LP	F	d.f.
Professional reality	23.54	21.83	23.79	21.65	9.65	296/3
Bureaucratic reality	21.10	20.21	18.23	17.87	15.70	296/3

Second, the linear correlations between the ideal professional and bureaucratic roles and the discrepancy score of each role, considered independently, showed their joint effects produced greater discrepancy in role than either role does independently. For example, a small proportion of the professional discrepancy score was explained by the professional ideal score than by the professional–bureaucratic score.

TABLE 3. TYPES OF BUREAUCRATIC-PROFESSIONAL ROLE ORGANIZATION
ADOPTED BY DEGREE AND DIPLOMA STUDENT NURSES*

STUDENT NURSES' TRAINING	ROLE ORGANIZATION								
	HB–HP		HB–LP		LB–HP		LB–HP		
	No.	PER CENT	No.	PER CENT	No.	PER CENT	No.	PER CENT	TOTAL No.
Degree	5	26	3	16	4	21	7	37	19
Diploma	12	23	13	25	14	27	13	25	52
Total	17	24	16	23	18	25	20	28	71

$\chi^2 = 1.46$ d.f. $= 3$ Not significant

* For explanation of headings see n. to Table 1.

But the greatest differences appear in the mixed conceptions of role. Significantly enough, while degree nurses are unlikely to hold high bureaucratic–low professional conceptions, this is a popular choice among diploma nurses. On the other hand, degree nurses, more frequently than diploma nurses, combine low bureaucratic and high professional role conceptions.

On the other hand, conceptual organization of diploma and degree students does not differ (Table 3). It appears that degree and diploma nurses experience conflict in roles in different ways only *after* graduation as the influence of the bureaucratic role in nursing becomes more prominent.

In general, then, the professional conception retains more, the bureaucratic conception relatively less, prominence among degree than among diploma nurses. But, after graduation, degree nurses also frequently attempt to combine it with high bureaucratic conception, which probably increases the conflict. On the other hand, among diploma nurses the popularity of both low bureaucratic and low professional conceptions provides them with an escape. Degree, more than diploma, programs stress the professional more effectively than they do the bureaucratic conception, as expected.

Do discrepancies between ideal and real perceptions of role increase after graduation?—If the nursing faculty and the hospital staff uphold institutional and official ideals in different ways, then the discrepancy between ideals and the perception of reality is likely to be completely realized only after the passage from school to work. If so, the discrepancy in roles may increase after graduation. However, this is not necessarily the case because there is an alternative: the original ideals may be modified.

Diploma nurses express lower professional and service conceptions of role than diploma students do, suggesting that these are modified after graduation while bureaucratic conceptions are apparently maintained (Table 4). On the other hand, among degree nurses the professional conception seems to be maintained after graduation, while an inconsistently held service con-

TABLE 4. MEAN DIFFERENCES IN ROLE CONCEPTIONS* BETWEEN
STUDENT AND GRADUATE STAFF NURSES WITH
DIPLOMA OR DEGREE TRAINING

ROLE CONCEPTION	DIPLOMA TRAINING				DEGREE TRAINING			
	STUDENT NURSES	GRADUATE NURSES	CRITICAL RATIO	F-RATIO OF VARIANCE	STUDENT NURSES	GRADUATE NURSES	CRITICAL RATIO	F-RATIO OF VARIANCE
Bureaucratic:								
Mean	21.88	21.63	0.50	....	19.63	21.09	1.77†	....
Variance	9.26	10.85	....	1.17	12.36	7.71	....	1.60
Professional:								
Mean	28.44	26.71	2.39‡	....	27.21	28.08	0.50	....
Variance	14.59	33.71	....	2.31†	1.44	31.99	....	2.22†
Service:								
Mean	28.30	26.74	4.56‡	....	28.42	25.35	1.16	....
Variance	1.06	14.66	....	13.83‡	15.81	141.42	....	8.94‡

* High mean indicates high scores on the role-conception scale. High scores indicate strong allegiance to the conception. However, since there is an unequal number of items in the scales, the total score possible for the bureaucratic conception is 30; for the other two scales, 40.
† Significant at .05 (one tail).
‡ Significant at .01 (one tail).

ception declines; at the same time, the bureaucratic conception increases after graduation.

In short, the professional allegiance of diploma nurses declines after graduation, while their initial loyalty to the hospital is maintained; but the reverse is true for degree graduates who maintain professional conceptions while increasing their allegiance to the bureaucracy after employment.

Comparisons may be made between like cells in Table 4 and Table 5. Because the diploma nurses' professional conceptions of role are modified after graduation, the discrepancy does not increase; but, because modification does not occur among degree nurses, discrepancy increases among them. On the other hand, in spite of the fact that degree nurses have increased their allegiance to it, they still sense a discrepancy between their ideal bureaucratic conception and their perceived opportunity to fulfil it properly, while diploma personnel neither change their role nor sense a discrepancy after graduation. Thus, just as the formation of conceptions of role and their style of organization are influenced by the training program, so are the intensity and form of discrepancy.

So, there is evidence that role conflicts and discrepancies are underlying career themes. This is a normal process, but only in the sense that certain ways of organizing work are normal. For conflict is a product of at least one fundamental characteristic of modern work—that is, the partial separation of training from career.

TABLE 5. MEAN DIFFERENCES IN ROLE DISCREPANCY* BETWEEN
NURSES AND STUDENT NURSES WITH DIPLOMA
OR DEGREE TRAINING

ROLE DISCREPANCY	DIPLOMA TRAINING				DEGREE TRAINING			
	STUDENT NURSES	GRADUATE NURSES	CRITICAL RATIO	F-RATIO OF VARIANCE	STUDENT NURSES	GRADUATE NURSES	CRITICAL RATIO	F-RATIO OF VARIANCE
Bureaucratic:								
Mean	2.13	2.64	1.04	....	2.26	3.41	1.67†	....
Variance	8.71	8.98	....	1.00	10.94	10.44	....	1.00
Professional:								
Mean	4.85	4.99	0.24	....	4.05	7.64	2.49‡	....
Variance	11.08	15.42	....	1.40	19.05	27.80	....	1.48
Service:								
Mean	2.88	2.31	−1.23	....	5.26	3.87	−1.19	....
Variance	7.34	9.15	....	1.24	16.96	10.30	....	1.60

* High mean indicates high role discrepancy.
† Significant at .05 (one tail).
‡ Significant at .01 (one tail).

Precisely because conflict in roles is an inherent characteristic of the *structure* of work, the individual can, and does, make adjustments which modify its impact upon him. The capacity to organize roles is theoretically important, demonstrating as it does the fallacy in assuming a necessary connection between structural disorganization and personality conflict. While dilemmas of career confront those who simultaneously uphold divergent principles, individuals can reduce conflict and thereby maintain their security in what seem to be conflict-ridden situations by refusing to identify themselves with some or all of the alternative roles (though perhaps at the cost of the good opinion of coworkers and superiors who believe otherwise).

Strategically placed as he is in situations which may demand impossible alternatives, the plight of the professional employee skirts one of the curious puzzles of society—the fact that people do not always *do* what they believe they *should*. This is probably a normal result of an institutional conflict which forces a choice between highly regarded but conflicting principles. For, while it is quite possible to express belief in conflicting principles, the natural consequence of demands to conform to them simultaneously is their compromise.

It is hazardous to generalize about other types of professional employees from this small sample of nurses; for, while nursing is currently engaged in a drive to professionalize, it is not a mature profession, and the fact that it is almost exclusively a woman's occupation further distorts its vocational uniqueness. Yet, one suspects that, as bureaucratization increases, similar problems will be encountered among the mature professions, with perhaps even more intense impact as well-established professional traditions are absorbed by large-scale organization.[19]

---

[19] The number of lawyers and doctors employed by government and business agencies and law "factories" seems generally to be on the increase. There is reason to believe that the conflict between bureaucratic and professional conceptions will increase. E.g., both Whyte and Friedsam observe that a conflict between loyalty to an organization and loyalty to an indirectly based individualism is already a popular literary theme (see William H. Whyte, *The Organization Man* [New York: Simon & Schuster, 1956], Part VI, pp. 243-267; and H. J. Friedsam, "Bureaucrats as Heroes," *Social Forces,* XXXII [March 1954], 269-274).

Interpersonal Conflict in the Outpatient Department

MARY MALONE · NORMAN H. BERKOWITZ ·
MALCOLM W. KLEIN

Much has been written of the importance of the relationships within the health team, and between team members and the patient. Saunders points out that the social relationships between the practitioner and his client are an "integral and necessary part of practice." He states that, "If we are unable to establish a relationship which gives satisfaction to the patient we cannot give good care."[1]

Jourard stresses the nurse-patient relationship, taking the position that "effective nursing calls for a high degree of interpersonal competence."[2]

He believes that anything that interferes with the nurse getting to know the patient as a person interferes with the effectiveness of her care.

Lambertsen proposes that the patient is influenced in his response to the nurse and his perception of her competence by the nature of the relationship he feels exists between the nurse and the physician. She believes that the patient accepts the nurse as technically skillful but that the degree of his satisfaction is dependent on the relationship occurring on an emotional rather than an intellectual level.[3]

These factors take on added importance in the outpatient department,

Reprinted with permission from the *American Journal of Nursing*, Vol. 62, No. 3, March 1962, pp. 108-112.

where the ambulatory patient must assume major responsibility for his own care. Not only does the patient need to understand what to do, how to do it, and why, he must also somehow be motivated to do it. A patient who does not follow through with his recommendations has in effect received poor care, irrespective of the accuracy of the diagnosis, the effectiveness of the treatment in the clinic, and the comprehensiveness of the prescription. These latter are but portions of "good patient care." They are not, in and of themselves, "good patient care."[4]

The interpersonal relationships of the nurse in the outpatient department could be studied in at least two ways. Researchers who believe the problems are primarily due to personality characteristics of the individuals involved would concentrate on personality variables. Those who believe the problems are primarily due to some aspects of the system within which these individuals work would concentrate on organizational and role relationship variables.

Both approaches are valid and useful. However, they are quite different and thus lead to different recommendations for change. The first group's suggestions would be directed toward change in individuals, or selection of individuals, while the second group would suggest changes in the work setting or educational process.

The information presented here is based on a study of some of the organizational factors within the outpatient department suspected of influencing the interpersonal relationships of the nurse, as well as her performance. This approach was selected because it represents the major interest of the writers. Also, in many ways, it seems that changes in the organizational framework hold more promise.

Many system factors are more easily manipulable, are less dependent on the constellation of personalities in contact with one another, and have a more permanent effect in situations where the number of individuals interacting and the specific individuals interacting are constantly changing. In most nursing settings, this is the case, and effecting change in personalities of so many people from so many disciplines seems impractical, if not impossible.

SEEKING INFORMATION

From the host of relationships in the outpatient department which could be discussed, this paper concentrates on those between the nurse and the outpatient department as a system, the supervisor, the physician, the patient, and the ward nurse. Findings presented here were obtained in the first two years of a study of the role of the nurse in the outpatient department. Approximately 90 nurses in seven outpatient departments in the Boston area participated in this study. The information was collected by questionnaires and interviews. It should be kept in mind that these are not observed data.

In order to obtain information about some of the problems the nurse faces, 13 cartoons picturing different common clinic situations were devised. The respondent was asked to identify with the nurse in the cartoon and write in a box what she thought the nurse would say. Usually there was another box in which she would write what she thought another individual—physician, supervisor, patient, other nurse—would say. Sometimes she was to write in what she was feeling but not expressing or what she thought the other person was thinking or feeling. Much of the information to be presented was obtained in response to these cartoons.

THE OUTPATIENT SYSTEM

When a nurse goes to work in the outpatient department, in addition to her professional role she takes on an organization role; that is, she is a professional nurse and a staff nurse or head nurse in a specific clinic. She brings with her the values, norms, skills, and goals of her profession and then is expected to take on the values and goals of her employing institution.

In the outpatient department, both ultimate goals are congruent. Both are dedicated to the best possible care for all patients. However, it is possible that the ultimate goal is replaced by a series of short-term goals. Many times the values and short-term goals of the profession and the organization are in opposition. Then the nurse is placed in conflict and must decide to favor one of the forces, work out a compromise solution, or do nothing.

Different expressions of emotion would be expected, according to the mode of resolution chosen. If we assume that tension accompanies conflict, we can expect tension to decrease when both sets of forces are reduced. This would be the case when the individual compromises or integrates the opposing forces. However, if one of the forces is favored, the demands of the other continue to exert pressure and keep tension high. If we accept the possibility that tension might be expressed as hostility, more would be expected when one force is favored than when an integrative response is made.

Two of the cartoons depicted situations in which the nurse was faced with the conflicting demands of profession and organization. In one, a nurse and a physician were outside a series of examining rooms. He was saying to her, "Miss Jones, I am not going to examine this patient until we can locate his record. It is unfair to the patient and poor medical care." The nurse was to write in one place what she would say to the doctor and in another what she was thinking.

The opposing forces were immediate care of the patient and the requirement that the patient's record be at hand. In responding to this cartoon, nurses who resolved conflict in favor of either the professional value or the organizational regulation expressed more hostility toward the agent they perceived as placing them in the situation—the physician or the record room— than did those who found an integrative solution.

In the second cartoon illustrating conflict between an organizational regulation and a professional value, a nurse was standing at the clinic desk and a patient was saying that she felt miserable. The clock on the wall showed 1:30 P.M. while the posted clinic hours were 10:00 A.M. to 1:00 P.M. The nurse was to write in what she would say to the patient and, in another box, what she was feeling.

The conflict here is probably more apparent. Nurses are committed to caring for ill people, but as staff nurses or nurses in the clinic, they are responsible for maintaining the clinic schedule. Again, nurses who resolved the conflict in favor of either the organization or the profession showed more hostility than those who compromised.

These are but two examples of conflict between the nurses' professional and organizational roles. It should be mentioned that the demands of both roles are perfectly legitimate. In the first situation, one can easily accept the importance of the patient's record and, in the second, one can understand that it is impossible to have fully staffed clinics open from dawn to dusk. On the other hand, it should also be easy to see how these organizational policies, instituted to implement patient care, may act as opposing forces to the attainment of a most important nursing goal—immediate care for a particular sick person.

The data indicate that compromise is associated with less hostility than decisions favoring either of the opposing forces. Because of the work setting in the outpatient department, the roles most likely to be involved in such conflicts with the nurse are those of patient and physician. As these are two of the most critical relationships for the nurse, the need for helping her compromise this kind of situation is apparent.

USING COMPROMISE

A conflict situation can be compromised only when there is a compromise alternative available. In the cartoons already discussed, the compromises most often used were to send the clerk for the record and send the patient to the emergency ward. If there is no clerk or no emergency ward, then neither of these are possible alternatives.

If we assume that compromise is the cause of reduced tension rather than merely accompanying it, then the first remedial step would seem to be to make compromise solutions available. This problem could be approached by discovering through research the common conflict situations faced by nurses in an outpatient department and making explicit the compromise alternatives available, and instituting others when feasible. Naturally, we cannot expect to eliminate conflict, but certainly it is not unrealistic to expect to find ways of affecting many such situations.

Another approach might be to help those involved to understand the forces operating in the conflict situation. Increased knowledge of the situation, the possible solutions, and their consequences might help the nurse to make better decisions, with a reduction of frustration and tension and consequent improvement in the relationships between the roles involved.

Because of the close working relationship between the nurse and the physician, there is increased opportunity for tension to arise. The problems between these two groups might be partially due to differing perceptions of the nursing role. A cartoon in which there was a nurse and a physician with a patient in an examining room provided us with some information related to this hunch. The physician was saying to the nurse, "Could you. . . ." The respondent was to write in what she thought the physician was asking.

The majority of the nurses indicated that they thought the physician would request help with an examination or treatment, performance of a technical nursing procedure, or attention to some administrative details. It is of particular interest to note that only two out of 90 thought he would ask them to teach the patient.

We infer from these data that the physician was perceived as viewing the nurse as his technical assistant first and, secondly, as one who can take care of those administrative duties that will help him treat his patient—obtaining records, x-ray results, and so forth. He was almost never thought to consider her as a teacher of patients. Sixty-five per cent of the nurses' covert responses indicated reluctance to follow through with the physicians' requests, or expressed outright refusal or hostility. There was almost equal hostility when the request was for a nursing or non-nursing activity.

Therefore, we cannot dismiss the possibility that hostility may not be primarily job related, but may be due to a more general variable such as status. The Boeks discuss the friction between nurse and doctor as a function of their positions within the hierarchy—the nursing group striving to increase their status, and the medical group striving to hold on to theirs.[5] They also refer to the tension resulting from the nurse's taking on responsibility for hospital policy and, in many instances, behaving more like an administrator than a nurse in her relationship with the physician. They infer that she may fall back on this aspect of her role if she does not wish to carry out physicians' request. It sounds very much as if they think nurses have more ability to resist influence and thereby have a more independent status as administrators than as nurses.

Several questions were asked relative to the nurses perception of the supervisory role, and the results indicated that there is some friction here. Only half of the respondents thought their supervisor was well qualified, while only one third thought they were receiving excellent supervision. They felt that they were supervised closely but that most of this help was with administrative problems—little with nursing care problems. The majority of interactions they had with their supervisors were said to be about organizational matters. Also, less than half believed that the supervisor's evaluation of their work was accurately based on sound information about the quality of their performance.

RELATIONSHIP WITH THE SUPERVISOR

Responses to a cartoon, in which a very perturbed nurse was telling her supervisor that she was ready to quit the outpatient department, indicated that only one third of the nurses felt that their supervisor would be understanding or sympathetic. The physician was often mentioned as the source of their frustration.

Little positive feeling was suggested by the results obtained to a question soliciting the nurses' relative loyalties to the following six groups—"the nursing profession, the medical field, this hospital, this hospital's nursing service, this OPD, and your work group."[6] Nursing service received the lowest ranking. As the supervisor is the most immediate representative of nursing service, this could be taken as an indication of the nurses' feeling toward this position. Consistent with these feelings, Argyris and Pearsall found that very few nurses aspire to supervisory positions.[7,8]

It is quite possible that the negative attitudes toward supervisors are due to the fact that the supervisor was thought to be more of an administrator than a nurse. She was seen as being more concerned with the smooth functioning of the clinic than with the quality of nursing care patients receive. Her judgments of nurses were thought to be made on inadequate information, most of it administrative in nature. All this suggests that nurses are rewarded by the supervisor for their administrative rather than nursing skills.

If this is indeed the situation, then the supervisor's emphasis on administration influences the nurse to do more administrative activities and, consequently, fewer nursing activities. Thus, the nurse's behavior is less and less in accord with her idealized concept of the nursing role. This leads to an increase in "role deprivation" and its effects, which include negative feelings toward the supervisor.[9]

We have seen that the nurse believes the physician expects her to be his assistant and an administrator, and the supervisor also expects her to be an administrator. At the same time, leaders and writers in her profession indicate they expect her to be a teacher of patients. Which of these expectations has the greatest influence on the nurse's behavior? Some possible answers to this question were obtained from questionnaires and interviews. Findings obtained in this way do not necessarily represent the nurses' actual behavior in such situations.

FEAR AND HOSTILITY

In one cartoon a nurse was saying to the patient, "Now remember. . . ." This sentence was to be completed, after which the respondents were to write in a box what the patient was thinking. Sixty-five per cent of the nurses' communications dealt with organizational matters, while 35 per cent were concerned with care the patient would give himself at home.

It is interesting that 64 per cent of the covert responses attributed frustration, resentment, or confusion to the patient. The attitudes attributed to the patient are often considered responses to fear or anxiety, and we might reflect on the findings of Feshback, a psychologist from the University of Pennsylvania, that a high degree of anxiety leads to little learning and poor follow-through.[10] He also found that fear often precedes hostility, which may be displaced or directed toward the person who has either aroused the fear or failed to reduce it. It would follow that in the preceding situation, the patient could be expected to harbor hostile feelings toward the nurse who has done little to reduce his anxiety. This is only speculation, as no data have been collected from patients. However, if this should be true, it has great significance for the quality of the relationship between the nurse and the patient.

THE NURSE AND THE PATIENT

In the second cartoon, a patient said to the nurse that the doctor told him to take a bath every day but that he did not have a tub. The nurses' responses were coded for their degree of usefulness and for their emotional tone. Less than one third offered helpful suggestions and only slightly over one fourth indicated either sympathy or understanding. It was surprising to note that approximately 60 per cent of the nurses assumed that the bath was prescribed because the patient was dirty, although there was no indication that this was the case. If a nurse had any question about the recommendation, as reported by the patient, she could be expected to question the physician. Very few indicated they would do so. Analysis of the relationship between the usefulness of the nurses' suggestions and her attitude toward the patient showed that as the understanding or sympathy of the nurse decreased, so did the usefulness of her suggestion.

These findings raise some important questions about nurses' attitudes toward outpatients. The information does not fit into the philosophy that nurses accept patients as they are, try to understand their problems, and help them work out solutions. There was little indication in the responses to either of these cartoons that the nurse was interested in the patient or his problem. Also, there was little evidence to suggest that she took responsibility for seeing that he understood how to care for himself and was able to do so.

Indeed, little in their responses shows that the professional values had much influence on the nurses' behavior at least as indicated by these measures. It looks as though the expectations of the supervisor and the physician influence nurses' behavior more than do the values and pronouncements of her profession.

To learn how nurses in the outpatient department perceived their role, and how they thought other nurses conceived of it, we used a cartoon showing two nurses—one from the clinic, the other from the "house"—discussing the difference between these two nursing settings. The respondents said that the main distinguishing characteristics of the outpatient department were the regular hours and the kind of patient treated. Only eight specifically mentioned that there was more need for teaching in the outpatient department. The responses attributed to the house nurse by the nurses of the outpatient department showed that less nursing care and easier work were considered to be the most differentiating characteristics, followed closely by the statement that in the outpatient department patients are not so sick.

Thirty per cent of the respondents attributed hostility to the house nurse, although the content of the overt statement was not provocative. An equal number attributed jealousy to the house nurse. This was usually in response to the comments on working conditions in the outpatient department.

Why do some clinic nurses see house nurses as hostile toward them? From the responses attributed to the house nurse, we can infer that the respondents see the clinic nurse as deviating from the concept of the nursing role held by the profession. She does not give care to acutely ill, hospitalized patients and thus is seen as failing to live up to the expectations of her role. We can only speculate about the hostility and jealousy attributed to the house nurse. It might be a projection of the guilt of the outpatient nurses resulting from their failure to live up to the expectations inherent in the idealized concept of a nurse.

SUMMARY AND DISCUSSION

Now let us pull this information together, see what it means, and speculate on some of the directions for change. Essentially, we have been saying that the role of the nurse in the outpatient department is in conflict. Here, the general concept of the nursing role is inappropriate so that it is not possible for her to fulfill the concept.

Initially, her profession dictates that she should care for physically ill patients in bed, but there are no such patients in the outpatient department. She then is exhorted to teach patients, but she finds that, by their behavior, neither the physician nor the supervisor expect or encourage her to do so. It is not humanly possible to meet everyone's expectations. One cannot teach every patient, assist three to eight doctors, and administer the clinic all at the same time.

This means that priorities must be assigned. Indications are that administrative duties receive high priority, which automatically means that some nursing duties including teaching are accorded low priority. Actually, there is no objective reason for the nurse to make any other decision. In fact, it might be rather unwise for her to do so. If she taught patients, who would take care of the administrative tasks? How would the supervisor and physician react if she neglected such matters? The nurse evidently feels she would be in considerable trouble and tries to avoid this by seeing that the clinic runs smoothly.

How does this affect the relationship between nurse and patient? Present observations have shown that nurses have less contact with patients than would be considered desirable. Also, indications are that when nurses talk with patients they generally discuss those aspects of care which, if not done, would considerably inconvenience the department. For example, if patients do not keep their x-ray appointments or go unprepared, soon there will be difficulties between x-ray and clinic personnel. These is little evidence that those aspects of care of greater importance to the patient—the hows, whats, and whys of his treatment, information about his illness, complications, restrictions, and so forth—receive much attention. However, we believe that one of the main reasons for this situation is that the nurse cannot afford to spend her time with patients. If she should, then other duties which are considered more important by the influential roles of physician and supervisor will not be done. If the patient is not taught, few persons appear to know. It does not seem to cause the same stir as problems with other departments, physicians, and so forth.

If we feel that ambulatory patients need help in understanding how to care for themselves and that nurses are the most suitable group to take major responsibility for seeing that they get this kind of help, what changes should be made? First, conditions must be provided which allow nurses in the outpatient department to give the kind of nursing care patients require.

It seems rather futile to educate nurses to be skillful in a highly specialized field of practice and then set up the work situations so they cannot use these skills. Therefore, the first suggestion in many ways echoes that being made for much of nursing practice. Nurses should take responsibility for nursing and give up their responsibility for administration.

To bring about this change is easier said than done. Lip service to the value of patient care and patient teaching will not bring it about. Unless the roadblocks to the achievement of these goals are removed, we will find that pronouncements like these will only build up greater frustration and tension within the nurses who are caught in the conflict.

How can these obstacles be removed? First, make nursing care important. This can be done by rewarding nurses for the quality of their nursing performance, not their administrative efficiency. Second, remove all responsibility for clinic administration from nurses—not just the activities themselves but the responsibility for these. Third, institutionalize patient teaching so that no patient leaves the clinic without first seeing a nurse.

It is also recommended that the profession, through its educational process, expand the concept of the nursing role to include those nurses who are not giving direct care to physically ill, hospitalized patients. Then fulfillment of this concept will be possible for nurses in practice, teaching, supervision, or research in all nursing settings.

These, then, are some of the changes which seem to be fundamental to freeing the nurse for increased contact with patients and for better utilization of these contacts. Without these changes, even those nurses competent in interpersonal relationships cannot reach their maximum effectiveness.

REFERENCES

1. Saunders, Lyle, *Cultural Differences and Medical Care.* New York: Russell Sage Foundation, 1954, p. 243.
2. Jourard, Sidney, How well do you know your patients? *Amer. J. Nurs.* 59:1568-1571, November 1959.
3. Lambertsen, Eleanor, *Education for Nursing Leadership.* Philadelphia: J. B. Lippincott Co., 1958, p. 103.
4. Klein, M. W., and others, Problems of measuring patient care in the outpatient department. *J. Health and Human Behavior* 2:138-144, Summer 1961.
5. Boek, W. E., and Boek, Jean K., *Society and Health.* New York: G. P. Putnam's Sons, 1956, pp. 219-220.
6. Bennis, W. G., and others, Reference groups and loyalties in the outpatient department. *Adm. Sci. Quart.* 2:481-500, March 1958.
7. Argyris, Chris, *Diagnosing Human Relations in Organization; A Case Study of a Hospital.* New Haven, Conn.: Labor and Management Center, 1956.
8. Pearsall, M., *Nursing Supervisors; A Social Profile.* Boston, Mass.: Massachusetts General Hospital, 1957. (Unpublished manuscript)
9. Malone, Mary, *Some Effects of Role Deprivation on Selected Aspects of the Behavior; Values and Attitudes of Nurses in Out-Patient Departments.*

Boston, Mass.: Boston University School of Nursing, 1958. (Unpublished master's thesis)

10. Feshbeck, Seymour, A talk presented to the Massachusetts Public Health Association, Boston, Mass., January 1960.

Social Influence and the Social-Psychological Function of Deference: A Study of Psychiatric Nursing

William A. Rushing

▨   In recent years sociologists and social psychologists have shown an active interest in the phenomena of influence attempts[1] and deference behavior.[2] Researchers and writers interested in each of these phenomena, however, have not turned their attention to the connection between the two

---

[1] See, for example, Kurt Back, "Influence through Social Communication," *Journal of Abnormal and Social Psychology*, XLVI (1951), 2-23; Leon Festinger, *et al.*, "The Influence Process in the Presence of Extreme Deviates," *Human Relations*, V (1952), 327-346; and Stanley Schachter, "Deviation, Rejection and Communication," *Journal of Abnormal and Social Psychology*, XLVI (1951), 190-207. For reviews of recent research on influence, see George C. Homans, *Social Behavior: Its Elementary Forms* (New York: Harcourt, Brace and World, Inc., 1961), pp. 83-111 and James G. March, "An Introduction to the Theory and Measurement of Influence," *The American Political Science Review*, XLIX (1955), 439-451.

[2] See Erving Goffman, "The Nature of Deference and Demeanor," *The American Anthropologist*, LVIII (1956), 473-502; see also, Rose Laub Coser, "Insulation from Observability and Types of Social Conformity," *American Sociological Review*, XXVI (1961), 28-39.

Reprinted with permission from *Social Forces*, Vol. 41, 1962-1963, pp. 142-148. Published by The University of North Carolina Press.

This paper reports on one phase of a broader study of the mental health professions. See William A. Rushing, "Professional Adaptive Problems on a Psychiatric Service" (unpublished dissertation, Department of Sociology and Anthropology, University of North Carolina, 1961). The author would like to express thanks to Harvey L. Smith, who directed the research, for his suggestions and guidance throughout the course of the study. A version of this paper was read at the twenty-fifth annual meeting of the Southern Sociological Society, Louisville, Kentucky, April 13, 1962.

—that is, deference as social influence. The first objective of this paper will be to redress this omission by pointing out, with empirical illustrations, how deference behavior may be viewed as an influence attempt.

A second objective is to conceptualize these two phenomena—influence attempts and deference behavior—within the context of an institutionalized or normative social order. Most studies of influence attempts have been conducted in the laboratory with *ad hoc* experimental groups—groups lacking in a tradition of established social norms and ties and, therefore, lacking in a stable, crystallized group structure.[3] Consequently, the relationship of influence attempts to the normative social structure is not clear. On the other hand, there is the tendency to assume that deference behavior *is* institutionalized behavior. That is to say, an individual is deferential toward another because of the status or role relationships between him and another actor; deference behavior tends to be viewed as a component of one's social role and the result of social norms which define the role.[4] No doubt this normative assumption is a valid one in many instances. However, data will be presented in this paper which reveal that under at least some circumstances deference behavior is more accurately described in terms other than institutionalized (role) behavior. Nevertheless, deference behavior, like all social behavior, takes place only within a normative context, the description of which is necessary if social behavior is to be understood. The conceptualization of deference behavior in terms of the functions it performs for the psychiatric nurse in her relationship with the psychiatrist will uncover certain empirical linkages between deference behavior as an influence attempt and the normative order.

In achieving these two objectives I will present empirical illustrations of the concept of power strategy and then indicate the function these behaviors perform for the psychiatric nurse in her relationship with her superior, the psychiatrist.

Data are based on interviews with 16 psychiatric nurses who work on the inpatient service of a teaching mental institution, where strong emphasis is placed on the nurse-patient relationship as an important aspect of the patient's therapeutic milieu.[5]

NORMATIVE COMPONENTS OF THE NURSE ROLE

The performance of the psychiatric nurse role involves two moral principles or commitments. (1) The nurse, like the doctor, is morally obligated

---

[3] Homans, *op. cit.*, p. 84.

[4] Goffman, for example, regards deference behavior as behavior guided by ceremonial *rules. Op. cit.*

[5] Material for the present paper may be found in more extended form in Rushing, *op. cit.*, Chapter XII, "Psychiatric Nursing: Role Conflict and Maintaining Power Strategies," pp. 388-434.

to help the patient recover from his illness. The present group of nurses indicate their acceptance ("internalization") of this commitment on two different ways. First, 14 of 15 nurses state that they are trying to help the patient to "get well," to "return to normal," to "return to society," or to "get back on their feet and be socially accepted again."[6] This moral commitment is also revealed by the responses nurses give to the question of how they feel about a drug research project. Doctors are supposed to place all patients requiring day-time sedation on a project where they will receive one of three drugs or an inert placebo. The project is so designed that no one, including the patient's doctor, knows what drug the patient is receiving, or if indeed he is receiving a drug at all. (Such procedure is necessary to control for possible contaminating effects due to patients responding in terms of their knowledge of the drug's alleged effects, and effects due to ward personnel interacting with patients in terms of their expectations of the drug's effects.) Of 16 nurses 13 express disapproval of placing patients on this project. Reasons given for this objection are: the patient may be given a placebo which will not help him; the drugs are administered by random placement and not according to the patient's needs; and the project drugs are slow acting, thus leading to unnecessary expense to the patient. The nurse's moral obligation to the patient rather than to the objective of scientific research is aptly summed up by the following nurse:

> It's the drug that happens to come up that the patient gets. I disagree very strongly with this. If it's not helping the patient, we have no *right* to keep him on it. It's okay for people wanting to know about drugs—they want to know about them and that's all right, but what about the patient? *It's the patient's welfare that is utmost, not knowing about some drug.*[7]

(2) Although all nurses were not asked specific questions regarding the doctor's authority over them, it was assumed that the nurse is the subordinate in the doctor-nurse relationship: she is subordinate to the doctor relative to the responsibility for the patient and the doctor's authority (i.e., she carries out the doctor's "orders"). This assumption is consistent with findings regarding the doctor-nurse relationship in other mental hospital set-

---

[6] These responses are replies to the question: "What specifically are you—as a psychiatric nurse—trying to accomplish in the performance of your nursing duties?" The fifteenth—who states that the objective of the nurse is "to carry out the doctor's care and treatment plan"—implies a similar objective since it is the doctor's ethical obligation to do what he can to facilitate the recovery of the patient. Although 16 nurses were interviewed, only 15 were asked the above question.

[7] These data are based on the nurse's response to the question: "How do you feel about the drug project?" If the answer was not unambiguous, the respondent was asked, "Are you for it or against it?" Reasons for the nurse's position were probed in all cases.

tings, as well as previous studies conducted in the present setting.[8] Therefore, the nurse's function may be described as the responsibility to carry out the doctor's orders. A head nurse expresses this the following way:

> As I see it, the function of the psychiatric nurse, the major function, is to carry out the doctor's care and treatment plan. The doctor is head of the team and it is the nurse's responsibility to carry out his treatment plan . . . She is the go-between the doctor and the patient. She relates to the patient so as to support him when he needs it and so on. [But] she relates to him in terms of the doctor's care plan.

These two normative components of the nurse's role are clear enough. The interesting question arises, what does the nurse do when these two principles are in conflict? For example, what does she do when she thinks the orders prescribed by the doctor are unsuitable for meeting the patient's therapeutic needs. Such situations are especially likely in a hospital setting which emphasizes the nurse-patient relationship as an adjunct to therapy because the nurse is with the patient eight hours of the day while the doctor is with him only during the therapeutic hour. Also, most doctors on the inpatient service of this hospital are first-year residents and, therefore, are lacking in psychiatric experience.[9] For these reasons the nurse may come to think she knows more than the doctor about the proper treatment procedure for particular patients.

The existence of a conflict between these two moral commitments—responsibility for the patient and his welfare and responsibility to carry out the doctor's order—can be seen from the fact that 15 of 16 nurses replied in the affirmative when asked if doctors ever gave them an order which they thought was contrary to the patient's welfare. Data reveal two types of reactions to this conflict: conforming to the doctor's authority and attempts to influence the doctor's treatment decision.

Four nurses report that they usually continue to carry out the order as stated by the doctor. When questioned why they did this although they felt

---

[8] See, for example, Ivan Belknap, *Human Problems of a State Mental Hospital* (New York: The Blakiston Division, McGraw-Hill Book Co., 1956); Robert G. Brown, "Problems of Social Organization of a New York Psychiatric Inpatient Service" (unpublished Ph.D. dissertation, Department of Sociology and Anthropology, University of North Carolina, 1960); William Caudill, *The Psychiatric Hospital as a Small Society* (Cambridge: Harvard University Press, 1958); and Dorothea Scott, "The Relation of the Uniform to the Professional Self-Image of the Psychiatric Nurse" (unpublished Master's thesis, Department of Sociology and Anthropology, University of North Carolina, 1960).

[9] For a discussion of this problem, see Harvey L. Smith, "Professional Strains and the Hospital Context," in Milton Greenblatt, Daniel J. Levinson, and Richard H. Williams (eds.), *The Patient and the Mental Hospital* (Glencoe: The Free Press, 1957), pp. 3-9.

the order was an incorrect one, the general response was that it was the doctor's decision to make and the nurse's responsibility was to carry out his decision. For example, one states, "If he gives an order that I disagree with, I go along with it because that's supposed to be his decision. The nurse is supposed to carry out his decision." Another says, "It's sort of an unwritten law . . . The nurse accepts it that way. She takes her orders from the doctor and carries them out. It may be that I do not agree with him, but it's his decision and, so, I go on and carry it out the way he thinks it should be." Certainly these responses are explicit manifestations of the internalization of the doctor-nurse authority relationship which implies that the doctor possesses superior knowledge and competence to that of the nurse.

POWER STRATEGIES

More interesting, for purposes of this paper, are the 11 nurses who report that, rather than conforming to the doctor's orders, they try to *influence* the doctor to modify or change his order. Three different types of influence attempts were reported.

Influence through the Doctor's Superior. Nine nurses report that they go to the chief resident or ward chief and let them take the matter up with the resident in an effort to elicit a change in the treatment plan.

Reporting Observations that are Contrary to the Doctor's Order. Because nurses are with the patients on the ward eight hours a day, they have an opportunity to observe many aspects of the patients' behavior. Consequently, in an attempt to get the doctor to change his treatment decision, eight nurses confront him with aspects of the patient's behavior that suggest some other treatment plan is indicated. For example:

> I will tell him things about the patient that are contrary to the order given. I just let him know about these things in hopes that he will change the order. I will merely tell him things about the patient that are contrary to the order.

Asking Questions. Finally, four nurses state they ask the doctor questions about the order indicating they do not understand it.

> I will ask if this was intended in the order or should it be something else. Or I might say that I thought it would be thus-and-so. If he puts something in the order that I disagree with, I will sometimes say, "I've never seen it like this before." Work around it this way . . . without coming right out and telling him. You have to do it this way—you have to be more tactful. I can't come right out and tell him what I think the order should be.

A pertinent question is: are these three influence attempts conforming behavior or deviant behavior? To the extent that they are actions which call into question the legitimacy of the doctor's order they might be considered deviant actions. At the same time, however, they are carried out in the interest of the patient; in this sense they are actions which conform to one of the major normative principles of the nurse's role.

Correctly viewed, these actions are neither a form of conformity nor a form of deviancy. Rather, they are actions that are caused by conflict between two normative principles of the nurse's role: the patient's welfare and the doctor's authority. Both principles are components of the definition of the nurse role, but the influence attempts are *not* actions specified in that definition. The definition does not say that the nurse should try to influence the doctor's decision, nor how she should go about this when she does try. Therefore, they are not role behaviors.[10]

Greater understanding of these influence attempts can be obtained by viewing them as *power strategies*: behaviors designed to influence the behavior of another, but behaviors that are oriented *to*, rather than in conformity *with*, institutionalized normative orders.[11] The nurse's influence attempts are efforts to get the doctor to change his order; therefore, they are not in conformity *with* the legitimate order—the doctor's authority. This is not to say that they are expressions of disrespect for the doctor's authority and competence; the contrary is the case because they are *oriented* to his greater authority and competence.

An example will illuminate. A nurse thinks doctors often prescribe drugs when they are not indicated. She tries to influence doctors to revoke their decision by asking questions, e.g., "I would say that I *wonder* if this drug is helping the patient. I may think that the drug isn't helping the patient but I wouldn't tell him that." She does not tell the doctor what she thinks—

> Because I respect him. If I don't respect him as a person, I respect his title . . . because he's a doctor and I'm a nurse. (That) means that he's more educated and knows more and is more able to handle the situation than I, or at least he's supposed to.

---

10 The author is aware of the lack of agreement among sociologists and social psychologists regarding the definition of the concept of role; see Neal Gross, Ward S. Mason, and Alexander W. McEachern, *Explorations in Role Analysis* (New York: John Wiley and Sons, Inc., 1958), pp. 11-18. The concept is used in this paper to refer to behaviors that are the enactment of positions or statuses in a social structure, or to the "dynamic aspect of status." See Ralph Linton, *The Study of Man* (New York: D. Appleton-Century Company, 1936), p. 114. Linton's formulation—as well as the formulations of Parsons, Merton, and Kingsley Davis—views "role behavior" as *institutionalized* behavior.

11 A discussion of this concept and its relevance to general sociological theory can be found in Rushing, *op. cit.*, pp. 3-4, 22-25, 28-29, and 30-34. The concept power strategy is borrowed from John W. Thibaut and Harold H. Kelley, *The Social Psychology of Groups* (New York: John Wiley and Sons, 1959), 119-122; however, the exact formulation of power strategy in this paper and in the author's above work are the author's.

We therefore have the situation in which the doctor is defined as possessing greater knowledge than the nurse, but where the nurse thinks she knows more about the needs of specific patients than the doctor. In her attempts to influence his decision, however, the nurse does not openly indicate that she *thinks* she knows more about the patient than the doctor. Clearly, the nurse's power strategies are types of deference behavior, if by deference we mean expressions of "regard," "respect," and "appreciation" for another and his role responsibilities.[12] For example, a nurse who says: "I have to be careful. I can't let it look like I am trying to tell him what to do. I have to approach him in a manner so it looks like I am not telling him."

It is true that the influence attempts originate with the nurse thinking she is better informed than the doctor. At the same time they are expressions of respect and regard for the doctor's superiority and greater competence. In being "careful" the nurse orients her actions to the doctor's superior status. Such "careful" actions may also be viewed as "avoidance rituals"[13]—taking care not to infringe upon the duties and responsibilities of another role performer. It is important to keep in mind that although the nurse engages in the above described deference behaviors, she is doing so with the intention of influencing the doctor's treatment orders. Her power strategies then are influence at the price of deference: she attempts to exchange[14] her deference behavior for a change in the doctor's treatment plan.

Not only are these actions oriented to the normative authority structure, they are oriented to a power structure as well. To understand the nature of the doctor's power over the nurse, it is necessary to realize that the role of the psychiatric nurse involves an interpersonal relationship with patients.[15] Nevertheless her background and training may not have prepared her for this role. Her task is to meet the emotional needs of patients, but she has received little training in the skills necessary to recognize, identify, and meet these needs. Consequently, she must turn to the doctor for direction and guidance to determine how she shall "relate to" patients. Nurses are quite explicit in expressing their dependence on the doctor.[16] One states, for example:

> He's the one who has to tell us how to handle the patient. We don't want to overdo, or underdo, something with the patient, and we look to him for direction . . . Everything comes from him. He tells us how we should treat the patient. He's our guide, the one we look to in order to know whether what we are doing is right.

---

[12] Goffman, *op. cit.*

[13] *Ibid.*

[14] George C. Homans, "Social Behavior as Exchange," *American Sociological Review*, LXIII (1958), 597-606.

[15] See Rushing, *op. cit.*, esp. pp. 397-401.

[16] *Ibid.*, esp. pp. 401-403.

What the nurse does in her relationship with the patient is thus dependent on what the doctor instructs her to do. Accordingly, the doctor has a high degree of power over her.[17] It should be noted that directives and guidance are not given solely through the medium of written instruction. Verbal instructions are issued during team meetings and ward rounds,[18] and in response to questions nurses have throughout the day. Several nurses volunteer that instructions given through face-to-face contacts are more useful than written orders.[19] A head nurse says, for example, "there's not much in the form of written orders" since most directions come through face-to-face contact by "sitting down and talking to (the doctor), and in team meetings." Therefore, the nurse's interpersonal relationship with the patient is dependent on a face-to-face relationship with the doctor, a relationship in which the patient's illness and methods of treatment are discussed. With this in mind we can begin to understand the function performed by the nurses' deferential power strategies.

First, however, the distinction between the power and the authority of the doctor should be made explicit. Regarding power, the nurse is dependent on the directions and orders of the doctor—directions are needed to determine how she shall perform her interpersonal role with the patient. In reference to authority, the nurse is responsible for conforming to the doctor's directives and "orders." Otherwise stated, authority is a normative phenomenon; power is not. The nurse is ethically obligated to carry out the doctor's orders because of the nature of the general norms of medicine: the doctor is defined as the superior, and it is on the basis of his greater knowledge and competence that decisions should be made. On the other hand, the doctor has power over the nurse because of the nature of their work: with his superior knowledge and competence, the doctor is a source to whom the nurse must turn to determine how she shall relate to patients. In any concrete course of action (a particular nurse-patient relationship), the nurse does, of course, respond to both orders. The distinction is, then, an analytic one: it refers to different aspects or properties of the nurse's action in her relationship with the patient. Nevertheless, the distinction is crucial for understanding the function of the nurses' power strategies.

---

[17] For similar formulations of power and its relationship to dependency, see Thibaut and Kelley, op. cit., Chapter 7; Robert Dubin, The World of Work (Englewood Cliffs, N. J.: Prentice-Hall, Inc., 1958), pp. 29, 48; and Richard M. Emerson, "Power-Dependence Relations," American Sociological Review, XXVII (1962), 31-41.

[18] Ward rounds are held each morning and are attended by the chief ward psychiatrist, chief resident, psychiatric residents, nurses, psychologist, occupational therapist, recreator, and aides and orderlies. Each resident has his own individual team meetings which are attended by the "ancillary professions" (psychology, social work, etc.) and nurses. Both ward rounds and team meetings are devoted to a discussion of patients, their problems, and how the "team" might best cope with them.

[19] See Rushing, op. cit., p. 390.

FUNCTION OF DEFERENCE

Goffman has stated that deference behavior serves to confirm the conception of selves.[20] In a recent analysis, Coser observes that deference also functions to "maintain the relational system."[21] According to the latter formulation, the nurses' power strategies should function to maintain the nurse-doctor relationship. As I have indicated, the relational system between nurse and doctor is a continuous face-to-face one. The continuity of this relational system is made difficult if the nurse-doctor relationship is strained. A nurse says, for example:

> I think that there should be a good relationship between the nurse and the doctor because if there are hard feelings neither one will want to help each other with the patient . . . You should be able to talk to him, (and) I think he should discuss with the nurse why he does something.

One method of creating strain (e.g., "hard feelings") in this relationship is for the nurse to try to invert the status differences (e.g., to question the doctor's superior knowledge and competence by questioning his order). In a previous study of the nurse-doctor relationship in this setting, it was found that doctors withdrew from their relationship with nurses when the latter questioned their orders.[22] This, however, deprives the nurse of something she *values*—a close relationship with the doctor. Consequently, by questioning the doctor's order the nurse runs the risk of incurring unpleasant *costs*— having to forgo the value of doctor-nurse relationship.[23] Such costs are illustrated by two nurses who speak of the doctor putting the nurse in a "bad position" and making her "insecure": When he fails to instruct the nurses in how they should handle his patients, "We don't know if we are doing the right thing. We might even be doing something to hurt the patient. We don't know."

Therefore, to prevent this costly situation from occurring, the nurse must maintain her relationship with the doctor. Her strategies of deference are to be viewed in these terms. By refusing openly to question the doctor's orders she does not alienate him, thereby maintaining her relationship with him; the function of this is to prevent the cost of having to "relate to" patients without knowing what to do—that is, without sufficient direction from the

---

20 Goffman, *op. cit.*

21 Rose Laub Coser, *op. cit.,* p. 29.

22 See Brown, *op. cit.,* p. 90.

23 George C. Homans defines cost as a "value forgone." See his *Social Behavior: Its Elementary Forms, op. cit.,* p. 59. For a study of power strategies, their relationship to social norms and to different stages of the institutionalization process, and the use of the concept of cost to conceptualize these relationships, see Rushing, *op. cit.*

doctor. Support for this inference is provided by comments from nurses regarding the use of each of the three previously described power strategies.[24]

One nurse goes to the ward chief rather than express her opinion to the doctor, so she will not "threaten" the doctor. If she openly questions his order, he is threatened and becomes angry. She also says that she must have "good interpersonal relationships" with the doctor so she can talk to him. If she "threatens" the doctor by questioning his order, her relationship with him is strained—"I can't talk to him." Consequently, "I go to the ward chief and tell him what the situation is," rather than openly questioning the doctor's order. Another states that she has openly questioned doctors about their orders, but that this "ruined" her relationship—a relationship in which she "would feel comfortable in talking to the doctor about the patient's problems, and he would feel the same way about talking to me; he would listen to me when I have something to say . . . Our relationship was ruined when I went directly to him." This nurse states that now she always goes to the ward chief and lets him handle the matter.

A nurse who reports that she confronts the doctor with observations that are contrary to the order he has given says she does so because, upon voicing her disagreement to the doctor in the past, "He would get angry and I would get hostile. The whole relationship would blow-up—he would get so mad." Another reports the following as reasons for confronting the doctor with a report of the patient's behavior, rather than expressing her opinion to him.

> Well, I guess a nurse in talking to a doctor has to be a little more diplomatic . . . Our observations are important, but we can't tell the doctor what to do. We aren't doctors. They are the ones who are supposed to be right; but a lot of times they aren't. But when they are not right, we can't tell them. It's a matter of inter-personal relations . . . he's the doctor and it's his decision to make, not mine. When you tell him, then . . . He has to take the position that whether you like it or not, I am right. He can't let you tell him what to do. If you do, he has to put you in your place and then your interpersonal relationship with him is destroyed. I have to be careful not to do this. The nurse and the doctor have to have a good interpersonal relationship in order to work as a team.

Obviously, this nurse's power strategy is determined by the doctor's power over her, as well as by his normative authority.

Finally, a nurse who says that she is "insecure" when the doctor does not provide her with orders is quite explicit about the function of asking questions: it enables her to maintain her relationship with the doctor and so prevents her from incurring the cost of foregoing the value of the doctor's orders and directives. If she expressed her opinion rather than utilize this strategy,

---

[24] For additional data and elaboration, see *ibid.*, pp. 425-429.

The doctor wouldn't like it and this would make me insecure. He would get mad and wouldn't discuss the patient with me at all then. It works out better if we just ask him; work around it this way. If I told him (what I think), it would make me feel insecure —I wouldn't be able to find out anything about the patient then.

CONCLUSION

The above data indicates that the concept of power strategy is a useful one for describing actions which are sociologically relevant. They are actions an actor performs in reference to another actor, but they do not fit the category of institutionalized role behavior. The concept also enables us to conceptualize noninstitutionalized behavior—influence attempts—in terms of the institutionalized order. Power strategies are not institutionalized in the sense that they are actions which are in conformity with the prescriptions of a social order; however, they cannot be understood unless seen in terms of the institutionalized order within which they are enacted—they are actions which are *oriented to* (rather than in *conformity with*) the legitimate (institutionalized) order.[25] For example, the nurse's deferential influence attempts are oriented to the legitimate order (doctor's authority): the nurse thinks she knows more than the doctor, but she is "careful" not to act as if she thinks she does. When these behaviors are considered *only* as actions which are oriented to a normative order—that is, only in terms of the property of deference involved, the important property of influence attempt is ignored. The nurse not only "respects" the doctor's authority, she also attempts to elicit a change in his order. Only when the doctor's power over the nurse is considered, and its analytic distinction from his authority made explicit, is the function of nurse's power strategies revealed. The conceptualization of power in terms of dependency and of authority in terms of the responsibility to comply with the orders of another allows us, in turn, to conceptualize influence attempts in terms of their relationship to the normative order.

---

[25] Max Weber has recognized this distinction between actions that are in conformity with an institutionalized social order and actions which are oriented to that order. "It is possible for action to be oriented to an order in other ways than through conformity with its prescriptions . . ." Max Weber, *The Theory of Social and Economic Organization*, trans., A. M. Henderson and Talcott Parsons (Glencoe: The Free Press, 1947), p. 125.

Status-Orientations in Nursing

ROBERT K. MERTON

The current state of dissatisfaction, prompted by the need for status has become one of the collective assets of the profession of nursing. It means that nurses are no longer willing to be regarded merely as the handmaiden of the physician. It means that their professional association has developed a sense of autonomy, prepared to take its own informed stand on issues affecting the public health, rather than simply following the positions taken by the American Medical Association and the American Public Health Association. And it means that nurses do not accept the status currently assigned them as their unchanging and final status.

The phrase, "needs for status," ordinarily refers to the identifiable desire of human beings for favorable recognition of who we are and what we are. It is a tacit or expressed wish for positive evaluation by our fellows. From the evidence provided by sociology and anthropology, it appears evident that this wish for favorable recognition, this need for status, is found in every society and among men and women in every walk of life.

Indeed, a generation ago, the then dean of American sociologists, W. I. Thomas, suggested that the "wish for recognition" was one of the four primeval wishes of all men everywhere (the others being the wish for new experience, with all its excitements; the wish for security, which curbs the all-out search for new experience with its attendant dangers; and the wish for response, to give and receive personal appreciation, love, and affection).

Whether man's profoundest requirements actually number four, or four times four, we should note that the desire for recognition is so widespread and so deep rooted that it is included in every inventory of man's fundamental concerns. This concern, as Thomas also reminded us, "is expressed in the general struggle of men for position in their social group, in devices for securing a recognized, enviable, and advantageous social status."[1] Nor did that analyst of social life, Thorsten Veblen, permit us to forget how pervasive the struggle for status can become.

More recently, this fundamental observation was taken up by Vance

Reprinted with permission from the *American Journal of Nursing*, Vol. 62, No. 10, October 1962, pp. 70-73.

Packard, who converted it into the proposition that we Americans are all hungry for status. The ideas of the sociologists about status and recognition become popularized—and distorted. In short order, the woods were full of amateur sociologists, talking of status and status-symbols, of status-hier-archies, and status-seeking.

The fact is that Packard succeeded in converting a truth into that most dangerous thing, the half-truth. From his work, we might suppose that only Americans are a tribe of status-seekers. Yet, the search for recognition is found the world over, although it is not found everywhere in the same degree. For one thing, the greater the change in social system, the greater the concern of people with their social status. And for another, the higher the rate of social mobility, the more rapidly changing the position of individuals and of aggregates of individuals, the greater the concern with social status.

All this may seem remote from the subject of the status-needs of profes-sional nurses and of practical nurses. But this is not really so. If we are to understand these needs for status among various kinds of nurses, we must first understand the general workings of status-needs in human society. Otherwise, we are subject to the illusion of centrality: to the illusion that what we find among nurses (or physicians, or plumbers, or even pickpockets) is peculiar to them alone.* But this is not the case. Status-needs enter into the relations between various types of nurses just as they do in the relations between people in other groups. By continuing a bit longer on the general subject of status and recognition before turning to the specific case in which we are most interested, we can escape the human tendency to become emo-tionally involved in what is closest to our own interests.

Rapid social mobility tends to make for increased concern with status. Status-hunger grows by what it feeds upon; the appetite for status comes with eating. Rapid advancement in position shows that a rise in status is possible and each rise in status provides a new plateau from which to take off for a further rise. Only in groups and societies which are thoroughly traditional, in which social mobility is at a minimum, will there be little hunger for improved status.

SOCIAL ASCENT OF NURSING

From these general observations, you will at once infer that the need for improved status, the need for heightened public and professional approval, should be fairly intense among nurses of every grade and variety. For the history of nursing in recent generations exhibits a marked advance in the skills, accomplishments, and position of the nurse. The social ascent of the occupation of nursing may seem painfully slow to the practitioners of

---

* Ample evidence testifies that there is as definite a status-hierarchy among pick-pockets as in any other occupation.

nursing, but from the long perspective of the social historian, it has been remarkably rapid. And this rise in status seems to have become accelerated in recent decades.

Nurses may ask: What is this nonsense about our rapid rise in status when we are notoriously underpaid and overworked? And yet there may be no contradiction here. The improved status of the nurse and nurses' complaints about the status accorded them may both have the same sources. This is only a seeming paradox. For as Stouffer and his research associates found, the branches of the military having the highest rates of promotion also had the most criticism of opportunities for promotion.[2] Thus, the Air Corps had higher mobility than, say, the Military Police, and yet the Air Corps men were far more critical than the MP's about the chances for promotion. So, too, the better-educated soldiers, although they had notably higher rates of promotion in general, were more critical of opportunities for promotion than their less-educated associates.

The explanation of this apparent paradox is this: A generally high rate of mobility induces high expectations among members of the group so that those who are not promoted are especially apt to be dissatisfied. They feel themselves *relatively* deprived. But in groups with altogether low rates of promotion, comparison of one's own status with that of one's fellows more often leads to acceptance of things as they are.

The same process can be observed, I believe, in the occupation of nursing. As the mobility of individual nurses and particularly as the rise in the standing of the entire occupation have accelerated, there develops an understandable dissatisfaction among nurses with the status accorded them. The profession of nursing begins to compare its status—its economic and social position—with that of other pertinent professions—say, teaching—and feels relatively deprived.

So much, then, in general terms about the significance of status for the nurse. With other people, nurses share a concern for the positive social recognition of their qualities and accomplishments. With other occupations that have experienced rapid social mobility, they share an intensified concern with status. With each rise in status, their horizons have expanded further. Nurses take other professions as their reference groups, as their basis for judging the status accorded them, and they feel relatively deprived. Accordingly, they reach out to enlarge their own competences further, to expand their accomplishments and their collective strength and, as a by-product, to raise their status a little more. They are the beneficiaries of status-discontent.

DIFFERENTIATION OF NURSING ROLES

This matter of status-needs also operates *within* the generic occupation of nursing. It enters, for example, into the relations between the registered professional nurse and the licensed practical nurse. Note, first, that the modern history of nursing has recorded a continuing and marked differentiation of roles. As the role of the professional nurse has evolved, there differentiated out the role of the licensed practical nurse. In the wake of this differentiation, also, all manner of auxiliary workers have developed at the periphery: nurses' aides and orderlies, to say nothing of technicians of every stripe, diet maids, ward maids, messengers, receptionists, clerks, hospital housekeepers, and other vocational groups that comprise the army of workers that staff the contemporary hospital and other health facilities.

To the informed, there is a clear distinction, on the one hand, between the professional nurse and the practical nurse who alone engage in the practice of nursing, and the rest of this varied and indispensable crew. But to the patients, all these constitute a vast assemblage among whom it is difficult to distinguish.

The continued differentiation of roles within nursing, and within the vocations that facilitate the provision of nursing care, has put a special responsibility upon the professional nurse. She must keep complexity from deteriorating into confusion. She must keep complexity from becoming fragmentation and even chaos. By virtue of her special education, her knowledge of basic principles and her trained capacities, the professional nurse must see to it that the public health is not jeopardized by allowing auxiliary workers, unqualified by training or education, to engage in nursing procedures. The professional nurse must maintain that precarious balance in the allocation of functions that enables auxiliary workers to do all that they responsibly can to assist in nursing care without permitting them to do more than they are qualified to do.

SOCIAL DEFINITION OF A NURSE

More than anything else, it is this vast proliferation of roles in and around nursing that has imposed upon the professional nurse the task of defining and maintaining the scope of each role of nursing personnel. In pursuit of this task, the professional association of nurses has clearly demarcated the status of the professional nurse and the licensed practical nurse, who are directly engaged in the practice of nursing, from all the rest of the technical and vocational roles which variously support and facilitate that practice. This represents a decisive clarification. Registered nurses and licensed practical nurses discharge the general function of nursing. All auxiliary workers facilitate and support the practice of nursing. They do not nurse.

It is this *functional* fact of nursing practice that marks off the relations between the professional nurse and the licensed practical nurse from the relations between all other members of the health team. It is a fundamental fact. As Etta Rasmussen points out in her article, the difference between the registered nurses and the licensed practical nurses is a difference in degree of responsibility for the function, not a difference in function. This is not like the relation between the physician and nurse, or the lawyer and account-ant, or the physicist and engineer. In all those cases, the generic functions of the paired occupational groups are connected, but remain distinctive.

In the case of registered nurses and licensed practical nurses, however, both are engaged in the practice of nursing. They are primarily differentiated in terms of the legally recognized responsibilities assigned to the professional nurse chiefly on the basis of her distinctive professional education.

It is a matter of common notoriety that the formal education of those engaged in nursing covers an extraordinary range of variability. At one extreme are practical nurses who have had only eight years of schooling all told before they entered upon a program of practical nurse education. At the other extreme are some professional nurses who hold doctorates. In between are the great majority. Most of those entering upon education for practical nursing are now high school graduates. Professional nurses have followed up their high school education with a two-year associate degree program, or a three-year diploma program, or four-year baccalaureate degree program or, beyond that, with a master's degree program. These differences are bound to have implications for distinctions of status.

The only other occupational field that approaches this range of variation in formal preparation is that of teaching. Primary school teachers, high school teachers, college teachers, and teachers in the graduate and profes-sional schools of universities are all engaged in the generic practice of teach-ing. Their own education varies greatly from only two years of training beyond high school to postdoctorate training.

Nevertheless, the case of teaching is not strictly comparable to the case of nursing. For ordinarily, teachers of vastly different kinds of preparation are not engaged in the same generic practice of teaching within the *same organization and with the same clientele*. The teacher in the elementary school is not directly linked up with the teachers of graduate students in a single educational organization. But in nursing, of course, every kind of nurse may be functionally linked together within the same health facility. Licensed practical nurses and registered nurses comprise parts of one another's work environment. This is bound to accentuate concern with comparative status among those who are thus interrelated.

For the reasons that have been indicated, we must expect that with every rise in the status of professional nurses there will develop a connected drive for higher status on the part of practical nurses. Their destiny is bound together by functional interdependence. That is why the American

Nurses' Association, as the established professional association of nurses, has for years done all it can to assist the development of the newer occupational association of practical nurses, the National Federation of Licensed Practical Nurses. But as the latter organization develops, it tries to achieve an increasing degree of autonomy. At each stage of development, also, existing status-interests are accentuated and new status-interests are originated.

In this process of changing aspirations, licensed practical nurses tend to take the registered nurses as reference models. This gives rise to questions such as this: If professional nurses have an expanding scope of responsibilities, why not also practical nurses? At times, the parallel is drawn between the position of the professional nurse vis-à-vis the physician and the position of the practical nurse vis-à-vis the professional nurse.

STATUS NEEDS AND STATE BOARDS

One recent expression of this thrust for heightened status by practical nurses is found in the concern to be represented on state boards of nursing, which administer the licensure of practical nurses. Here, once again, we see the effort to take the philosophy and policies of professional nurses as a prototype. Just as professional nurses insist on being members of state boards for their licensure rather than accepting the notion that physicians should comprise these boards, so, it is said, practical nurses should be on state boards administering their licensure rather than having only professional nurses on them.

It is in matters of this kind, I believe, that one detects the workings of a desire for enhanced status taking the place of a detached appraisal of the problem. For there is, of course, a fundamental difference between the generic function of the physician and the generic function of the professional nurse. The one is engaged in the practice of medicine, the other in the practice of nursing.

As noted earlier in this article, it is functionally otherwise with the professional nurse and the practical nurse: both are engaged in nursing. By virtue of her education and training, designed to provide a broad concept of all nursing, the professional nurse is legally obliged to exercise more judgment about medically delegated acts. The practical nurse is not held legally responsible to exercise this degree of judgment since her curriculum does not prepare her for it. Moreover, the education of the professional nurse fully encompasses all that is contained in the education of the practical nurse, whereas the education of the physician does not encompass all that is contained in the education of the professional nurse.

The broader understandings of professional nurses, based not upon their individual differences but upon their education, qualifies them to prepare board examinations for practical nurses, since they can draw upon the broad concept of nursing.

In all of this, of course, it must be recognized that professional nurses should meet especially exacting criteria to serve effectively on state boards. Not every professional nurse is equal to the demanding requirements of this position. But to meet these requirements, she must at least have the scientifically based and broad-gauged education designed for the best exercise of judgment within the entire range of nursing.

I have dwelt upon this one example because it brings out essential issues in the social consequences of status-needs developing among professional and practical nurses (as in other occupations). Historically, as an occupation evolves enlarged competences, it seeks ever higher status and public recognition. This *can* serve socially useful purposes. It can provide deepened motivations that can be harnessed to socially beneficial activities. But if status-needs become so rapidly intensified that they run far ahead of the competences that must underlie heightened status and enlarged responsibilities, this can only be at the expense of the society. More will then be asked than society can responsibly grant.

Samuel Butler once remarked, "Woe to the specialist who is not a pretty fair generalist, and to the generalist who is not also a bit of a specialist." That makes so much good sense that I should like to echo it and go on to paraphrase it. Woe to the licensed practical nurse who is not under the direction and guidance of a registered nurse and to the registered nurse who has no licensed practical nurses to work with her. And most of all, woe to the patient if personnel supportive of nursing are allowed to undertake the practice of nursing.

Once said, all this will probably be recognized as the restraints society must impose upon the rate of rise in status accorded functionally advancing groups in society. But it is useful to have it periodically reaffirmed. Both professional nurses and licensed practical nurses can earn the right to growing public recognition of their growing capabilities. But to be authentic rather than spurious, this rise in status must be earned. Greater knowledge, enlarged skills, a capacity for self-criticism, and ever deepened social responsibility are, in the end, the sound foundations for improved social status.

REFERENCES

1. Thomas, W. I., *The Unadjusted Girl*. Boston: Little, Brown and Co., 1923, pp. 1-40.
2. Stouffer, S. A., and others, *The American Soldier*. Princeton, N. J.: Princeton University Press, 1949, Vol. 1, pp. 250-279.

Nurses and Patients: Time, Place, and Distance

BERNARD E. SEGAL

⚑   The findings in this paper are part of a larger inquiry that was set in a private psychiatric hospital in metropolitan Boston. The patients in that hospital, between two hundred and two hundred forty during the course of the study, had considerably higher social status, conceived in extra-hospital terms, than the nurses who worked there.[1] The major questions the larger study attempted to answer were: Does the high status of the patients affect the nurses' views of nurse-patient relationships, and, if so, are the nurses' views of these relationships related to their conceptions of the nature and proper treatment of mental illness?

Part of the answer to these questions is included in this paper. Here I am concerned with the effects of (a) ward type and (b) work shift on (c) the nurses' impressions of the effect of patients' social status on nurse-patient relationships, and on (d) nurses' conceptions of mental illness and its treatment. Phrased as a single question—"Do, where and when nurses work in a given hospital make a difference in how they think of their patients and of their own jobs?"

One hundred and one of 103 nurses were interviewed and 95 completed

---

[1] The judgment of the higher external social status of the patients was based on the following facts: a) The cost of a three months stay in the hospital exceeded half of most nurses' annual salaries. b) The mean occupational level of the patients on the North-Hatt scale was more than ten points higher than the nurses' mean level (assuming that a nurse has a rank equal to a schoolteacher). The difference in the mean levels was about fifteen points between the male patients and the husbands of married nurses. Information about the patients came from a detailed study of the case records of all the patients in the hospital on a day chosen at random from the middle month of the study. The case records did not have information about the occupational history of about a third of the female patients—a good number of them had never been employed since they never had any ostensible need for the income from gainful employment. c) Over ten per cent of the patients had their total hospital costs paid for out of the income from principal wealth. d) With age and sex controlled, the patients on the average had over two years more formal education than the nurses.

Reprinted with permission from the author and *Social Problems*, Vol. 9, No. 3, 1962, pp. 257-264.

questionnaire forms. In this article attention is limited to the 52 nurses who worked on the day and relief shifts, and to the 24 nurses who worked on the night shift. All were graduate registered nurses; their official positions ran from staff nurse to head nurse. The nurses not included in this report were either on the faculty of the school of nursing or were part of the nursing service administration.

THE VARIABLES

There were fifteen wards in the hospital, classified as follows by the hospital staff: two admission wards, two disturbed wards, four open wards, two "active treatment" wards (intermediate between disturbed and open), three chronic and two geriatric wards.

Both male and female patients lived on four of the wards, but the other eleven housed exclusively males or females. The largest ward never had more than twenty resident patients; the smallest, never fewer than eight.

Discussion of the effects on nurses' attitudes of the type of ward on which they worked will apply only to the day and relief shifts. The character of the whole hospital changed drastically on the night shift, and differences among the wards were minimized. For example, by ten p.m. all the wards were locked, almost all interward communication by staff or patients was over, and then at eleven a new set of personnel came on.

One specific instrument assessed nurses' impressions about the effect of patients' social status; another assessed their attitudes about the nature and treatment of mental illness. The first was a Likert-type scale called the Status Disaffection Scale.[2] It was composed of ten items. The following are representative: "With all the menial tasks that patients here expect you to do, it's sometimes hard to feel like a professional person." "Patients here are more selfish than in other hospitals where the patients have fewer possessions." "Patients here use their educations to make nurses feel inferior."[3]

The aim of the scale was to discover the effect of the patients' high extra-hospital social status on the nurses' occupational self-images. The

---

[2] The scale's split half reliability (odd-even) was .85; each item discriminated between the top thirty and bottom thirty scores (nearly two-thirds of all the respondents) at less than the .001 level of confidence by "t" test.

[3] Most of the items were paraphrases of comments made by nurses in conversations I had with them before any formal interviewing program began. Sixty such items were given in pre-test to fifty student nurses. Thirty-five items discriminated between the top and bottom thirds of the pre-test respondents at less than the .05 level of confidence, by "t" test. I selected thirty of these items to be included as part of the questionnaire form administered to the research universe of graduate nurses. The ten-item scale reported on here consists of the items among the thirty that most clearly discriminated between the top and bottom thirty scorers of the graduate nurses. The rank-order correlation between the ten item scale and the complete set of thirty items was .87.

higher the score, the more a nurse was thought to be expressing the attitude that the patients' high status upset her, at least in terms of the manifest content of the scale items. Somewhat less directly, a high score on this scale is an indication by the nurse that she believes the status of the patients prevents her from performing her duties in a manner that is mutually satisfactory for her and for the patients.

Scale score was the summation of the scored answers to each of the ten questions on the scale. Each item was answered along a range from one to six (strongly disagree, disagree, mildly disagree, mildly agree, agree, strongly agree). The theoretical range of scale scores thus ran from 10 to 60; the actual range was from 12 to 54; the mean was 28.6, indicative of mild disagreement.

The CMI Scale (Custodial Mental Illness Ideology), developed by Gilbert and Levinson,[4] measures conceptions of the nature and treatment of mental illness. An extreme high score on this scale represents a custodial orientation that emphasizes social and physical distance between mentally ill and normal people. Custodialism as the term is used here refers to scores on this scale. It does not refer to a form of behavior, although previous research has demonstrated some relationship between endorsing custodial points of view and acting restrictively toward psychiatric patients.[5]

The CMI scale has eighteen items, of which the following are representative: "As soon as a person shows signs of mental disturbance he should be hospitalized." "A mental patient is in no position to make decisions about even everyday living problems." "Patients need the same kind of control and discipline as an untrained child."

Scores on this scale were computed according to Gilbert and Levinson's directions.[6] That is, they are a summation of the scored responses on each of the eighteen items, then divided by eighteen and multiplied by ten. This makes it possible to express the total score in terms of ten times the mean score per item. (The same result occurs, of course, by adding each of the item scores on a ten item scale.) Each CMI item ran a range from one to seven (strongly disagree, disagree, mildly disagree, mildly agree, agree, strongly agree); a hypothetical neutral point was scored as four. CMI scale score thus had a theoretical range from ten to seventy; the actual range was from fifteen to fifty; the mean was 29, indicating mild disagreement.

The rank-order correlation between CMI and Status Disaffection scores

---

[4] Doris C. Gilbert and Daniel J. Levinson, " 'Custodialism' and 'Humanism' in Staff Ideology," in Milton Greenblatt, Daniel J. Levinson, and Richard H. Williams: *The Patient and the Mental Hospital* (Glencoe, Ill.: Free Press, 1957).

[5] Doris C. Gilbert and Daniel J. Levinson, "Role Performance, Ideology, and Personality in Mental Hospital Aides," in Milton Greenblatt *et al., op. cit.*

[6] Doris C. Gilbert and Daniel J. Levinson, " 'Custodialism' and 'Humanism' in Staff Ideology," in Milton Greenblatt *et al., op. cit.*

was .495.[7] An element that appears to be common to both scales is that patients are difficult people to deal with, unpleasant people with whom to spend a good deal of time. In a sense, the items on the Status Disaffection Scale most of which were derived from statements made by nurses in conversations before any formal interviewing program began, were uttered by people who were at the moment expressing a kind of custodialism as well as dissatisfaction with the patients' high standing. This, because the items imply that patients are not conforming to the nurses' conceptions of the patient role, but are instead attempting to assert their individuality. Indeed, an interpretation of the correlation will appear below[8] that some respondents use status disaffection attitudes to justify their custodial viewpoints.

CUSTODIALISM AND STATUS DISAFFECTION BY WARD TYPE

A nurse in the hospital under discussion may be subject to a status contradiction as well as to conflicting role demands. The status contradiction results from the inversion of the respective social statuses of the nurse and of the patient in the hospital as contrasted with the community.[9] Within the hospital, the nurse has control and influence over patients who would at least be informally superordinate to her outside the hospital. Further, the control the nurse exerts can apply to intimate details of the patients' lives and is

---

[7] Rank-order was used because it does not depend on assumptions about the normality of either distribution. There is some evidence to indicate that the relationship is not an artifact of having the two scales appear on the same questionnaire form. With a sample consisting of a quarter of the respondent universe, the rank-order correlation between the Status Disaffection Scale and a "response set" scale developed by Arthur Couch (unpublished, Harvard University, 1959) was .15; the correlation between CMI and response set was .04.

[8] In the section on night nurses, who simultaneously showed the most status disaffection and the most custodialism of any group of nurses.

[9] In a different private psychiatric hospital, Hollingshead and Redlich summarized staff attitudes toward patients' extra-hospital class positions thus: "The comfort, welfare, and treatment of patients within the genteel tradition is the acknowledged function of the institution. The administrators and the staff know the patients pay for these surroundings, and they are aware of the manifest and latent values in this setting. Administrators, receptionists, psychiatrists, nurses, maids, aides, groundskeepers, and chauffeurs know the earmarks of high and low status from long experience. In unguarded moments they may state this fact plainly. For example, a chief nurse in a noted private hospital summarized her status awareness in these words: 'I can tell from their grooming, their clothes, their luggage and the way they talk what they are. One has to be aware of these things or you will be in difficulty all the time. Good care means knowing who the patients are and how they expect you to regard them.'" August B. Hollingshead and Frederick C. Redlich, *Social Class and Mental Illness,* Wiley, New York, 1958, pp. 325, 326. Of the hundred nurses in this study, over eighty per cent had moments in their interviews that were at least as unguarded as the one that Hollingshead and Redlich reported.

sustained over rather long periods of time—from several weeks to several years.

The conflicting role demands are illustrated a) by the nurse's having both control over and services for patients as part of her job, and b) by the ideological conflict between universalistic affective neutrality and particularistic concern for individual patients.

To some extent, every nurse is ultimately guided by universalistic role-expectations regarding her performance with the sick, who are themselves subject to a different set of expectations from those that would apply to them if they were well. This situation is a specific example of the larger "sick role" theory, derived from Parsons,[10] wherein psychiatric illness legitimates the suspension of the usual hierarchy of social relations.

This suspension is not complete in the empirical situation discussed here. It is most nearly complete on geriatric wards, where patients are looked upon as if they were almost purely physical units, and nurses' duties are both limited and rather clearly specified. It is least complete on the open wards, where patients are looked upon as being but a step away from returning to the extra-hospital community, and nurses' duties are neither clear nor explicitly limited. These examples should show that nurses' roles and their conceptions of them vary from one type of ward to another. There are parallel variations from ward type to ward type in the ways nurses view their patients, and in the ways they think they ought to treat them.

Two propsitions account for the patterns of custodialism and status disaffection by ward type among the nurses under study here: 1. If a nurse can derive the impression that she is performing her occupational duties competently, she is less affected by the status contradiction between herself and her patients, and will show less status disaffection. Status disaffection is thus tied to the nurse's perception of her role performance. 2. Custodialism is more directly related to the demands of the work situation. A nurse whose set of tasks is concentrated around protection, restriction, and physical care tends to be more custodial than one whose tasks are centered around rehabilitative and mutually participant interaction with patients.

Custodialism by ward type occurs, with one exception, in direct relation to the extent that the patients with whom a nurse works are removed from daily contact with the extra-hospital community. The exceptional case is the open wards; it will be discussed below.

However, there is no such single condition over the range of ward types that will account for nurses thinking that they are achieving satisfactory performance goals. It is therefore useful to spend some time discussing some of

---

10 Talcott Parsons, "Illness and the Role of the Physician," in Clyde Kluckhohn, Henry A. Murray and David M. Schneider, *Personality in Nature, Culture, and Society*, Knopf, New York, 1953.

TABLE 1. STATUS DISAFFECTION AND CUSTODIALISM BY
WARD TYPE AND SHIFT

	NUMBER OF NURSES	CUSTODIALISM MEAN SCORE	RANK	STATUS DISAFFECTION MEAN SCORE	RANK
Ward type					
Geriatric	7	31.4	2	23.7	5
Chronic	10	32.4	1	27.2	4
Disturbed	7	28.1	4	30.0	2
Active treatment	8	26.8	5	28.9	3
Admission	9	26.2	6	20.7	6
Open	11	28.3	3	30.8	1
Shift					
Day—relief	52*	29.0		27.0	
Night	24	33.5		34.3	

* Total of all the nurses on the above ward types.

the strains and satisfactions of psychiatric nursing that are unique to each ward type.

Consider that the nurses on the geriatric wards, who show the least status disaffection (see Table 1), are considerably less upset by the high status of the patients than the nurses on the disturbed wards. Why? After all, the patients on the disturbed and on the geriatric wards are clearly the "sickest" patients in the hospital. However, the nature of the patients' illnesses on these two types of wards is different, hence the nurse's tasks are different, and—most important—the possibility of a nurse perceiving that a patient responds to her professional efforts is different.

On a geriatric ward, a nurse can offer the whole range of her medical competence, although there is little obvious need for and little profit from the application of psychiatric knowledge and techniques. Geriatric ward nurses don't expect their patients to improve; they do expect to see that patients are made more comfortable or are kept alive several more months or years. By contrast, on a disturbed ward the nurse has little opportunity to use any but the most rudimentary medical (in the sense of physical medicine) techniques. Her primary concern is with the patients' behavior, not with their physical well-being. The ethos of the disturbed ward definitely leans toward interpersonal therapy and the application of psychiatric skills, but always there is a fairly low probability of success and a fairly high probability that the patient will reject the nurse and her efforts.

Admission ward nurses also seek useful interpersonal relations with patients who are often as ill as those on the disturbed wards. What accounts for the relative absence of status disaffection among them? On admission wards, patients are unaccustomed to living in the hospital. Admission to a psychiatric ward is a new and often terrifying experience for them.[11] Therefore, because patients must place particular reliance on the ward staff in order to become acclimated to the hospital world, nurses have a good opportunity to display their competence in applying psychiatric skills. Moreover, patients move from the admission wards after about three weeks, not long after or just about at the time when they have become well enough adjusted to the hospital surroundings to make their requests and demands known. It appears that for nurses in this hospital there is less tension and more satisfaction in being an agent of short-term socialization than in being an agent of long-term treatment.[12]

Nurses' goals are least clear on the open wards. Previous research has shown, for example, that psychiatric nurses on open wards find it difficult to define their own roles satisfactorily, because their patients are not obviously ill.[13] Once nurses begin to think that patients have little direct need for them, then some of the services for which the patients call on nurses appear demeaning (e.g., drawing tubs, arranging interward visits), if only because they seem to be quite within the capabilities of patients who are "almost well." The relatively great status disaffection among open ward nurses thus stems from a basic ambiguity: the nurses cannot be certain whether they are performing useful professional tasks for patients, or are being imposed on by patients.

Calling attention to this ambiguity also helps to account for the relatively high degree of custodialism among open ward nurses.

It is only on the open wards that the relative extent of custodialism clearly tends to exceed demands on the nurse for protection, restriction, and actual physical contact with patients. Emphasizing that patients are sick, emphasizing control over patients and over difficult situations on the ward, can be important in sustaining a nurse's impression that she is really doing her job well. Nurses attach significance to their image of themselves as skilled and hard working people who are performing a worthwhile service. If they lose their chance to serve, either through the patients or through their own negative impressions of the patients, they also lose an important

---

[11] What is probably still the best article on this subject is Tamara Dembo and Eugenia Hanfmann: "The Patient's Psychological Situation upon Admission to a Mental Hospital," *American Journal of Psychology*, 47 (1935), 381-408.

[12] The distinction between these two functions of psychiatric hospital personnel is rather fully presented in Talcott Parsons, "The Mental Hospital as a Form of Organization," in Milton Greenblatt, *et al.*, eds., *op. cit.* It is implicit in much of Erving Goffman, "On the Characteristics of Total Institutions," in *Symposium on Preventive and Social Psychiatry*, Government Printing Office, Washington, D.C., 1958.

[13] William Caudill, Frederick Redlich, H. R. Gilmore, and E. B. Brody, "Social Structure and Interaction Processes on a Psychiatric Ward," *American Journal of Orthopsychiatry*, 22 (1952), 314-334.

source of their self-respect. Open ward nurses may use a relatively custodial point of view defensively, either as a rationale for exerting authority over patients who in many ways appear to be quite well, or to maintain composure before patients who are almost able to press on a nurse the weight of their extra-hospital positions.

CUSTODIALISM AND STATUS DISAFFECTION ON THE NIGHT SHIFT

At night, inactivity and silence are a great contrast to the activity everywhere in the hospital till sundown, or till nine or ten o'clock on the wards. By 11:30 almost all the patients are in bed, except for a few who have late television privileges. The only personnel in the hospital are two night nursing supervisors, one resident on call, and the aides and nurses who work on the wards.

The night nurse is in full charge of her ward. (In over twenty nights that I spent at the hospital, each ward always had one, but only one, graduate nurse on duty.) She sees a supervisor who makes regular rounds two or three times during the course of the night; she never sees a physician unless he's summoned for an emergency. The nurse may work alone or with one aide on some open wards; she may work with as many as four or five aides on either disturbed ward. In either case, the night shift is a time when the label "charge nurse" fits particularly well.

For some, the night shift has some definite advantages. There are no superiors around, and hardly any people to make the nurse conform to hospital policies with which she might disagree. She is her own boss, and boss over the patient if she chooses. This is indicated by a night nurse's description of her job:

> Keep the ward as quiet as possible. But they (patients) should feel free to come and talk with me. You can't order a person to sleep. Give them something to eat, if they wake up and can't sleep and ask for it. Sometimes we get too lenient. I restrict them a little. If they're hungry enough, they'll eat crackers and milk.

In general, night nurses were considerably more bothered than others by the patients' high status. To account for this finding, two factors should be called to attention. First, compared to the nurses on the day and relief shifts who tended to display relatively great status disaffection, the night nurses have little opportunity to display the professional competence of the trained psychiatric nurse, let alone apply it successfully. Indeed, other people around the hospital do not think that night nurses are a part of the "therapeutic team." Instead they are thought of as though they were well trained and responsible baby-sitters.[14]

Second are the desiderata which a great proportion of the night nurses specify as exemplifying good performance by patients. Patients are supposed to sleep, to stay quiet. They are not supposed to bother the nurses or upset the ward routine. When they do, they are infringing on what the nurses think are their own rights on the ward. Many night nurses saw their own dominant positions threatened by what they thought were patients' attempts to establish theirs.

Night nurses show not only more status disaffection than others, but also more custodialism. In fact, the night shift can be characterized in terms of the large number of people on it who simultaneously show high degrees of both. (For example, 18 of 24 night nurses earned scores above the respective hospital median of each of the scales. Only 11 of the 52 other nurses did so.)

The major reason for the night nurses' custodialism is the same as it was among the day and relief nurses who tended to be relatively custodial; that is, night nursing consists mostly of protecting, restricting, and ministering to simple physical aches and pains. But other things about the night shift are also conducive to developing relatively custodial attitudes.

Nurses who work at night consider themselves virtually alone. They do not think very highly of the aides who work with them. As much as they can, they like to keep their wards in strict control to avoid any emergency—partly because they think they might be blamed for their occurrence, partly because they are a little afraid about spending eight lonesome hours with psychiatric patients.

Thus, they are anxious about possible disasters, and they must attune themselves to expect the unexpected. They are insecure in their positions because they do not know what the other members of the hospital staff expect of them. Finally, they have little contact with the daytime—some might say the real—hospital that has left custodial attitudes behind and is establishing a new level of understanding of the meaning and effects of patients' behavior.

All these factors combine to leave night nurses with a rather narrow definition of what constitutes proper patient behavior. In fact, it is so narrow that a sizeable number of night nurses think that patients who do not conform to it are attempting to assert themselves at the nurses' expense. In this connection, the following interview excerpt demonstrates—more clearly than comparative scale scores can—a point that was made above; viz., there are respondents who make use of elements of status disaffection in order to justify their custodial attitudes.

---

[14] The parallel between the duties of some nurses and of baby-sitters was suggested in a personal communication from Rose Coser.

A spoiled brat type of attitude is the impression I have of most of them. Some of them need about two years work in the Russian salt mines to know what work is. It's too easy for them, and I don't know how to cope with it. The way they're treated here is that they're well catered to and they wouldn't think of getting out. If they're transferred to a state hospital—they get out. This is a hotel rather than a hospital. They say this is what you're paid for, and thus there are five or six of them making a ritual of having a glass of milk at four in the morning. A hospital is supposed to discipline a patient to conform to reality. The administration is supposed to back you up. They're not at home and they should get used to the idea. It's not conducive to getting them well.

Even though there is only limited interaction between nurses and patients at night, the nurses are able to find elements in that interaction which are to them indicative of patients' attempts to retain the prerogatives of high extra-hospital status in a ward setting.

CONCLUSION

Previous research has demonstrated that nurses' attitudes about (a) the nature and treatment of mental illness (custodialism) and about (b) the effects of patients' extra-hospital social status on nurse-patient relationships (status disaffection) vary from one type of psychiatric hospital to another.[15] This paper has attempted to show that these attitudes also vary from one type of ward to another and from work shift to work shift within the same hospital.

Custodialism was linked to the set of tasks that nurses had to perform, while status disaffection was related to the nurses' impressions of how well they were able to carry out their assigned duties. Their tasks, and their opportunities for performing them in competent and successful fashion, varied from ward to ward and from shift to shift. Thus night nurses, among whom the simultaneous occurrence of considerable custodialism and considerable status disaffection was concentrated, tended to use their antipathy toward patients as a means of justifying their restrictiveness toward patients. In general, nurses were more custodial when they worked where there was greater emphasis placed on protection, restriction, and physical contact, and they showed more status disaffection when their attempts to apply interpersonal psychiatric nursing techniques were unsuccessful.

---

[15] Doris C. Gilbert and Daniel J. Levinson, " 'Custodialism' and 'Humanism' in Staff Ideology," *op. cit.*, and August B. Hollingshead and Frederick C. Redlich, *op. cit.*

Index

Aasterud, Margaret, 57
  article, 82-87
Adams, Harold, 205
Admission of patient, 7
American Nurses' Association, 382
Anderson, Barbara J., 4
  article, 16-26
Anthropologist, medical, 196
Anxiety, in diagnosis and treatment, 158-159
  at onset of illness, 156
Apathy as response to overprotection, 161-163
Apple, Dorrian, 206-212
Argyris, Chris, 361

Baumann, Barbara, 141
  article, 206-219
Baziak, Anna T., 232
  article, 272-277
Beals, Ralph, 205
Berkowitz, Norman H., 325
  article, 356-366
Bird, Brian, 17, 59
  article, 101
Blau, Peter, 299
Brauer, Paul H., 140
  article, 167-178
Brill, Henry, 312
Brown, Esther Lucile, 4, 139
  article, 6-15

Callahan, Josephine, 231
  article, 266-271
Care function, 4 (*See also*, Patient care)
Caudill, William, 199
Communications, barriers to, 53-57, 69-73
  due to specialized terminology, 278-279

Communications—(*Cont.*)
  consequences of limitation, 77-79
  effects, on patient stress reaction, 92-100
  of physical illness on, 107
  elements of, 51-52
  failure of in hospital setting, 14-15
  importance in rendering nursing care (experiment), 110-119
  meaning and function to patient, 61-68
  nonverbal, examples, 104-107
  relief of pain, 110-119
  structured, examples and results, 94-98
Community, definition, 312-313
  Studies, Inc., 266
  therapeutic, 312
Convalescence, 163-166
Corwin, Ronald G., 325
  article, 341-356
Coser, Lewis A., 304
Coser, Rose L., 233
  article, 292-306
Culture, American, attitude toward health, 215
  conditioning of hospital personnel, 275-276
  gap, health workers and beneficiary population, 199-226
  hospital, compared with prison, 316-317
  mental (article), 306-322
  influence, on nurse-patient interaction, 143-155
  on patient behavior, 141
  patient, 314
  traits, misdiagnosed as psychosis (case history), 184-195
Cure, function, 4

Cushing, Harvey, 233
Custodialism, 387-393

Davis, Marjorie, 206
Death, attitudes toward, 172-173
  as possible consequence of fear, 19
De Cicco, Lena, 206, 212
Defense mechanism, of terminally ill
  patient, 177-178
Deference, social influence and psy-
  chological function
  article, 366-376
Dentan, Robert K., 232
  article, 272-277
Dependence of patient, 161, 223
Depersonalization of patient, 4, 8-11,
  274
Dodge, Joan S., 58
  article, 87-92
Dumas, Rhetaugh Graves, 4, 5, 41
  article, 16-26

Egocentricity in illness, 160
Elder, Ruth G., 59
  article, 102-109
Ethnoculturicity of hospital person-
  nel, 232
Ethnopsychology, 184
"Evil Eye," 200
Expressive function, definition, 30

Family, attitudes of, 170, 177, 179-
  184
  of patient, staff views, 168
Fear(s), common, in hospital patients,
  64
  patient reaction to, 93
  as possible cause of death, 19
  "talking out," 102-103, 105
Feshbeck, Seymour, 362
Food service, hospital, 10
Foster, George M., 198, 205
Freedman, Maurice, 203
Freeman, Howard, 206

Galton, Sir Francis, 318
Gilbert, Doris C., 386
Gregg, Dorothy, 60
  article, 127-136

Guilt as accompaniment of illness,
  157

Hall, Edward T., 314
Hayworth, Donald, 298
Health, conceptions of, diversities in
  (article), 206-219
  educational influence, 218
  definition, 215
  practices, in hierarchy of cultural
    values, 200
  impediment, cultural, 201-202
  somatic, sociologic definition, 215
Home, loss of by patient, 8-9
Hospital, administration, comparison
  with business (article), 245-251
  community relationships, 244
  diffusion of authority in, 240-241
  functionaries, attitude toward own
    roles, 74-77
  hierarchy of, 238-240
  individualism, vs. bureaucracy,
    242-243
  specialization of, 248-249
  functions, primary, 229-231, 235-
    236, 252-253
  humor (article), 292-306
  language and culture conditioning
    (article), 272-277
  mental, culture of (article), 306-322
  organization, charts, 254, 256, 258
  regulations, patient expectations,
    64-65
  social structure (article), 233-244
Hughes, Everett C., 253, 296, 345

Illness, "accepted," 160-163
  cultural influences on incidence, 196
  terminal, patient and staff attitudes,
    167-178
Instrumental function, definition, 30
Involvement, emotional, nurse-patient,
  38-41

Jacobs, Melville, 318
Janis, Irving L., 88, 93
Jewell, Donald P., 140
  article, 184-195
Johnson, Miriam M., 4, 17, 41, 251
  article, 29-39

Johnson, Nelson A., 307
Jones, Maxwell, 311
Jourard, Sidney, 356

King, Stanley, 232
Klein, Malcolm W., 325
    article, 356-366
Koos, Earl L., 206, 212, 291

Lambertsen, Eleanor, 356
Larson, Richard F., 232
    article, 278-291
Lederer, Henry D., 140
    article, 155-167
Leonard, Robert C., 4, 59
    articles, 16-26, 110-119, 120-126
Levinson, Daniel J., 386
Listening, to patient, 101

Malone, Mary, 325
    article, 356-366
Mangin, William, 204
Martin, Harry W., 4, 17, 41, 251
    article, 29-39
Mauksch, Hans O., 229, 325
    articles, 245-251, 251-265, 327-
      340
Medical terminology, patient knowl-
  edge of (article), 278-291
Merton, Robert K., 326
    article, 377-383
Meyers, Mary E., 58
    article, 92-100
Morgan, Norman C., 307
Morris, Charles W., 277

Neurosis, amelioration of through
  physical illness, 157
New, Peter Kong-Ming, 231
    article, 266-271
Nimkoff, Meyer, 315
Nite, Gladys, 231
    article, 266-271
"No-society," concept of, 318
Nurse, attitude of, toward family of
      patient, 168
    toward geriatric patients, 389
    toward high-status patients (arti-
      cle), 384-393
    toward informing patient, 87-92

Nurse—(Cont.)
    as coordinator of patient care (arti-
      cle), 251-265
    patient communication, interpreta-
      tion, 102-109
    patient expectations of, 66-73
    from patient point of view (article),
      219-227
    personality, as perceived by pa-
      tient, 224
    psychiatric, difficulty of role defini-
      tions, 390
      normative components of role,
        367-369
    student, adolescent dilemma, 330-
      331
      characteristics of, 335
      contact with patient, 331-332
      difficulties and conflicts, 333-334
      first impressions, 328-329
      impact of reality on, 329
      loss of initiative and motivation,
        338-339
      reactions to illness and death, 332-
        333
      relationships with peers, 334-335
      role orientation, 339-340
      status relationships, 346
Nursing, communications, effect in
      pain relief (experiment), 110-
      119
    deference in, functions, 374-376
    explanation to patient, 82-87
    improvement of through patient
      participation, 120-126
    licensed practical, 380-382
    in outpatient department, conflicts
      (article), 356-366
    overstaffing on unit (article), 266-
      271
    patient-centered, 270
    professionalization of, 267, 344-
      345
    psychological preparation of surgi-
      cal patient, 24-27
    role, conflicts in (article), 341-356
      bureaucratic vs. professional
        roles, 343-345, 350-351
      educational idealization, 342

Nursing role—(*Cont.*)
  perceptions, real and ideal, 353-356
  transition from student to practitioner, 346-355
  expressive, 5, 17, 30, 40-47
  limitations of, 33-36
  instrumental, 30
  sociologic analysis of, 29-39, 40-47
  task subdivision, 10
  social ascent of, 378-379
  social definition of, 380-382
  staff, effects of departmentalization on, 253-259
  State Board of, 382-383
  status orientations (article), 377-383
  strategy in influencing physician, 370-373

Ogburn, William F., 315
Osmond, Humphry, 233
  article, 306-322
Outpatient department, interpersonal conflict in (article), 356-366
  system, 358-359

Pace, Robert E., 315
Pain, cultural attitudes toward, 215-217
  effect of communications on (experiment), 114-119
Parsons, Talcott, 215, 388
Patient, at "accepted illness" stage, 160-163
  care, complaints, 298
  concern with medical and nursing errors, 221-222
  convalescent, 163-166
  culture, 314
    influence on interpersonal relationships, 141, 143-155
  dependence and powerlessness, 223-224
  depersonalization of, 4, 8-11, 274
  effects of hospital language on (article), 272-277

Patient—(*Cont.*)
  explanations to, 82-87
    blockage of, 85-87
    timing, 84-85
    type and extent, 83-84
  fears and dissatisfactions, 222-223
  "good," concept of, 222, 226
  humor (article), 292-305
  "illness role," 64
  information, 87-92
  knowledge of medical vocabulary (article), 278-291
  mental, social life (article), 306-322
  orientation at onset of illness, 155
  perception of by staff, 11
  preparation of, psychological aspects, 16-26
  progressive, 270
  psychosocial needs, 6-15
  "rights" of, 63, 69
  role in own treatment, 120-126
  society, 308
  stress reactions, effect of communications on, 92-100
  terminally ill, attitudes and approaches, 167-178, 179-184
  unit, effects of nurse overstaffing on (article), 266-271
  functions, 259-263
Paul, Benjamin D., 141
  article, 195-206
Pearsall, M., 361
Physician, attitudes toward nurse role, 360
  patient expectations of, 62-65, 68
  relationship to hospital, 236, 255
Polgar, Steven, 198

Rasmussen, Etta, 381
Reassurance, 20
  article, 127-136
Regression, emotional, in illness, 161-163, 170
Rehabilitation of convalescent, 165-166
Rhymes, Julina P., 59
  article, 110-119
Rossen, George, 242

Ruesch, Jurgen, 109
Rushing, William A., 325
    article, 366-376

Samora, Julian, 232
    article, 278-291
Saunders, Lyle, 232, 356
    article, 278-291
Schulman, Sam, 251
Scotch, Norman, 204
Segal, Bernard E., 326
    article, 384-393
Simmel, Georg, 337
Skipper, James K., Jr., 5, 58
    articles, 40-47, 61-82
Smith, Harvey, 252
Social science, place in nursing cur-
    riculum, 3-5
system, doctor-nurse-patient, 31, 40
Society, definition, 308-309
Sommer, Robert, 233
    article, 306-322
Staff, hospital, attitude toward patient,
    13-14
    reaction to diagnosis, 12-13
    socialization, 11-12
Status, as fundamental need, 377-378
    gap, patient-health personnel, 203
Stern, B. J., 318
Stigma, social, of illness, 157
Surgery, psychological preparation of
    patient for, 16-26

Sykes, Gresham, 318
Symptoms, orientation to health, 213

Tagliacozzo, Daisy, 18, 142
    article, 219-227
Tao-Kim-Hai, André, 140
    article, 143-155
Tarasuk, Mary B., 59
    article, 110-119
Taylor, Paul S., 205
Textor, Robert B., 201
Thomas, W. I., 377
Thorner, Isadore, 41, 251
Triad, doctor-nurse-patient, 31-33, 40
Tryon, Phyllis A., 59
    article, 120-126

Valzey, John, 309
Veblen, Thorsten, 377
Von Mering, Otto, 307, 308

Weeks, H. Ashley, 206
Wertenbaker, Lael, 170
White, Leslie A., 319
Wilmer, Harry A., 312
Wilsensky, Harold, 244
Wilson, Robert N., 229
    article, 233-244
Woodson, W. W., 318

Zborowsky, Mark, 215